Advances in Joining of Ceramics

Related titles published by The American Ceramic Society:

Progress in Nanotechnology
©2002, ISBN 1-57498-169-2

Innovative Processing and Synthesis of Ceramics, Glasses, and Composites VI (Ceramic Transactions Volume 135)
Edited by Narottam P. Bansal and J.P. Singh
©2002, ISBN 1-57498-150-1

Advances in Ceramic Matrix Composites VIII (Ceramic Transactions Volume 139)
Edited by J.P. Singh, Narottam P. Bansal, and Mritunjay Singh
©2002, ISBN 1-57498-154-4

Innovative Processing and Synthesis of Ceramics, Glasses, and Composites V (Ceramic Transactions Volume 129)
Edited by Narottam P. Bansal and J.P. Singh
©2002, ISBN 1-57498-137-4

Advances in Ceramic Matrix Composites VII (Ceramic Transactions Volume 128)
Edited by Narottam P. Bansal, J.P. Singh, and H.-T. Lin
©2001, ISBN 1-57498-136-6

Boing-Boing the Bionic Cat and the Jewel Thief
By Larry L. Hench
©2001, ISBN 1-57498-129-3

The Magic of Ceramics
By David W. Richerson
©2000, ISBN 1-57498-050-5

Boing-Boing the Bionic Cat
By Larry L. Hench
©2000, ISBN 1-57498-109-9

Ceramic Innovations in the 20th Century
Edited by John B. Wachtman Jr.
©1999, ISBN 1-57498-093-9

Ceramic Joining (Ceramic Transactions, Volume 77)
Edited by Ivar Reimanis, Charles Henager Jr., and Antoni Tomsia
©1997, ISBN 1-57498-022-X

Structural Ceramic Joining II (Ceramic Transactions, Volume 35)
Edited by Arthur J. Moorhead, Ronald E. Loehman, and Sylvia M. Johnson
©1993, ISBN 0-944904-65-3

For information on ordering titles published by The American Ceramic Society, or to request a publications catalog, please contact our Customer Service Department at 614-794-5890 (phone), 614-794-5892 (fax),<customersrvc@acers.org> (e-mail), or write to Customer Service Department, 735 Ceramic Place, Westerville, OH 43081, USA.

Visit our on-line book catalog at <www.ceramics.org>.

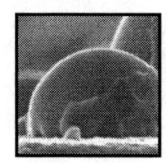

Ceramic Transactions
Volume 138

Advances in Joining of Ceramics

Proceedings of the Joining of Ceramics symposium held at the 104th Annual Meeting of The American Ceramic Society, April 28–May 1, 2002 in St. Louis, Missouri.

Edited by
Charles A. Lewinsohn
Ceramatec, Inc.

Mrityunjay Singh
QSS Group Inc.
NASA Glenn Research Center

Ronald Loehman
Sandia National Laboratory

Published by
The American Ceramic Society
735 Ceramic Place
Westerville, Ohio 43081
www.ceramics.org

Proceedings of the Joining of Ceramics symposium held at the 104th Annual Meeting of The American Ceramic Society, April 28–May 1, 2002 in St. Louis, Missouri.

Copyright 2003, The American Ceramic Society. All rights reserved.

Statements of fact and opinion are the responsibility of the authors alone and do not imply an opinion on the part of the officers, staff, or members of The American Ceramic Society. The American Ceramic Society assumes no responsibility for the statements and opinions advanced by the contributors to its publications or by the speakers at its programs. Registered names and trademarks, etc., used in this publication, even without specific indication thereof, are not to be considered unprotected by the law.

No part of this book may be reproduced, stored in a retrieval system, or transmitted in any form or by any means, electronic, mechanical, photocopying, microfilming, recording, or otherwise, without prior written permission from the publisher.

Authorization to photocopy for internal or personal use beyond the limits of Sections 107 and 108 of the U.S. Copyright Law is granted by the American Ceramic Society, ISSN 1042-1122 provided that the appropriate fee is paid directly to the Copyright Clearance Center, Inc., 222 Rosewood Drive, Danvers, MA 01923 USA, www.copyright.com. Prior to photocopying items for educational classroom use, please contact Copyright Clearance Center, Inc.

This consent does not extend to copying items for general distribution or for advertising or promotional purposes or to republishing items in whole or in part in any work in any format.

Please direct republication or special copying permission requests to the Senior Director, Publications, The American Ceramic Society, PO Box 6136, Westerville, Ohio 43086-6136, USA.

Cover photo: "Poor wetting was observed in TZP/Au/Ti systems in vacuum, ~4at%Ti, 1175°C/15min" is courtesy of S. Agathoploulos, S. Pina, and R.N. Correia, and appears as figure 3a in their paper "A Review of Recent Investigations on Zirconia Joining for Biomedical Applications" which begins on page 135.

For information on ordering titles published by The American Ceramic Society, or to request a publications catalog, please call 614-794-5890.

Printed in the United States of America.

4 3 2 1–05 04 03 02

ISSN 1042-1122
ISBN 1-57498-153-6

Contents

Preface vii

Designing Joints in Ceramics

Selection and Function of Interlayer Materials in
Ceramic/Ceramic Joining 3
 E.D. Case

Numerical Modeling of Solid State Bonding Based
on Fundamental Bonding Mechanisms: For Bonding
between Dissimilar Materials 29
 Y. Takahashi

Designing Joints with Graded Layers 49
 J. Stamile, I.E. Reimanis, and J. Chapa-Cabrera

Engineering High-Quality Ceramic-Metal Bonds 61
 V.A. Greenhut and T.R. Chapman

Brazing

Particulate Loading of High Temperature Brazes for
Joining Engineering Ceramics 103
 K.M. Knowles, D.R. Ormston, D.B. Conquest, L.T. Ecclestone, and J.A. Fernie

Development of a Copper Oxide-Silver Braze for
Ceramic Joining 119
 K.S. Weil and J.Y. Kim

Biomedical Applications

A Review of Recent Investigations on Zirconia Joining
for Biomedical Applications 135
 S. Agathopoulos, S. Pina, and R.N. Correia

Joining Zirconia and Alumina Bioceramics 149
 H.W. Shin, E.D. Case, B.D. Brooks, P. Kwon, and C.K. Kok

Graded Coatings for Metallic Implant Alloys 159
E. Saiz, A.P. Tomsia, S. Fujino, and J.M. Gomez-Vega

High Temperature Applications

Thermal Cycling of Advanced Compressive Seal for
Solid Oxide Fuel Cells. 175
Y.-S. Chou and J.W. Stevenson

Brazing a Mixed Ionic/Electronic Conductor to an
Oxidation Resistant Metal. 185
K.S. Weil and J.S. Hardy

Brazeless Approaches to Joining Silicon Carbide-Based
Ceramics for High Temperature Applications. 201
C.A. Lewinsohn, C.H. Henager Jr., and M. Singh

Processing Issues in Fabricating Ceramic Micro-Heat
Exchangers by Joining Components. 209
P. Kwon, C.K. Kok, D. Fickes, C.W. Somerton, H.W. Shin, and E.D. Case

Index. 221

Preface

Joining remains an enabling technology in several key areas related to the use of ceramics. Development of ceramic materials for electronic, biomedical, power generation, and many other fields continues at a rapid pace. The inherent cost of technical ceramics, as compared with metals, usually drives device designers to specify that ceramic components possessing desirable properties to be used only in critical locations in an assembly. Hence, joining of ceramics is a critical issue in the integration of ceramic components in engineering design.

The papers contained in this volume were a result of an international symposium on Joining of Ceramics held at the 104th Annual Meeting of The American Ceramic Society, April 28–May 1, 2002 in St. Louis, Missouri. Twenty speakers from North America, Europe, and Asia presented their papers during this symposium. Some of the papers reviewed the state-of-the-art of ceramic joining, whereas others presented results from recent studies concerned with developing new joining materials and methods. Several of the papers described innovative ways to model joint behavior and properties.

The papers in this volume were peer-reviewed and divided into four general categories: designing joints in ceramics, brazing, biomedical applications, and high temperature applications. The selection of materials for joints (Case and Greenhut), approaches to modeling joint properties (Takahashi and Stamille), and a review of the state-of-the-art of ceramic joining methods (Greenhut) are presented in the section on designing joints in ceramics. In the section on brazing there are two papers describing innovative brazing compositions and methods (Knowles and Weil). In the section on biomedical applications there is a review of the state-of-the-art (Agathopoulos) and two papers describing recent advances (Shin and Saiz). In the section on high temperature applications there are two papers on the development of joints for new applications of ceramic materials (Chou and Weil), a paper on new joining methods for silicon carbide-based ceramics (Lewinsohn) and a paper illustrating the use of ceramic joining to fabricate ceramic components (Kwon).

The editors thank all the contributors, speakers, and attendees at the symposium for making it such a rewarding forum for discussion of recent advances in joining. We also thank the staff of The American Ceramic Society for their support and assistance in publishing this volume.

Charles A. Lewinsohn

Mrityunjay Singh

Ronald Loehman

Designing Joints in Ceramics

SELECTION AND FUNCTION OF INTERLAYER MATERIALS IN CERAMIC/CERAMIC JOINING

Eldon D. Case
Chemical Engineering and Materials Science Department
Michigan State University
East Lansing, MI 48824

ABSTRACT

The ability to join ceramics with ceramics is important to both the design and function of ceramics. Ceramic/ceramic joining can allow ceramic components to be fabricated with a greater range of both external and internal morphologies (where "internal" morphology can refer to channels within the component, for example). Also, ceramic/ceramic joining can allow one to integrate ceramics of different properties and function into a single structure. A variety of interlayer materials and interlayer fabrication techniques have been used to successfully join ceramics. This paper reviews the function of interlayer materials and aspects of the choice of interlayer materials and/or interlayer application techniques in ceramic/ceramic joining.

INTRODUCTION

Ceramic/ceramic bonding has been of technological importance for a very long time. For example, joining stoneware cups and handles has long been performed by first "throwing" the cup from clay then allowing the cup to dry to "leather hard" consistency. A freshly pulled handle then can be joined to the cup by first abrading the intended joint region with a scribe and attaching the cup and handle using slip. This simple example highlights the use of joining to obtain morphologies that may not otherwise be practical or even feasible. More recently, many different ceramics have been joined, where the ceramics may be either in the "green state" (unfired) or densified prior to joining.

THE FUNCTION OF CERAMIC/CERAMIC BONDING

It can be difficult to machine or form intricate shapes in ceramic components. However, ceramic/ceramic joining can facilitate the fabrication of more complex shapes. It can be useful to consider the topic morphological complexity of ceramic components in terms of an external geometry or shape as well as an "internal geometry", which can consist, for example, of channels that penetrate the bulk of the component [1]. Such channels could serve as a conduit for a variety of fluids, including cooling fluids for electronic devices, medicine in bioceramics, fuel or coolant in engine components, and a variety of other uses.

Channels in ceramics can be formed by a number of different techniques. External channels in ceramics can be formed by cutting or by ultrasonic grinding [2,3], or by "stamping" or "pressing in" of channels into a powder compact [4]. Shallow channels (channels with submicron depths) can be formed by photolithographic techniques [5]. External channels with dimensions of up to several hundred microns or more can be formed by pressing fugitive phase elements into the surface of a powder compact, with the external channels formed when a fugitive phase is burned out of the powder compact [6,7]. Likewise, internal channels in ceramics can be formed by the burnout of fugitive phase elements that have been pressed into a powder compact, for example [6-8]. (In the case of the direct formation of channels using fugitive phase elements, it is important that the elements are "burned out" by a pre-sintering heat treatment that allows sufficient time for the volatile phase to escape from the powder compact. Otherwise, an over-rapid binder burnout can lead to bloating and cracking).

However, internal channels in ceramics also can be formed by joining ceramic components having external channels (Figure 1). In this technique, typically sintered ceramic specimens containing exterior channels are joined using an interlayer. This technique of forming internal channels by joining specimens with external channels has at least one inherent advantage over the method of directly forming internal channels by fugitive phase burnout; namely the external channels can be examined in detail prior to joining. Thus, the accessibility of external channels allows one to sort out defective channels or to make detailed measurements of channel dimension prior to joining the specimens.

When interlayers are used in ceramic/ceramic joining, there are a number of different methods of applying the interlayer, as will be discussed below. Also, the thickness of the interlayer can potentially be important in ceramic/ceramic joining. However, before we discuss the selection and function of interlayer materials in joining, we shall briefly discuss ceramic/ceramic joining for which no interlayer material is applied prior to joining.

SYSTEMS THAT JOIN WITHOUT THE USE OF AN INTERLAYER

The presence of an interlayer is not universally required for ceramic/ceramic joining. There are two significant types of ceramic/ceramic joining for which one does not apply an interlayer material prior to joining, namely:

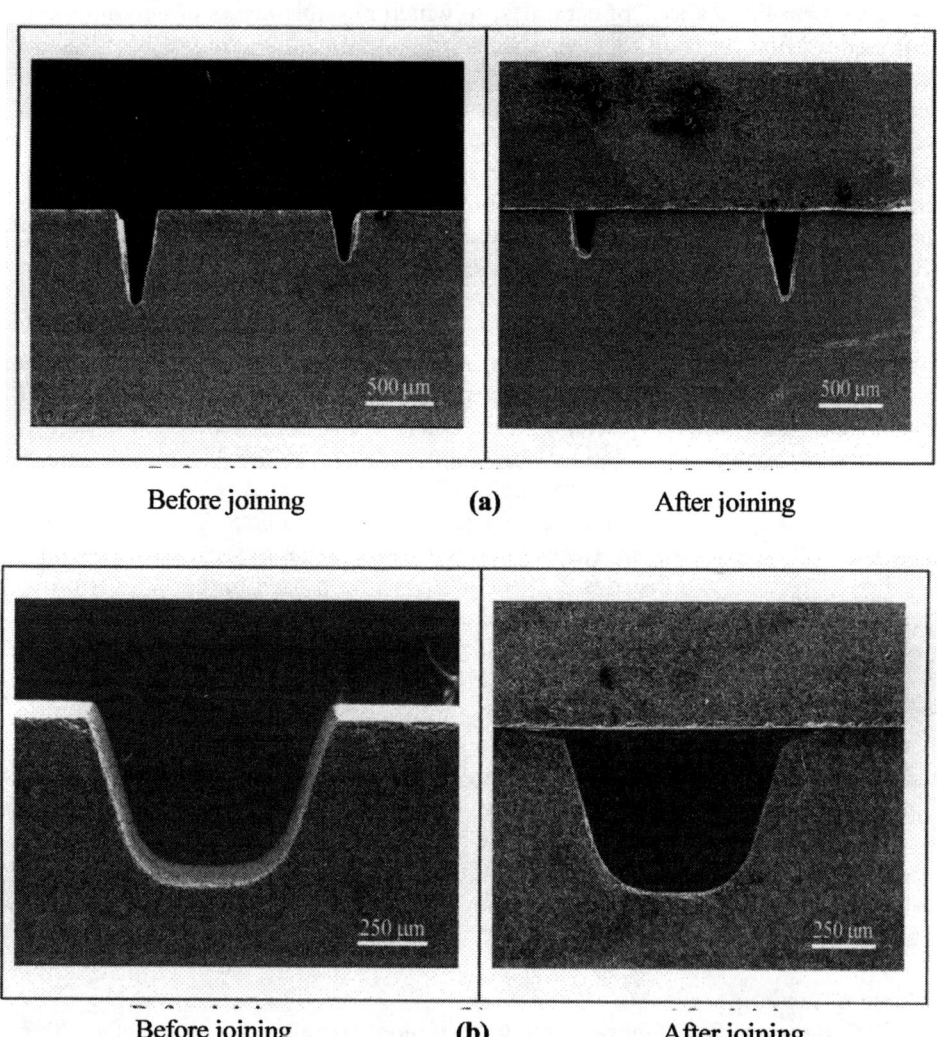

Figure 1. Microwave-joined specimens of (a) MaCor[TM] and (b) alumina (Reprinted with permission from [2], Copyright CRC Press, Boca Raton, Florida).

(a) "Freeform fabrication" of ceramics, in which multiple layers of ceramics can be joined by first pressing together sheets with significant loading of binders and plasticizers, then sintering the body, allowing for binder burnout. Thus, joining in the green state is facilitated by the binder phase. The specimen is then densified after the individual layers are joined in the green state.

(b) Diffusion bonding can be used to join densified specimens at high temperatures and applied pressures. Joining by superplastic deformation is a special case of diffusion bonding. Although interlayers or surface dopants are often used in diffusion bonding, diffusion bonding has been done without the presence of an interlayer.

Ceramic/ceramic joining via green tape (Freeform fabrication)

Ceramic/ceramic joining has been accomplished via the pressing together of "green tape" material [9,10], where green tape is a term used to describe ceramics that are impregnated with a binder phase and produced in flexible sheets. Green tapes typically incorporate binders such as polyvinyl butyral (PVB) [11,12] and plasticizers such as polyethylene glycol (PEG) [11] or dibutyl phthalate (DBP) [12], where the sheets are cut, stacked and pressed together to form a component.

For more than two decades, green tapes have been used in the fabrication of electronic ceramics, including multilayer ceramic capacitors and multilayer electronics packaging [13,14]. The binder and plasticizers must be removed prior to sintering the capacitors, but binder burnout can involve processing problems. For example, Tavernor et al. note that "the most common defects found in multi-layer ceramic capacitors are derived from residual porosity formed when solvents and binders are released from a ceramic green body" [15]. Another difficulty with green tape materials is that (especially for components made of multiple layers) the time that is required for binder burnout can be very lengthy. For example, the binder burnout time for multilayer capacitors or multilayer ceramic piezoelectric components can range from tens of hours to more than one week [16,17].

Diffusion Bonding

Diffusion bonding can be used to join both metals and ceramics at high temperatures and pressures. In diffusion bonding, the mass transfer across the joined interface is due to solid-state diffusion, but additional interlayer materials that act as fluxes are sometimes also used in order to enhance the mass diffusion rates [18]. Diffusion bonding (and creep) can be a sensitive function of grain size. The tendency for both creep and successful diffusion bonding increases as the grain size decreases. For example, Elssner et al. showed that alumina plates with a mean grain size of 18 microns did not join, while similar alumina plates with a one micron average grain size joined when processed under nominally identical conditions [19].

Using superplastic joining at pressures of up to 35 MPa and a joining temperature of 1400^0C, Dominguez-Rodriguez and co-workers [20, 21] were able to form bonds between partially stabilized zirconia specimens for which the interface could not be distinguished from the bulk material. Dominguez-Rodriguez et al. intentionally avoided the use of an interlayer material, terming it "deleterious" [20, 21]. The microstructure near the joint was apparently identical to the microstructure far from the joint. However, the superplastic flow induced plastic strains of up to 10 percent in the specimens [20, 21].

JOINING FACILITATED BY LOW MELTING POINT PHASES

Bonding can occur without an applied interlayer between ceramic components that include significant phase fractions of glassy or low melting temperature phases. In this case, the interlayer evolves in-situ during joining. More than a decade ago, Fukushima observed that microwave heating could induce joining between 92% and 96% purity alumina specimens, while 99% alumina specimens failed to join [23]. When Fukushima inserted billets of 92% alumina between the faces of 99% alumina specimens, the specimens did join. In addition, Fukushima was unable to join yttria-doped silicon nitride by microwave heating until a low-purity silicon nitride billet was inserted between the specimen faces [23]. The enhancement in microwave joining as the impurity level increases results from at least two factors. First, microwave heating is proportional to the dielectric loss of the material [37], and dielectric loss increases as the impurity level increases in a given material [4, 37, 42]. Second, the impurities often favor the formation of glassy grain boundary phases which can lead to a glassy interlayer being formed at the interface between the low purity specimen and another specimen.

More recently, Binner et al. [24,25] have shown that in both alumina and in silicon carbide, the presence of low melting point phases can affect joining behavior. For example, Binner et al. were able to microwave join RBSC (Reaction Bonded Silicon Carbide) specimens while more pure silicon carbide specimens did not join under similar conditions. In addition, in a series of micrographs for joints processed at a series of differing joining temperatures, Binner et al. observed a glassy phase that appeared to "bleed" out from the RBSC and form an interlayer that bonded the specimens together.

As demonstrated by the work of both Fukushima [23] and Binner et al. [24,25], low melting point phases can lead to the formation of interlayers that lead to joining. Thus, interlayers can in this circumstance lead to bonding, although interlayer materials where not externally applied to the specimens prior to heating.

HEATING TECHNIQUES FOR CERAMIC/CERAMIC JOINING

Ceramic/ceramic joining has been accomplished by conventional heating, microwave heating, capacitive discharge, laser heating, and frictional heating.

Microwave heating

Microwave heating has been used by a number of researchers to process ceramics [2,3,9,10,26-55]. The author and co-workers have used microwave energy in a variety of ceramic processing studies which has included sintering [9, 10,26-31], binder burnout [32,33], crack healing [34-36], modeling of refractory heating [37-41], thermal etching [42] and joining of similar ceramics, dissimilar ceramics and ceramic composites (Figures 2 - 6) both oxide ceramics [2,3,34,40, 43-48] and non-oxide ceramics [46, 49,50].

Laser heating

An example of a joining technique involving laser heating is gas-phase selective area laser deposition (SALD). In this technique, an interlayer is deposited in situ during the joining process [56]. Using the SALD technique for joining means that a laser beam is rastered over the joint region to induce the desired chemical reactions in the gas phase that is introduced into a vacuum chamber. For example, Harrison and Marcus [56] used SALD in which the laser heating induced thermal decomposition of tetramethylsilane and hydrogen gas mixture in a vacuum chamber to produce solid SiC that was used to join Hexoloy (Carborundum) tubes with an outer diameter of 0.95 cm.

Capacitive discharge joining

Alumina and PSZ (a partially stabilized 3 mol% yttria-zirconia) have been joined using a capacitor discharge system [57]. Specimens polished with 1 micron diamond paste prior to joining. Plate-shaped specimens were joined with specimen dimensions of 10 mm X 10 mm X 4 mm and 5 mm X 4 mm X 10 mm. The interlayer materials were Ti or Al foils or amorphous aluminum-rich $Al_aNi_bY_c$ foils, where the foil thickness was about 10 - 75 microns thick. The alumina joints were approximately 40 microns thick, with a significant porosity. However, the zirconia joint thickness were about 15 microns thick for the $Al_aNi_bY_c$ amorphous foil [57].

Frictional heating

Iijima and Watanabe [58] were able to join silicon nitride plates without an interlayer material using friction heating. Applying a 19kHz ultrasonic signal (with the direction of the vibration being parallel to the silicon nitride/ silicon nitride interface), Iijima and Watanabe achieved a silicon nitride/ silicon nitride joint within 10 seconds, where the highest joint strength achieved was approximately 33 MPa [58].

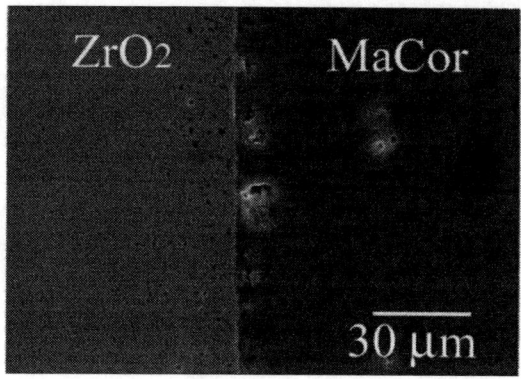

Figure 2. SEM micrographs of microwave-joined ZrO_2 with MaCor™ joined at 1020^0C for 20 minutes, using a 20 gm dead weight (after [79]).

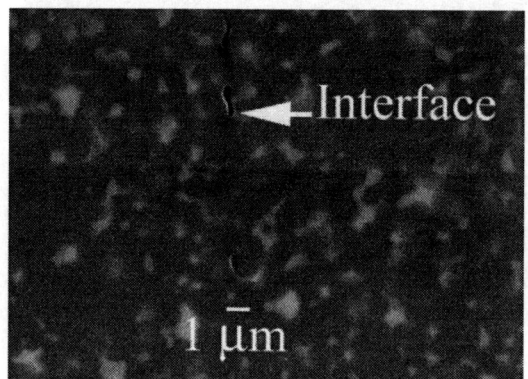

Figure 3. SEM micrographs of microwave-joined alumina/zirconia composites joined at 1450°C for 20 minutes (after [79]). Occasional porosity aids in locating the interface, but much of the interface was without porosity that could be resolved with the SEM.

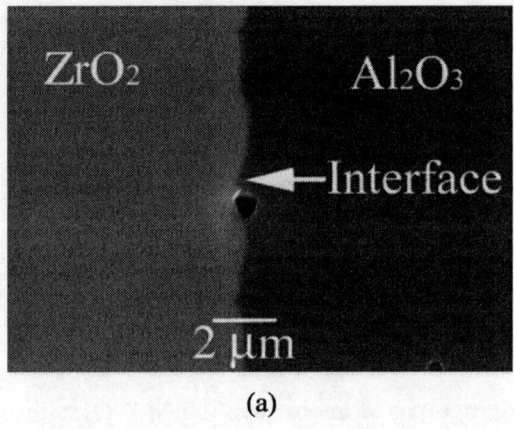

(a)

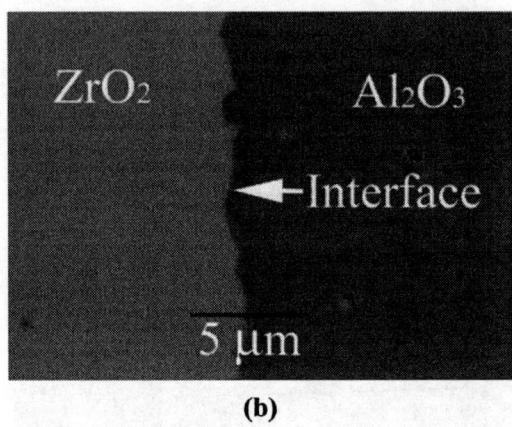

(b)

Figure 4. SEM micrographs of microwave-joined ZrO_2 /Al_2O_3, using a 50 gm dead weight, joined at 1500^0C for 20 minutes using a silica interlayer (Figure 4(a) is reprinted with permission from Journal of Advanced and Specialty Materials II, ASM International, Materials Park, OH, 44073-0002, Fig.3 pg 14, reference [45]). The same type of interlocking microstructure observed in the above two micrographs also were observed for conventionally joined ZrO_2 /Al_2O_3 specimens [85].

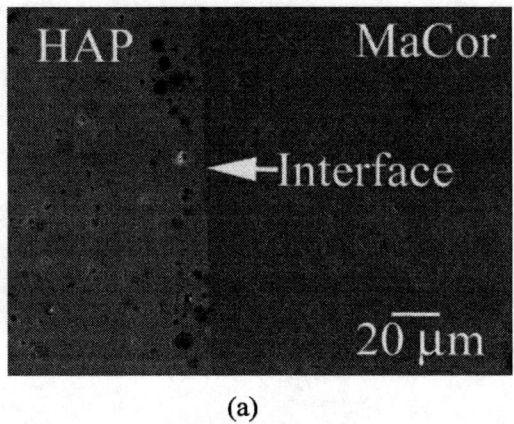

(a)

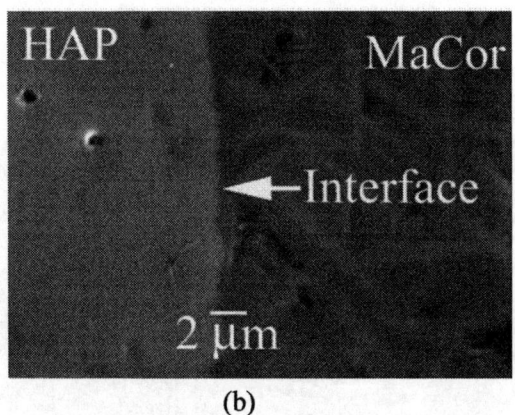

(b)

Figure 5. SEM micrographs of microwave-joined MaCor^{TM} and HAP, joined at 1020^{0}C for 20 minutes using a 20 gm dead weight using a silica interlayer (after [79]). For the higher magnification micrograph (Fig. 5b), one can observe the randomly-oriented mica platelets in the MaCor^{TM} microstructure.

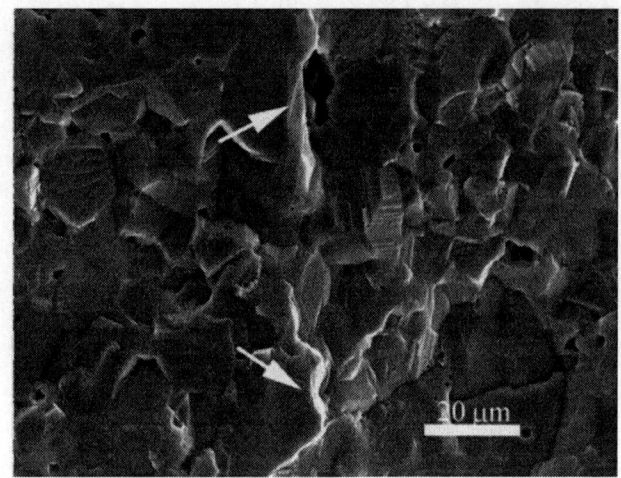

Figure 6a. The fracture surface of alumina speicmens that were microwave-joined at 1625°C for 10 minutes. The arrows indicate the position of the joined interface (after [34]).

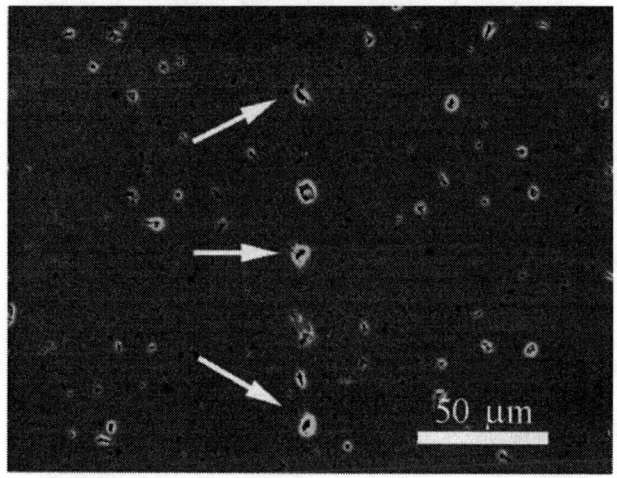

Figure 6b. A polished surface of the microwave-joined alumina specimen, joined at 1625°C for 10 minutes. The arrows indicate the position of the joined interface (after [34]).

APPLIED STRESS DURING JOINING

The applied stress during joining is a crucial processing variable. Many researchers apply high stresses during joining; especially those researchers that fabricate joints via diffusion bonding, superplastic deformation, or by hot pressing. For diffusion bonding and superplastic deformation, a high-applied stress is indispensable, since the mass transport that is involved is facilitated by creep conditions of high-applied stress at high temperature. Researchers that use metallic interlayers or other thick interlayers often employ hot pressing. If one is using initially thick interlayers, then the high applied pressures available via hot pressing can enable the foil or interlayer to conform to the gap between the materials to be joined.

A disadvantage of applying high stresses during bonding is the fixturing needed to apply the load to the specimen. In hot pressing (as well as in diffusion bonding and superplastic deformation) one needs to have sections of the load train adjacent to the specimen fabricated from materials that can perform under the temperatures and stress conditions

In addition to fixturing considerations, high stress at the joining temperature can induce creep in the specimens, depending on the times, temperatures, and the details of the creep mechanisms for the particular materials [20,59]. Of course, a problem that can be induced by creep is the loss of dimensional tolerances during joining. Joining by diffusion bonding does involve high-applied stress, and such stresses can lead to significant deformation of the specimens [20]. High-applied stresses sometimes are used even when interlayer materials are used. For example, many researchers have employed hot pressing to apply stresses in the range of 1 to 5 MPa in order to join materials for which an interlayer has been included.

CHEMICAL COMPOSITION OF THE INTERLAYER MATERIAL

A wide variety of materials have been used as an interlayer. For example, ceramic/ceramic joining has been successfully performed using metallic interlayers [57,60,61], ceramic interlayers [59,62], carbon-based interlayers [63] and glass interlayers [64-67].

Metallic interlayers

Metallic interlayers have been used to join a variety of oxide and non-oxide ceramics. A number of the metal interlayer joining processes involve reactive metal brazing, in which the metal reacts with the ceramic, forming a compound that is more readily wet by molten metal. For example, for the multilayer interlayers used by Young and Duh [68] to join AlN to AlN. AlN is not wet by Cu, Al, Ag, or Ni [56], but a Ni alloy that has been electroless-plated onto the AlN forms an AlNi compound that is more readily wet by molten metal than AlN.

Young et al. joined AlN with AlN by using a multilayer metallic bond phase in which the AlN plates were first coated with Ni [68]. Young et al. then placed a copper metal foil between the Ni-coated AlN plates and the specimen was then vacuum hot pressed for 30 minutes at temperatures between 600^0C to 700^0C with an applied pressure of 6.5 MPa [68].

Wu et al. used Ti/Ni/Ti metallic foil interlayers to join silicon nitride with silicon nitride at temperatures between 1000^0C and 1150^0C at pressures from 0 to 7.5 MPa and hold times of 0 to 180 minutes [69]. Wu et. al. found that a series of intermetallic compounds was formed in the bond layer region Ni_3Ti, NiTi, TiN, Ni_3Si, and other Ni, Ti, N, Si intermetallic compounds. The optimum bond strengths were obtained at applied pressures of 2.5 MPa, hold times of 60 to 120 minutes, and temperatures of approximately 1050^0C.

Reichel and Warlimont joined silicon nitride specimens using a range of cobalt-based braze materials, with a CoTi10 alloy brazed at temperatures ranging from about 1280^0C to 1500^0C [70]. Using vanadium foils, Fukai et al. [71] joined SiC to SiC at temperatures of 1200^0C to 1400^0C, with joining times of 30 minutes to 18 hours under an applied load of 30 MPa.

Turan et al. [57] used capacitive discharge heating to rapidly inject a high-energy electrical pulse in thin conductive metal foils, including amorphous metals as well as aluminum and titanium foils to fabricate alumina/alumina joints and zirconia/zirconia joints.

Dissimilar ceramics have also been joined by metallic interlayers. For example, Gam et al. [60] joined alumina to titanium diboride by hot pressing at 1470^0 C at 10 MPa for 30 minutes in a N_2 atmosphere. Gam et al. used a compositionally graded interlayer progressed from Ti foil on the TiB_2 face to Al foil at the alumina interface.

Joining using ceramic interlayers

Ceramic interlayers have been applied using several different techniques [2 – 4, 6, 8, 22, 43–52, 59, 72–74]. Interlayers have been applied as a slurry or paste, as a pre-densified billet, as a spin on layer of a liquid ceramic precursor.

Several researchers have performed ceramic/ceramic joining in the green state. For example, Zheng and Akinc joined SiC to SiC in the green state using an interlayer composed of a mixture of the ceramic precursor
allyhydridopolycarbosilane (AHPCS) and 25 to 35 volume percent of SiC powder [51]. The joint material (AHPCS with the SiC powder) was mixed up to form a paste and the paste was then applied to the surface of SiC powder compacts [51]. The specimens were first heated slowly in an ultrahigh purity argon atmosphere followed by densification at 2150^0C for 40 minutes.

Another method for the green state joining of ceramics using interlayers is that of the functionally gradient approach, where for example a powder compact is fabricated which has a compositional gradient that gradually transitions between the materials to be joined. For example, Lee et al. recently joined alumina and silicon nitride using a functional gradient approach [22]. The functional gradient between the alumina and the silicon nitride powders consisted of 20 layers, each 500 microns thick, of sialon polytoids. Sintering aids of alumina and yttria were added to the silicon nitride, yttria was added to the alumina as a sintering aid, and yttria was used as a sintering aid in the 12H sialon polytoid powder mixture with alumina and silicon nitride that made up the functional gradient [22]. According to Lee et al, the sialon polytoid powders were selected for use in the functional gradient layer since upon densification, a relatively glass-free microstructure is produced, which is advantageous for high temperature mechanical properties [22]. It should be noted that Lee et al. attempted to sinter an alumina/sialon/silicon nitride without a functional gradient (only a single sialon powder layer between the alumina and silicon nitride powders), however that attempt resulted in specimens with numerous large cracks running mostly normal to the alumina/silicon nitride interface [22].

Case and co-workers [1, 8] have also used functional gradients to join alumina and alumina composites are part of research on the design of meso-scale heat exchangers. In addition to inducing compositional gradients by layering, Case et al. have varied the particle sizes of the powders in order to enhance the particle packing [1, 8].

In those cases in which an interlayer is applied to already densified specimens before joining, the ceramic interlayers have been applied in a number of ways including application as a slurry [59, 73], insertion of the interlayer as a billet [72] and electrophoretic deposition [74]. Xie et al. used both superplastic beta-sialon interlayer [73] and interlayer composed of α-silicon nitride, yttria, silica and alumina powders [59] to join silicon nitride plates by hot pressing for two hours at 5 MPa. The interlayer material was applied as a slurry. For the beta-Sialon interlayer [73] joining temperatures ranged 1600^0C to 1750^0C and for the earlier work with the silicon nitride, yttria, silica and alumina powder slurry [59], joining was done at 1450^0C-1650^0C at pressures of up to 5 MPa at times between 10 minutes and 1 hour. The joints produced by Xie et al. varied from about 1 to 3 microns in thickness. Ravi and Chaim inserted a tape-cast billet of Y-TZP between densified Y-TZP specimens prior to joining the Y-TZP specimens via hot pressing at temperatures between 1000^0C and 1300^0C at pressures of 55 MPa [72]. Lessing et al. [74] used electrophoretic deposition to fabricate an interlayer for the joining of silicon carbide and silicon nitride components. The interlayer, which was a mixture of silicon nitride or silicon carbide powders and graphite or lamp black. When heated at 1450^0C, a the carbon-based components of the electrophoretic layer reaction with the silicon nitride or silicon carbide powders, resulting in a reaction bond layer joining the specimens. Although the carbonaceous material used by Singh [63] to join SiC is applied as a slurry, the general principal of reaction bonding of SiC materials used by Lessing et al. [74] is similar to that developed by Singh [63].

SELECTING THE INTERLAYER COMPOSITION

For ceramic/ceramic joining, one fundamental question is "what is the chemical composition of the interlayer that lead to successful joining of a given pair of ceramic specimens?". As a partial answer to this question, one can potentially utilize the development work that has already been done in sintering studies [75]. For example, the ceramics community has invested a great deal of time and effort into finding effective sintering aids for certain ceramic materials such as silicon nitride and silicon carbide [75]. (Highly covalent ceramics such as silicon nitride and silicon carbide typically require sintering aids since the mass diffusivity in pure, covalent solids is very low. Sintering aids can boost the grain boundary diffusivity and hence accelerate densification).

As a particular example, sintering aids such as Y_2O_3, MgO, Al_2O_3 and SiO_2 have been employed (in various combinations and doping levels) to enhance the densification of silicon nitride [75,76]. The glassy grain boundary phases that often result from the addition of sintering aids can adversely affect fracture and fatigue properties as well as oxidation behavior [75,76]. For silicon nitride, the typical rapid drop in strength at temperatures $> 1200^0C$ is generally attributed to glassy grain boundary phases. However, improvement in the grain boundary phase can be "engineered" by using a sintering aid of silica plus rare earth sesquioxides (Re_2O_3, where Re is a rare earth ion). The Re_2O_3 plus SiO_2 system tends to form a crystalline $Re_2Si_2O_7$ phase that enhances both high temperature strength and oxidation resistance for the sintered silicon nitride. Gopal et al. [75] have noted that the understanding gained in the design of grain boundary phases for sintering can be utilized in ceramic/ceramic joining. For example, additives of Yb_2O_3 and silica lower the joining temperature for silicon nitride to $\approx 1650^0C$ due to the existence of a $Yb_2Si_2O_7$ eutectic [75]. Furthermore, combining silica with two rare earth sesquioxides (such as Y_2O_3 and Yb_2O_3) deepens the eutectic and lowers the joining temperature for bulk silicon nitride to roughly $1550-1500^0C$ [75].

While the work of Gopal et al. in using sintering aids as a guide to identifying optimal chemistries for joining, this technique is not necessarily straightforward to apply universally to ceramic/ceramic joining studies. One difficulty is that sintering aids for most ceramic materials have not been studied as extensively as has been the case for ceramics such as silicon nitride and silicon carbide. Thus, for a given ceramic/ceramic pair to be joined, there may be limited or no work available in the literature that discusses sintering aids. In addition, the joining of dissimilar ceramics (SiC and an alumina/zirconia particulate composite as an example) are potentially more complicated that the joining of similar ceramics such as Si_3N_4/Si_3N_4.

However, it may be problematic to engineer the interlayer composition so that the chemistry of the as processed matches the chemistry of grain boundaries after sintering.

INTERLAYER/INTERFACE PROPERTIES IMPORTANT IN JOINING
Interlayer thickness

The thickness varies considerably for interlayers that have been used successfully for ceramic/ceramic joining [2,3,18,47,77-79]. For example, for spin-on interlayers [2,3,47,78,79], the thickness of spin-on interlayers (after curing) tends to be in the sub-micron range. Case and co-workers have joined a number of ceramics using spin-on layers that are roughly 200 to 500 nm thick after curing [2,3,47,78,79].

Not surprisingly, the thicker interlayer bonds seem to accommodate surface roughness of the joined parts. For example, with the joining method developed by Singh [63], one has the practical advantage that the surfaces to be joined can be in the as-cut condition, rather than requiring polishing. Reducing the polishing can potentially lead to large savings if ceramic/ceramic joining is attempted for large parts. However, thicker interlayers can also lead to higher residual stresses, as will be discussed in the next section.

Interlayer thickness and residual stress

If ceramic plates of thickness L are joined using a metallic interlayer of thickness 2H, then the residual stress decreases with the interlayer thickness decreases [80]. According to Kovalev et al., [80], when L/H is equal to or greater than the threshold value $(L/H)_{th}$, then the relative thickness of the adherent is essentially equivalent to an infinite thickness, that is, the residual stress is no longer sensitive to the relative thickness of the interlayer and adherent. Kovalev et al. used finite element calculations to model silicon nitride/silicon nitride joining using Ni, Al, or Si interlayers [80]. For thin metallic interlayers, the elastic-plastic properties of the interlayer determine the development of the residual tensile stresses in the ceramic rather than the thermal expansion mismatch [80], where plasticity in the metal interlayer leads to a relaxation of the residual stress.

As reviewed by Lewinsohn et al. [83], for interlayers formed from ceramic precursors, it is generally found that edge cracks are associated with thicker interlayers, especially interlayers exceeding a thickness of about 20 microns. According to Lewinsohn et al., the shrinkage associated with such precursors can induce considerable stresses in the specimen [83]. In addition, as the polymer is converted into a ceramic, the viscosity changes by many orders of magnitude such that in the temperature range in which the viscosity changes rapidly, one should heat the specimen relatively slowly to avoid cracking [83]. However, the research of Case et al indicates that if the interlayer is sufficiently thin, such problems may be reduced [2, 34, 43-49,79]. Case and co-workers have pyrolyzed spin-on layers of a silica ceramic precursor to form silica layers that are typically 200 to 300 nm in thickness when cured via heating in air at 200^0C. Heating rates of > 50^0C/minute from room temperature to 1000^0C during microwave heating did not induce cracking in the specimens [2, 34, 43-49,79], although viscosity of the silica precursor is likely changing dramatically over this temperature range.

Initial surface roughness of the specimens to be joined

For ceramic/ceramic joining, the effect of surface roughness of the components to be joined has not been studied in a systematic way. For two ceramics components that are to be joined, the surface roughness of each component can vary from that induced by cutting the ceramic to a relatively smooth and flat surface obtained by polishing with fine particle size abrasive pastes, for example. There are indications that this initial surface roughness should play a role in the design of the as cured interlayer thickness. The interlayer thickness is itself a function of the interlayer material and interlayer deposition technique.

SPECIMEN PROPERTIES AND THE INTERFACE
Strength

The strength of ceramic/ceramic joints of course sensitive to the interlayer material. For metallic interlayers, often the joint strength begins to show significant decreases in the range of 800^0C to 1000^0C [57,60,61]. In addition, metallic interlayers can be subject to oxidation and environmental degradation at elevated temperatures. In addition, glass interlayers [64-67] can be subject to softening at elevated temperatures. However, in addition to strength, other physical properties of joined ceramics can be affected by the nature of the interlayer. The next section discusses the relationship between the nature of the interlayer and optical properties of joined optical or infrared ceramics.

Optical properties

Yen et al. joined polycrystalline magnesium fluoride using diffusion bonding [81,82]. However, the transmittance of the joined MgF_2 was considerably lower than that of an unjoined MgF_2 of comparable thickness [81]. In order to enhance interfacial diffusion, Yen et al. followed up their initial work by joining MgF_2 specimens that had been coated with LiF by vacuum evaporation. (The LiF coated was applied in order to enhance diffusion in the region of the interface). For both the LiF coated specimens and the uncoated specimens, the transmittance of the joined and unjoined specimens were measured in the infrared wavelength range from 2 to 10 microns using an infrared spectrophotometer. Yen et al. attributed the loss in transmittance observed in the diffusion-joined MgF_2 to porosity and grain growth (due to plastic deformation and recrystallization in the MgF_2) that occurred at or near the MgF_2/MgF_2 interface due to the diffusion bonding process [81,82].

In another study in which optical transmittance of joined optical ceramics is affected by the bond layer, Lee et al. [44,78] used sodium silicate as an interlayer material to join MgF_2/MgF_2 by both conventional and microwave heating. Case et al. measured the IR transmittance over the wavelength range from 800 to 1600 nm using a monochromator. For both the microwave and conventionally heated specimens, joining was done at 700^0C for 20 minutes. As shown in Figure 7, the interfacial bond layer was about 10 microns thick for joining by both microwave and conventional heating [44,78]. However, the transmittance of the microwave joined specimen was essentially the same as an equivalent thickness of the unjoined material, while the optical transmittance of the conventionally joined materials was considerably lower [44,78]. As was the case for the work by Yen et al. [81,82], the mechanism for the drop in transmittance for the conventionally joined MgF_2 is apparently due to the microstructure of the bond layer. For the microwave joined specimen the bond layer appears homogeneous to relatively homogeneous (Figure 7a) while for the conventionally joined material, a second phase appears to be present in the interlayer (Figure 7b). In order to quantitatively compare the transmittance of the microwave joined, conventionally joined and microwave joined materials, Case et al. used the Lambert-Bouger law that takes into account optical reflection at each interface, namely

$$\frac{I_T}{I_I} = (1-R)^n \exp(-\alpha x) = T$$

where I_T = the transmitted intensity, I_I = the incident intensity, R = the reflection coefficient, n = the number of interface, α = the optical absorption factor, x = the specimen thickness and T = the optical transmittance. The values of the optical absorption factor measured for where 0.149, 0.156, and 0.342 for unjoined, microwave-joined and conventionally-joined MgF_2, respectively, which indicates the very large loss in transmittance brought about by the optical scattering in the conventionally-joined MgF_2 specimens.

As was the case in the MgF_2/MgF_2 joints fabricated by Yen et al. [81,82], optical scattering in the bond region likely is responsible for the drop in optical transmittance. Thus in the studies by Yen et al. [81,82] and the study by Case and co-workers [44,78] has shown that interlayer microstructure can degrade the transmittance of joined optical/IR materials such as MgF_2.

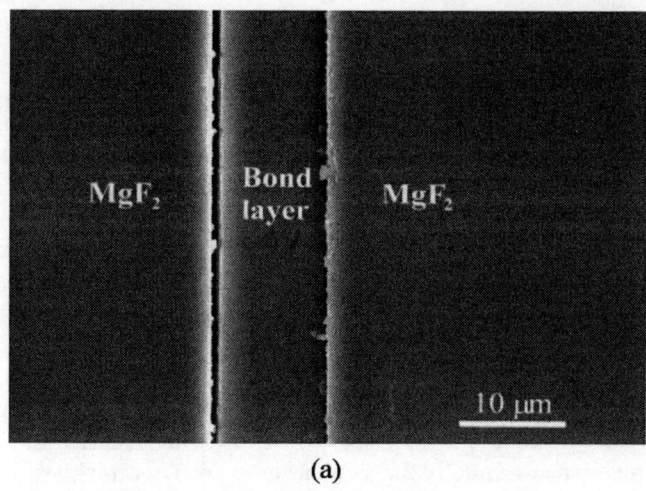

(a)

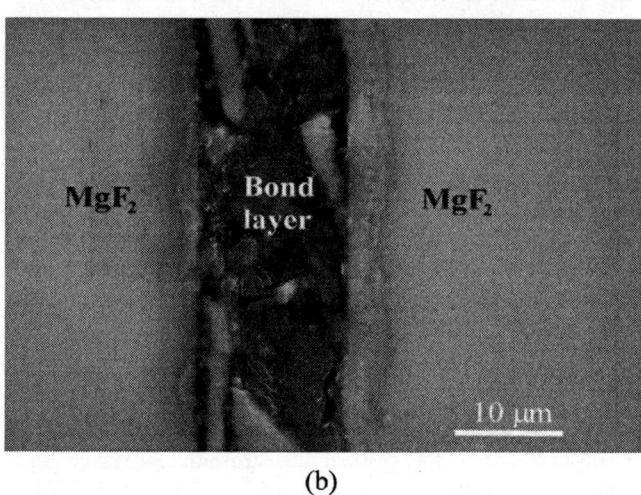

(b)

Figure 7. Joined MgF_2 specimens joined by (a) microwave and (b) conventional heating (after [78]). Note the microstructure of the microwave-joined specimen appears relatively homogeneous while second phases are present in the conventionally-heated interlayer.

Initial gaps between the interlayer and substrate

Due to typical lack of plasticity of ceramics, ceramic interlayers that are applied prior to heating will have "gaps" between the interlayer material and the ceramic substrate prior to heating [36]. It has been noted that interlayers formed from preceramic polymers are thin, such initial gaps can lead to interfacial porosity after the joint is fabricated [83]. However, such gaps may be important in microwave heating. Before the joint is fabricated, a ceramic interlayer will typically contact the opposing specimen surface at a few isolated contact points [36]. As the materials are heated and joining proceeds, Tyska and Case [36] have suggested that the joint region evolves, beginning with bonds being formed at the initial contact points. As joining proceeds the morphological changes that take place in the "gaps" likely have much in common with the crack healing process [36]. In regard to microwave processing, the "gaps" can be viewed much as a planar array of air capacitors. For the interaction of the microwave field with the "gaps", consider the relationship

$$\vec{D} = \varepsilon \vec{E}$$

where $\vec{D}$ is the electric displacement vector, $\vec{E}$ is the electric field vector, and ε is the permittivity (the real part of the dielectric constant). The normal component of the vector $\vec{D}$ is continuous across an interface between two dielectric media [84]. For air (in the initial "gaps" in the join region) $\varepsilon \cong \varepsilon_0$, where $\varepsilon_0 = 1 =$ the permittivity of a vacuum. For comparison, for alumina, $\varepsilon \cong 9$. If one joins alumina specimens, $\vec{D}$ (and hence the product $\varepsilon \vec{E}$) is continuous across the interface, which means that the electric field in the air gap in much higher than in the electric field in the alumina, which may lead to preferential heating at the alumina surfaces bordering the air gap. Such surface-limited heating would be difficult to experimentally detect but it may lead to apparent enhancement in joining via microwave heating compared to conventional heating [85].

SUMMARY

While interlayers are not necessary for ceramic/ceramic joining, interlayers have been used widely to join ceramics. Metallic interlayers have been used to join many ceramic oxides and non-oxides, but metallic interlayers limit both the use temperature and the service environment of the joined components.

Gopal et al. [72, 75] have suggested that one select the interlayer composition to match the composition of sintering aids for the given material. For silicon carbide and silicon nitride, this approach works well [72, 75]. However, sintering aids have exhaustively researched for silicon carbide and silicon nitride, while the sintering aid information is far less complete for most other ceramic systems.

Also, for dissimilar ceramics, the choice of interlayer material may not be straightforward.

The magnitude of the applied stress during joint fabrication is an important aspect of the ceramic/ceramic joining. High applied pressures can certainly enhance bonding, but if high pressures and high temperatures that are employed during joining, significant plastic deformation and loss of dimensional tolerance can occur. Also, the fixturing needed to apply high loads can (1) limit the geometry of the specimens that are joined and (2) complicate the furnace design and (3) perturb the microwave fields present if microwave joining is used.

Thicker bond layers can likely help to accommodate an initial surface roughness. However, thick bonds can elevate residual stress [80] and lead to edge cracks [83].

The interlayer can affect the final strength of the joined component, with metallic and glassy bond phases tending to have lower maximum service temperatures than do ceramic interlayers. However, in addition to mechanical properties, the transmittance of optical and infrared materials can be affected by joining [78, 81, 82]

REFERENCES:
1. H. W. Shin, P. Kwon and E. D. Case, "Novel powder processing techniques to fabricate efficient meso-scale heat exchangers", in press, Proceedings of the 30th North American Manufacturing Research Conference.
2. K. N. Seiber, K. Y. Lee, and E. D. Case, "Microwave and Conventional Joining of Ceramics using Spin-on Materials," pp. 941-949 in Proceedings of the 12th Annual Advanced Composites Conference, Technomic Publishing Co., Lancaster, PA, 1997.
3. E. D. Case, K. Y. Lee, J. G. Lee, and T. Hoepfner, "Geometrical Stability of Holes and Channels During Joining of Ceramics and Ceramic Composites," pp. 27 - 34 in Joining of Advanced and Specialty Materials, M. Singh, J. E. Indacochea, and D. Hauser, eds., ASM International, Materials Park, OH, 1998.
4. J. G. Lee, H. W. Shin, E. D. Case, P. Kwon, "The fabrication of smooth, submilliter-diameter channels in polycrystalline ceramics without machining", J. Mater. Sci. Lett., 20[2]: 107 - 109, 2001.
5. M. Kitayama, J. D. Powers, L. Kulinsky and A. M. Glaeser, J. Eur. Ceram. Soc. 19: 2191 - 2198, 1999.
6. H. W. Shin, E. D. Case, and P. Kwon, "Joining bioactive and bioinert ceramics", pp. 15-22, Joining of Advanced and Specialty Materials III, ASM International, Materials Park, OH, 2001.
7. H. W. Shin, P. Kwon and E. D. Case, "Fabrication of internal channels without machining in joined alumina and zirconia ceramics", pp. 23-30,

Joining of Advanced and Specialty Materials III, ASM International, Materials Park, OH, 2001.
8. H. W. Shin, E. D. Case, and P. Kwon, "Fabrication of internal channels in ceramics and ceramic composites", in press, Journal of Advanced Materials
9. J. Bansky, D. Bartley, J. Engemann, J. Asmussen, E. Case, and S. Connery, "Mechanical Characteristics of Hybrid Multilayer Green Tape Ceramics Sintered in a 2.45 GHz Single Mode Microwave Cavity," Scripta Metallurgica et Materialia, 28: 785-790, 1993.
10. J. Bansky, J. Engemann, E. K. Polzer, D. Bartley, and E. Case, "Advanced Processing and Novel Applications of Hybrid Multilayer Green Tapes," Proceedings of the Ninth European Hybrid Microelectronics Conference, ISHM, Nice, France, 107-115, 1993.
11. D. Rocak, M. Kosec and A. Degen, "Ceramic suspension optimization using factorial designs of experiments", J. European Ceram. Soc., 22[4]: 391 - 395, 2002.
12. J. H. Jean and H. R. Wang, "Organic distributions in dried alumina green tape", J. Am. Ceram. Soc., 84[2]: 267 - 272, 2001.
13. A. I. Y. Tok, F. Y. C. Boey and M. K. A. Khor, "Tape casting of high dielectric ceramic substrates for microelectronics packaging", J. Mater. Eng. Perform., 8[4]: 469 - 472, 1999.
14. M. J. Orkin, C. H. Sherwood and G. J. Ewell, "Characterization of cast green tape used in manufacturing multilayer ceramic capacitors", Am. Ceram. Soc. Bull., 59[8]:831, 1980.
15. A. W. Tavernor, H. P. S. Li, A. J. Bell and R. Stevens, "Improved compaction in multilayer capacitor fabrication", J. European Ceram. Soc., 19[9]: 1691 - 1695, 1999.
16. S. Masia, P. D. Calvert, W. E. Rhine, and H. K. Bowen, J. Mater. Sci, 24: 1907- 1912, 1989.
17. M. Kahn and M. Chase, "Effects of Heat Treatments on Multilayer Piezoelectric Ceramic-air Composites", J. Am. Ceram. Soc., 75[3]: 649-656, 1992.
18. M. L. Santella, "A Review of Techniques for Joining Advanced Ceramics", 1992, Amer. Ceram. Soc. Bull., 71: 947-954, 1992.
19. G. Elssner, W. Diem and J. S. Wallace, pp. 629-639 in "Surfaces and Interfaces in Ceramic and Ceramic-Metal Systems", Edited by J. Pask and A. G. Evans, Plenum Press, New York, 1981..
20. Jimenez-Pique, E., Dominguez-Rodriguez, A., Martinez-Fernandez, J., Lara-Curzio, E. and Singh, M., "Microstructure and mechanical properties of superplastically joined yttria-partially-stabilized zirconia (Y-PSZ) ceramics", J. Eur. Ceram. Soc., 20 [2] 147-151, 2000.

21. A. Dominguez-Rodriguez, F. Guiberteau and M. Jimenez-Melendo, "Heterogeneous junction of yttria partially stabilized zirconia by superplastic flow", J. Mater. Res., 13[6]: 1631-1636, 1998.
22. C. S. Lee, L. C. De Jonghe and G. Thomas, "Mechanical properties of polytypoidally joined Si_3N_4-Al_2O_3", Acta Mater., 49[18]: 3767 - 3773, 2001.
23. H. Fukushima, T. Yamanaka, and Matsui, "Microwave heating and its application to joining", J. Mater. Res. 5[2]: 397 – 405, 1990.
24. J.G.P. Binner, J.A. Fernie, and P.A. Whitaker, "An Investigation into Microwave Bonding Mechanisms via a Study of Silicon Carbide and Zirconia," J. Mater. Sci., 33 [12]: 3009-3015, 1998.
25. J.G.P. Binner, J.A. Fernie, and P.A. Whitaker, T. E. Cross, "The effect of composition on the bonding of alumina ceramics", J. Mater. Sci., 33 [12]: 3017-3029, 1998.
26. K.Y. Lee, E. D. Case, and J. Asmussen, Jr., "Sintering of Alumina Ceramics in a Single-Mode Microwave Cavity Under Automated Control," Ceramic Transactions, 59, 473-480, American Ceramic Society, Inc., Columbus, OH, 1995.
27. K.Y. Lee, E. D. Case, and J. Asmussen, Jr., "Microwave Sintering of Ceramic Matrix Composites and the Effect of Organic Binders on the Sinterability," Proceedings of 11th Annual Advanced Composites Conference, The Engineering Society, Ann Arbor, MI, 491-504, 1995.
28. K.Y. Lee, P. H. Dearhouse, and E. D. Case, "Microwave Sintering of Alumina Using Four Different Single-Cavity Modes," Journal of Materials Synthesis and Processing, 7[3]: 159 - 166, 1999.
29. K.Y. Lee and E. D. Case, "Microwave Sintering of Alumina Matrix Zirconia Composites Using a Single-Mode Microwave Cavity," Journal Materials Science Letters, 18[3]: 201-203, 1999.
30. K.Y. Lee, L. Cropsey, B. Tyszka, and E. D. Case, "Grain size, density and Mechanical Properties of alumina batch-processed in a single mode microwave cavity," Materials Research Bulletin, 32[3]: 287-295, 1997.
31. T. P. Hoepfner and E. D. Case, "Physical Characteristics of Sintered Hydroxyapatite", pp.53 - 66, Bioceramics: Materials and Applications III, Ceramic Transactions, Volume 110, American Ceramic Society, Inc., Westerville, OH, 2000.
32. K.Y. Lee, E. D. Case, J. Asmussen, Jr., and M. Siegel, "Binder Burnout in a Controlled Single-Mode Microwave Cavity," Scripta Materialia, 35[1]: 107-111, 1996.
33. K.Y. Lee, E.D. Case, J. Asmussen, "Binder Burnout for ceramics and ceramic matrix composites using a single-mode microwave cavity," pp. 539-546 in Microwaves: Theory and Applications in Materials Processing IV,

Ceramic Transactions, Volume 80, D.E. Clark, W.H. Sutton, and D.A. Lewis, Eds., American Ceramic Society, Inc., Westerville, OH, 1997.
34. K.Y. Lee, E. D. Case, D. Reinhard, "Microwave Joining and Repair of Ceramics and Ceramic Composites," Ceramic Eng. and Sci. Proc., 18: 543-550, 1997.
35. B.A. Wilson, K. Y. Lee, and E. D. Case, "Diffusive Crack Healing Behavior in Polycrystalline Alumina: A Comparison Between Microwave Annealing and Conventional Annealing," Materials Research Bulletin, 32 [12]: 1606-1615, 1997.
36. B.R. Tyska and E. D. Case, "Relationships between crack healing in ceramics and ceramic/ceramic joining," pp. 1 - 4 in Proceedings of the 35th International Microwave Power Symposium, International Power Institute, Manassas, VA, 2000.
37. K.Y. Lee, E. D. Case, and J. Asmussen, Jr., "The Steady-State Temperature as a Function of Casket Geometry for Microwave-Heated Refractory Caskets," Materials Research Innovations, 1[2]: 101-116, 1997.
38. M.Traub, K. Y. Lee, and E. D. Case, " The Effect of Casket Geometry on Microwave Heating and Its Modeling", pp. 69 - 80 in Ceramic Transactions, Volume 94, American Ceramic Society, Inc., Westerville, OH, 1998.
39. K.Y. Lee and E. D. Case, "Steady-State Temperature of Microwave-Heated Refractories as a Function of Microwave Power and Refractory Geometry," Materials Science and Engineering, A269: 8 - 20, 1999.
40. E.D. Case and J. G. Lee, "Techniques to minimize the effect of refractory casket 'hot spots' during microwave processing," pp. 5 - 8 in Proceedings of the 35th International Microwave Power Symposium, International Microwave Power Institute, Manassas, VA, 2000.
41. J.G. Lee, E. D. Case and K. Y. Lee, "Enhancing the Microwave Processing of Ceramics by Avoiding Hot Spots and Local Melting in Refractory Specimen Enclosures ", Journal of Advanced Materials, 34[2]: 49 - 59, 2002.
42. K.Y. Lee and E. D. Case, "A Comparison of theoretical and experimental profiles for thermally-induced grain-boundary grooving", European Physical Journal, Applied Physics, 8[3]: 197- 214, 1999.
43. E.D. Case, K. Y. Lee, and J. G. Lee, "Joining of Polycrystalline Ceramics and Ceramic Composites Using Microwave Heating," pp. 17 - 20 in Proceedings of the 33rd International Microwave Power Symposium (IMPI), International Power Institute, Manassas, VA, 1998.
44. E.D. Case, J. G. Lee, and K. Y. Lee, "Joining of Optical and Infrared Materials Using Spin-On Layers", pp. 17 - 26 in Joining of Advanced and Specialty Materials, M. Singh, J. E. Indacochea, and D. Hauser, eds., ASM International, Materials Park, OH, 1998.

45. E.D. Case, J. G. Lee, L. Zeng, and M. A. Crimp, "Joining of Dissimilar Ceramic Materials", pp 10 - 17 in Joining of Advanced and Specialty Materials II, ASM International, Materials Park, OH, 2000.
46. E.D. Case and J. G. Lee, "Joining Dissimilar Ceramics and Ceramic Composites for Biomedical and Structural Applications", pp. 318 - 324, Technology Convergence in Composites Applications, Proceedings of the ACUN-3 International Composites Conference, S. Bandyopadhyay, N Gowripalan, and N. Drayton, eds. University of New South Wales, Sydney, Australia, 2001.
47. E.D. Case and M. A. Crimp, "Joining of Ceramic Materials Using Spin on Interlayers", Advanced Engineering Materials, 3: 395-399, 2001.
48. L.Zeng, M. A. Crimp and E. D. Case, "The interfacial microstructure of Zirconia and MaCor^{TM} joined using spin-on interlayers", Materials Science and Engineering, A307: 74 - 79, 2001.
49. J.G. Lee and E. D. Case, "Joining of Non-Oxide Ceramics Using Conventional and Microwave Heating", 21[4]: 589 - 597, Ceramic Engineering and Science Proceedings, American Ceramic Society, 2000.
50. M.Ferraris, F. Paolini, E. D. Case, M. Salvo, "Microwave Joining of SiC", submitted, Journal of the American Ceramic Society.
51. J. Zheng and M. Akinc, "Green state joining of SiC without applied pressure", J. Am. Ceram. Soc., 84[11]: 2479 - 2483, 2001.
52. S.Aravindan and R. Krishnamurthy, "Joining of ceramic composites by microwave heating" Mater. Lett., 38[4]: 245-249, 1999.
53. T.Sato N. Takahashi and K. Shimakage, "Microwave joining of alumina to magnesia", J. Ceram. Soc. Jap., 104[10]: 905-907, 1996.
54. I. Ahmad, R. Silberglitt, T. A. Shan, Y. L. Tian and R. Cozzens, "Microwave assisted of SiC and its application to joining", pp. 357-365 in Ceram. Trans., Vol. 59, The American Ceramic Society, 1995.
55. R.R. DI Fire and D. E. Clark, "Microwave joining of zinc sulfide", pp. 381 - 387 in Ceram.Trans., Vol 59, The American Ceramic Society, 1995.
56. S.Harrison and H. L. Marcus, "Gas-phase selective area laser deposition (SALD) joining of SiC", Materials & Design, 20[2 - 3]: 147 - 152, 1999.
57. S.Turan, I. A. Bucklow and E. R. Wallach, "Capacitor-discharge joining of oxide ceramics", J. Am. Ceram. Soc., 82: 1242 - 1248, 1999.
58. M.Iijima and Y. Watanabe, "Ultrasonic joining of silicon nitride plates without an adhesive material using a 19 kHz vibration system", Jpn. J. Appl. Phys. Part 1 - Regul. Pap. Short Notes Rev. Pap. 40[5B]: 3789 - 3791, 2001.
59. R.J. Xie, L.P. Huang, Y. Chen and X.R. Fu, "Evaluation of Si_3N_4 Joints: Bond Strength and Microstructure," J. Mat. Sci., 34 [8] 1783-1790, 1999.

60. J.S. Gam, K. S. Han, S. S. Park and H. C. Park, "Joining of TiB2-Al2O3 using compositionally graded interlayers", Mater. Manuf. Process, 14: 537 - 546, 1999.
61. R.A. Marks, D. R. Chapman, D. T. Danielson and A. M. Glaeser, A.M., "Joining of alumina via copper/niobium/copper interlayers", Acta Mater., 48: 4425 - 4438, 2000.
62. M.Gopal, M. Sixta, L. De Jonghe and G. Thomas, "Seamless joining of silicon nitride ceramics", J. Am. Ceram. Soc., 84[4]: 708 - 712, 2001.
63. M.Singh, "Microstructure and mechanical properties of reaction-formed joints in reaction-bonded silicon carbide ceramics", J. Mat. Sci., 33: 5781-5787, 1998.
64. P.Lemoine, M. Ferraris, M. Salvo and M. Montorsi, "Vitreous Joining Process of SiCf/SiC Composites", J. Eur. Ceram. Soc., 16: 1231- , 1996.
65. M.Ferraris, M. Salvo, C. Isola, M. Appendino Montorsi and A. Kohyama, "Glass-ceramic Joining and Coating of SiC/SiC for Fusion Applications", J. of Nucl. Mat., 258-263: 1546-1550, 1998.
66. Y.Katoh, M. Kotani, A. Kohyama, M. Montorsi, M. Salvo, and M. Ferraris, "Microstructure and Mechanical Properties of Low-Activation Glass-Ceramic Joining And Coating For SiC/SiC Composites", J. Nucl. Mat. 283-287: 1262-1266, 2000.
67. H. L. Lee, S. W. Nam, B. S. Hahn, B. H. Park and D. Han, "Joining of silicon carbide using MgO-Al_2O_3-SiO_2 filler", J. Mat. Sci. 33 [20]: 5007-5014, 1998.
68. C.D. Young and J.G. Duh, "Bonding Mechanism of Electrodes Ni-P Film with AlN substrate and Cu Foil," IEEE Transactions on Components Packaging and Manufacturing Technology Part A, 21 [2] 330-344, 1998.
69. A. P. Wu, G. S. Zou, J. L. Ren, W. J. Li, "Heat-resistant joints of Si3N4 ceramics with intermetallic compounds formed in situ", J. Mater. Sci., 36[11]: 2673 - 2678, 2001.
70. U. Reichel and H. Warlimont, "Rapidly solidified CoTi alloys as brazing foils for high-temperature joining of silicon nitride ceramic", Z. Metallk., 90[9]: 699 - 703, 1999.
71. T. Fukai, M. Naka and J. C. Schuster, "Interfacial microstructure and reaction phases of solid state bonded at SiC/V joints", J. Mater. Synth. Process, 6[6]: 387 - 392, 1998.
72. B. G. Ravi and R. Chaim, "Joining of ZrO sub 2 -4.5 wt% Y sub 2 O sub 3 (Y-TZP) ceramics using nanocrystalline tape cast interlayers", J. Materials Science, 37[4]: 813-818, 2002.
73. R. J. Xie, M. Mitomo, G. D. Zhan, L. P. Huang and X. R. Fu, "Diffusion bonding of silicon nitride using a superplastic beta-SiAlON interlayer", J. Amer. Ceram. Soc. 84 [2]: 471-473, 2001.

74. P. A. Lessing, A. W. Erikson and D. C. Kunerth, "Electrophrotectic deposition (EPD) applied to reaction joining of silicon carbide and silicon nitride ceramics", J. Mater. Sci;, 35[2]: 2913 - 2925, 2000.
75. M. Gopal, L. C. DeJonghe and G. Thomas, "Silicon nitride: from sintering to joining", Acta Mater., 46: 2401 - 2405, 1998.
76. A. Bhatnagar, M. J. Hoffman and R. H. Dauskardt, "Fracture and subcritical crack growth behavior of Y-Si-Al-O-N glasses and Si3N4 ceramics", J. Am. Ceram. Soc., 83: 585 -596, 2000.
77. K. H. Sandhage, H. J. Schmutzler, R. Wheeler and H. L Fraser, "Mullite Joining by Oxidation of Malleable, Alkaline-Earth-Bearing Bonding Agents", J. Am. Ceram. Soc., 79[7]: 1839-1850, 1996.
78. J. G. Lee, K. Y. Lee and E. D. Case, "Joining of Diamond Thin Films to Optical and IR Materials," pp. 509 - 520 in Ceramic Transactions, Volume 94, American Ceramic Society, Inc., Westerville, OH, 1998.
79. J. G. Lee and E. D. Case, "Microwave Joining of Particulate Composites", pp. 571 - 581 in Advances in Ceramic Matrix Composites V, Ceramic Transactions Volume 103, American Ceramic Society, Inc., Westerville, OH, 2000.
80. S. P. Kovalev, P. Miranzo and M. I. Osendi, "Finite element simulation of thermal residual stresses in joining ceramics with thin metal interlayers", J. Am. Ceram. Soc., 81[9]: 2342-2348, 1998.
81. T. F. Yen., Y. H. Chang, D. L. Yu, F. S. Yen, D. S. Tsai, and I. N. Lin, "Diffusion bonding of MgF_2 optical ceramics," Mat. Sci. and Engineering, A147 121-128, 1991.
82. T. F. Yen, Y. H. Chang, D. S. Tsai, S. L. Duh and S. J. Yang, "LiF-film-assisted diffusion bonding of MgF_2 ceramics," Mat. Sci. and Engineering, A154, 215-221, 1992.
83. C. A. Lewinsohn, P. Colombo, I. Reimanis and O. Unal, "Stresses occurring during joining of ceramics using preceramic polymers", J. Am. Ceram. Soc., 84[10] 2240-2244, 2001.
84. J. R. Reitz and F. J. Milford, pp. 82 - 83 in Foundations of Electromagnetic Theory, Second Edition, Addison-Wesley Publishing Co., Reading, Massachusetts, 1967.
85. H. W. Shin, P. Kwon and E. D. Case, "Joining zirconia, alumina and HAP bioceramics", in this proceedings.

NUMERICAL MODELING OF SOLID STATE BONDING BASED ON FUNDAMENTAL BONDING MECHANISMS
----FOR BONDING BETWEEN DISSIMILAR MATERIALS----

Yasuo TAKAHASHI

JWRI, Osaka University

11-1, Mihogaoka, Ibaraki, Osaka, 567-0047, Japan

ABSTRACT

Numerical modeling methods that can be used as tools for developing and processing bonds between dissimilar materials are discussed. The solid state bonding process controlled by the intimate contact stage is modeled, based on the fundamental mechanisms such as plastic deformation, visco-plastic (creep) deformation, interface diffusion, and volume diffusion. An example of using these methods to predict the bonding process of Cu-Cu and Cu-Ni is described. For Cu-Ni bonding, the interdiffusion process between Cu and Ni is taken into account.

In ceramic/metal bonding, the solid state bonding of Ti/Al_2O_3 and Cu/SiO_2 were investigated in terms of the intimate contact stage, because Ti and Cu reduce the surface of Al_2O_3 and SiO_2, respectively. This idea is supported by the experimental results of valence Auger analysis. In Cu/SiO_2 bonding, it is suggested that the creep mechanism is dominant under the condition of the bonding pressure =10 MPa, the bonding temperature = 1173 K and the vacuum degree = 1×10^{-4} Pa. Ti/Al_2O_3 bonding is summarized in terms of intimate contact control. Finally, the problems of ceramic/metal bonding are discussed.

INTRODUCTION

The solid state bonding process needs at least two steps; interfacial contact and chemical binding at the contact area [1]. In metal/metal bonding, the surface oxide film inhibits the chemical binding between them, i.e. it is a main hindrance factor. If the bonding condition (temperature and vacuum degree) is chosen properly, the oxide film can be reduced [2,3]. Aluminum alloys, however, need additional elements (e.g. Mg) for reducing or granulating the oxide film. Even then, surface roughness remains as an inevitable hindrance factor. In other words, the interfacial contacting (or void shrinkage at the bond-interface) controls the solid state bonding process as a determining step. The void shrinkage and the interfacial contact defines the growth of real bond-area, which is carried out by two or more distinguishable mechanisms: plastic deformation, creep deformation, interface self-diffusion and volume self-diffusion [4]. The void shrinkage at the bond interface between similar metals has been studied by many researchers [4-7]. The prediction of the solid state diffusion bonding of similar metals (Cu, Ni, Ag, and Ti) is possible even when the spacing between voids at the bond interface changes during bonding [6]. In the case when the model parameters are unknown, the supporting system for predicting the bonding process between new similar metals has been developed [7].

The fundamental bonding mechanisms as stated above are considered to contribute to the bonding process for dissimilar materials, i.e. if the contacted area has no hindrance factors, the chemical binding will occur instantly. However, in the bonding processes for dissimilar materials, the interdiffusion and reaction diffusion occurs through the bonded interface. The interdiffusion continues during bonding but should be assumed to be an accompanying phenomena which is not necessary for the bonding process. However, the interdiffusion changes the properties of bonded interface and has a large influence on the contacting (void shrinkage) rate and, in addition, some interface reaction is necessary for ceramic/metal bonding.

In the present study, a two dimensional bonding model between Cu and Ni is proposed. The contribution of each fundamental mechanism to the bonding process and the relationship between the interdiffusion and the contacting process is discussed. Further, it is suggested from the experimental results that the solid state bonding between ceramics and metals such as Ti/Al_2O_3 and Cu/SiO_2 can be controlled by the contacting process at high temperature and high vacuum conditions. In particular, an attempt is made to identify the contacting mechanism for Cu/SiO_2 bonding. In Al_2O_3/Ti bonding, the necessary reaction (metallization of Al_2O_3 surface) is described.

CONTACTING (VOID SHRINKAGE) MODEL

Fig. 1 illustrates a two dimensional model of a (a) faying (bonding) surface, a (b) bond-interface and (c) void morphology at the bond-interface. The surface is assumed to be clean and have long triangular ridges with a regular peaks. Two

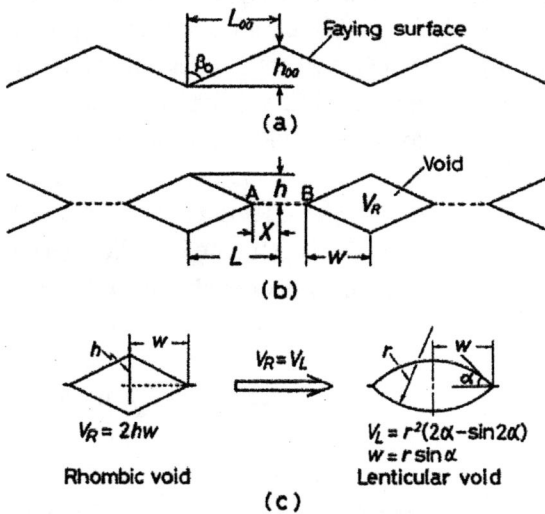

Fig. 1 Two dimenonal modesl of diffusion bonding process controlled by contacting process: (a) faying (bonding) surface, (b) void array at the bond-interface, and (c) translation from rhombic void to lenticular void. The void volume per length of void (or cross sectional area) of lenticular void $V_L = r^2(2\alpha - \sin 2\alpha)$ is assumed to be equal to that of the rhombic void $V_R = 2hw$. Surface diffusion is ignored by assuming $D_s \gg D_b$, where D_s is the surface self-diffusion coefficient [4].

faying surfaces are in contact peak to peak. In practice, the real shape of voids is not symmetrical with respect to the bond interface but the void shape in the model is symmetrical and the initial contact is assumed to be determined by plastic deformation of a soft material, i.e. Cu [*]. The initial bond ratio $S_o = X_o/L_o$ is given by

$$S_o = P/\{(1+\beta_o)\sigma_Y\}, \quad (1)$$

where P is the bonding pressure, σ_Y is the yield stress and β_o is the angle shown in Fig. 1 (a). Also, X_o is the half initial contact width and L_o is the half initial void spacing. The initial void height h_o was calculated using the principle of constant volume [5]. After the initial contact, the bonding process is produced by creep deformation and interface diffusion and volume diffusion [5, 6].

*) As mentioned below, the contacting process due to deformation mechanisms is affected by hard materials (i.e. Ni or ceramics). The yield stress for the initial contact must be changed from that of soft materials but the yield stress of the soft material is adopted to estimate the initial contact width $2X_o$. In the present study, half the initial contact width X_o is small enough, compared with half void spacing L, owing to the low pressure condition (<30 MPa), compared with pressure welding. The bonding process (the growth of X from X_o) after the initial contact is not so largely influenced by the value of X_o. The reason for this might be because the creep deformation compensates the error of the initial contact. In other words, even if X_o is somewhat overestimated, the creep deformation will correct that. As the bonding pressure P increases to above 30 MPa , the effective yield stress should also be taken into account.

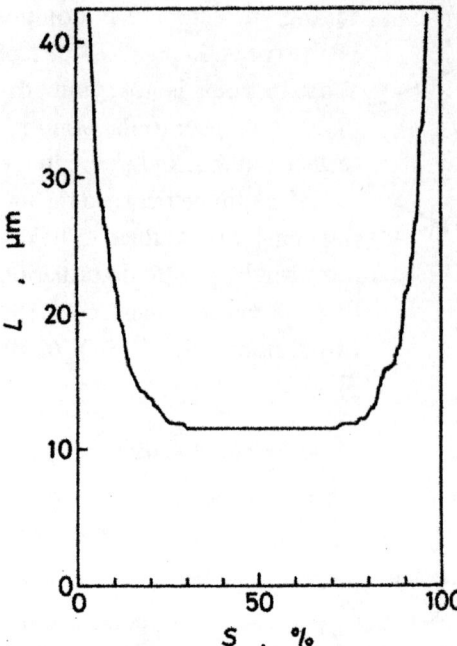

Fig. 2 Change in mean half void spacing, L, with bond ratio S, estimated by the overlap method [5]. This S-L curve is for Cu/Ni couple with the surface roughness parameters of $L_{oo} = 12$ μm and $h_{oo} = 2.5$ μm.

In general, as the surface roughness is not uniform, the void spacing $2L$ changes with increasing the bond-ratio $S = X/L$. In particular, the surface roughness is different between Cu and Ni (dissimilar materials). The change in half the effective void spacing L with S was estimated by the overlap methods proposed elsewhere [5]. Fig. 2 shows the change in L with S (S-L curve) for the Cu/Ni bonding. The value of L is averaged in each stage S. The S-L curve simulates the following process; the distance between voids becomes long in the early stage of bonding because of the scattering of surface roughness height h_{oo} and as S increases ($S = S_o \sim 50\%$), L decreases. In $S > 80\%$, L again increases due to small voids vanishing in the latter stage of bonding [5].

The contacting rates dS/dt for each mechanisms were given by

$$\left(\frac{dS}{dt}\right)_{creep1} = \frac{A \cdot S \cdot \left(\frac{\sqrt{3}}{2}\right)^{n+1}}{\{1-S^{2/n}\}^n} \left\{\frac{2P}{nG}\left(\frac{1-S}{S}\right)\right\}^n \quad (2)$$

for the creep deformation in the range of $S < 50\%$,

$$\left(\frac{dS}{dt}\right)_{creep2} = \frac{A(1-S)\left(\frac{\sqrt{3}}{2}\right)^{n+1}\left(\frac{2P}{nG}\right)^n}{\{1-(1-S)^{2/n}\}^n} \quad (3)$$

for the creep mechanism in the range of $S \geq 50\%$, and

$$\left(\frac{dS}{dt}\right)_{\text{diff}} = \frac{3\sin\alpha \cdot \Omega}{kT(2\alpha - \sin 2\alpha)rX^2}\left(\frac{P}{S} + \frac{\gamma_s}{r}\right)\left(\delta_b D_b + \frac{2L}{\pi}D_v\right) \quad (4)$$

for self-diffusion mechanisms, where G is the effective shear modulus, n is the stress exponent, $A = A_o \exp(-Q_c/RT)$, A_o the creep constant, Q_c the activation energy for interfacial creep deformation, R the gas constant, Ω the effective atomic volume, k Boltzmann's constant, T the absolute temperature, γ_s the mean surface energy, r the radius of surface curvature, δ_b the thickness of boundary, D_b the boundary self-diffusion coefficient, and D_v is the volume self-diffusion coefficient. The angle α is shown in Fig. 1 (c). The radius r is calculated from the assumption of $V_R = V_L$ (see Fig. 1 (c)) and the rate of change of the void height h was calculated from the volume conservation by $dh/dt = -hX/(L+X)$. Equations (1)-(4) were originally applied for the diffusion bonding of similar materials [4,5]. When these equations are applied to dissimilar material bonding, it is very important to use the proper model parameters such as n, A_o, G, D_b, D_v, Ω, and δ_b [**]. The interdiffusion between dissimilar materials is necessary to estimate these parameters. Values of the model parameters were calculated from the concentration ratio of elements, except for the creep parameters of A_o, n and Q_c. The effective self-diffusion coefficient D_{eff} was calculated by

$$D_{\text{eff}} = f_D \cdot \frac{D_A D_B}{c_A D_B + c_B D_A}, \quad (5)$$

where f_D is the correction factor for an increase of vacancy concentration due to the interdiffusion; D_A and D_B are self-diffusion coefficients for pure metals A and B, respectively, and also c_A and c_B are molar fractions of A and B, respectively ($c_A + c_B = 1$). Equation (5) is for interface and volume self-diffusion mechanisms. The atomic volume, Ω, and the interface thickness, δ_b, were assumed to be proportional to the ratio of molar fraction of A and B (for example, $\Omega = c_A \Omega_A + c_B \Omega_B$, where Ω_A and Ω_B are the atomic volumes for A and B, respectively). Because the creep rate was not proportional to the concentration ratio, the creep parameters were determined from experimental results. G was eliminated by substituting $A G^n$ for A in

---

[**] Although this may appear to be an oversimplification, the assumptions are justified by examination of the model results.

equations (2) and (3), i.e., the temperature dependence of the shear modulus G was neglected, compared with $\exp(-Q_c/RT)$ [7].

The present study deals with the interdiffusion between dissimilar materials such as Cu and Ni which have homogeneous solid solutions and do not produce any new phases. Even if the system of a homogeneous solid solution is adopted, the relationship between the bonding process and the reaction layer, δ_m, due to the interdiffusion can be discussed by giving the thickness, δ_m, of reaction layer in the range of Cu 10mass%~90mass%.

Table 1 Properties of copper and nickel and creep parameters during bonding.

Parameter	symbol	for Cu	for Ni	Unit
Melting temperature	T_m	1356	1726	K
Atomic volume	Ω	1.18×10^{-29}	1.09×10^{-29}	m^3
Interface thickness	δ_b	5.12×10^{-10}	4.98×10^{-10}	m
Frequency factor of D_v	D_{vo}	6.2×10^{-5}	1.9×10^{-4}	$m^2 s^{-1}$
Frequency factor of D_b	D_{bo}	0.10×10^{-4}	0.70×10^{-5}	$m^2 s^{-1}$
Activation energy for D_v	Q_v	2.08×10^5	2.72×10^5	J/mol
Activation energy for D_b	Q_b	1.05×10^5	1.15×10^5	J/mol
Surface energy	γ_s	1.72	1.73	$J \cdot m^{-2}$
Yield stress at 300 K	σ_{Yo}	1.79×10^8	3.35×10^8	N/m

Yield stress $\sigma_Y = \sigma_{Yo} (G(T)/G(300)) \Gamma(T)$
Shear modulus $G(T) = a_1 (T/T_m)^2 + a_2 (T/T_m) + a_3$
Correction coefficient $\Gamma(T) = b_1 (T/T_m)^3 + b_2 (T/T_m)^2 + b_3 (T/T_m) + b_4$

where $a_1 = -4.70 \times 10^{10}$, $a_2 = 1.35 \times 10^{10}$, $a_3 = 4.60 \times 10^{10}$ for Cu
$a_1 = -6.53 \times 10^9$, $a_2 = -4.25 \times 10^{10}$, $a_3 = 1.07 \times 10^{11}$ for Ni
$b_1 = 0.00$, $b_2 = -0.88$, $b_3 = 0.35$, $b_4 = 0.96$ for Cu
$b_1 = 6.14$, $b_2 = -10.1$, $b_3 = 3.52$, $b_4 = 0.66$ for Ni

Creep constants during bonding $A_o = 5.0 \times 10^{-28}$,
Stress exponent during bonding $n = 4.52$
Activation energy for creep during bonding $Q_c = 194.5$ kJ/mol
Correction factor $f_D = 2.0$

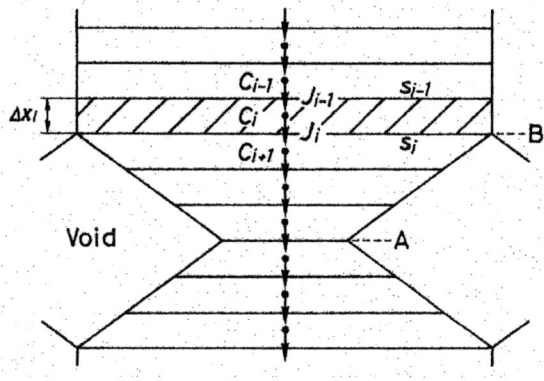

Fig. 3 Finite differential model of mutual diffusion without reaction phase. Mark A expresses the bond-interface and mark B is a top of the void. The upper side is copper and the lower side is nickel.

The interdiffusion gives rise to an increase of vacancy concentration at the bond interface. In applying equation (4) for the bonding process of dissimilar materials, it is necessary to assume that the vacancy concentration, c_{vo}, of the void surface with $r = \infty$ is always equal to the vacancy concentration, c_{vi}, at the bond interface under the condition without bonding pressure. If $c_{vo} < c_{vi}$, the void shrinkage is restrained by the interdiffusion and the condition of $c_{vo} \ll c_{vi}$ gives rise to the void growth. In the present study, $c_{vo} \approx c_{vi} > c_{eq}$ is assumed at the bonded area, where c_{eq} is the equilibrium vacancy concentration at $P = 0$ MPa.   Table 1 shows the model parameters for Cu and Ni and creep constants estimated from experimental results [7].   Creep parameters A_o, n, and Q_c were assumed to be constant during bonding.

INTERDIFFUSION MODEL

Fig. 3 shows a differential model of mutual diffusion across the bonded interface between Cu and Ni. The thickness, Δx_i, of differential meshes in the vicinity of the bond-zone AB was set to one twentieth (or thirtieth) of the initial half void height h_o (see Fig. 1) but increased with the distance from the bond interface. The distance of 500 μm from the bonded interface was meshed (the total distance for meshing was 1mm).

The flux of Cu atoms from cell $j-1$ to cell j is given by

$$J_i = -\tilde{D}(C_{i,i+1}) \cdot \frac{C_{i+1} - C_i}{\Delta x_{i,i+1}}, \qquad (6)$$

where $\tilde{D}(C_{i,i+1})$ is the interdiffusion coefficient at the copper content of $C_{i,i+1} = (C_i + C_{i+1})/2$, $\Delta x_{i,i+1} = (\Delta x_i + \Delta x_{i+1})/2$ and C_i is the copper content in cell i. From the principle of mass conservation, the change of copper content in cell i in the time increment Δt is obtained by

$$\Delta C_i = \frac{s_{i-1}J_{i-1} - s_i J_i}{\Delta x_i \cdot s_{i-1,i}} \cdot \Delta t, \tag{7}$$

where s_i is the area per unit length of bond-zone in the direction perpendicular to the sheet at the ith mesh and $s_{i-1,i} = (s_{i-1} + s_i)/2$. The coefficient $\tilde{D}$ was determined according to ref [8] and assumed to depend on T and C_i.

The bonding process was simulated by coupling the interdiffusion with the contacting (void shrinkage) process and using the repetition (Euler's) method [5].

EXPERIMENTAL

The bonding tests for Cu/Ni were carried out to estimate proper model parameters of A_o, n, Q_c and f_D and to verify the model. The bonding tests for Cu/Cu and Ni/Ni were also carried out to compare with Cu/Ni bonding. The determination of the model parameters has been described in detail elsewhere [7, 9]. The interdiffusion layer was observed by EPMA and compared with the calculated results. The bonding conditions were P = 3 to 30 MPa and T = 1123 to 1273 K. The atmospheric pressure was about 1.3×10^{-3} Pa. The bonding tests for metal/ceramics (Ti/Al$_2$O$_3$

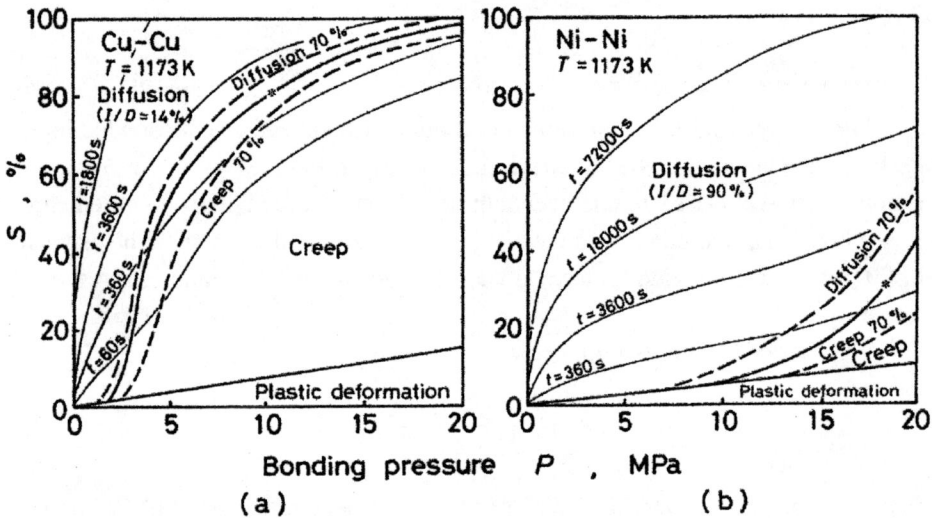

Fig. 4 Mechanism maps of bonding for similar metals. (a) Cu/Cu bonding and (b) Ni/Ni bonding.

and Cu/SiO$_2$) were also performed in order to suggest that the metal/ceramic bonding process can be controlled by the growth of the area chemically bonded, if the bonding was done under a proper condition of high temperature and high vacuum or a proper metalization for ceramic surfaces treated before bonding. The surface roughness of sample (Cu, Ni and Ti) was mechanically obtained by the lathe but the surface of SiO$_2$ and Al$_2$O$_3$ was flat ($h_{oo} \approx 0.05$ μm), compared with the surface of metals (Cu, Ni and Ti) . Valence Auger analysis across the bond-interface was carried out to examine the atomic interaction between metal and ceramics [2, 10]. The effect of metallization on alumina surfaces on Ti/Al$_2$O$_3$ bonding was examined. The metallization was carried out by vacuum deposition. The thickness, d_m, of Ti deposition layer onto the Al$_2$O$_3$ surface was changed from 0 to 160 nm. The annealing (metallizing) was carried out for 30 min at the bonding temperature before bonding.

RESULTS AND DISCUSSION
1. Bonding of similar materials

Fig. 4 (a) and (b) show the diffusion bonding mechanism maps for Cu/Cu and Ni/Ni bonding, respectively. They are the maps for surface roughness height $h_{oo} = 2.5$ μm and the roughness pitch $L_{oo} = 12.0$ μm (see Fig. 1 (a)) and the S-L curves shown in Fig. 2. The mechanism maps show the dominant mechanism in each domain [4]. The index I/D shown in Fig. 4 is obtained by

$$I/D = \frac{\delta_b D_b}{\left(\delta_b D_b + \frac{2L}{\pi} D_v\right)} \tag{8}$$

and indicates the contribution ratio of the interface diffusion against the total diffusion mechanisms to the bonding rate dS/dt. The solid line at the boundary between domains of creep (or diffusion) and plastic deformation expresses the initial contact ratio S_o due to the plastic deformation mechanism. The dotted curve of "Diffusion 70%" means that the contribution of diffusional mechanisms (interface and volume diffusion) is 70% to the total bonding rate. The solid curve with an asterisk (named as "equi-contributive curve") means creep : diffusion = 50 : 50 in the contribution to the total bonding rate. The time contour curve for each bonding time t gives the bond-ratio S achieved in the bonding time t. It has been accepted in the general diffusion bonding that the dominant bonding (void shrinkage) mechanism gradually changes from creep deformation to diffusion as S increases. However, as shown in

Fig. 4, the transition of mechanism from deformation to diffusion depends on the bonding condition and the kinds of materials. Creep deformation contributes more in Cu/Cu bonding than in Ni/Ni bonding. It is found from the ratio I/D that interface diffusion contributes more in Ni/Ni bonding. The mechanism maps for similar metals have been verified elsewhere [6] and can predict the bonding process controlled by the void shrinkage.

2) Bonding between Cu and Ni as dissimilar materials

The model parameters n, A_o, Q_c (for creep) and f_D (for diffusional mechanisms) were estimated experimentally (see Table 1). The Cu/Ni bonding was simulated by using these parameters, under various bonding conditions which were different from the conditions used for determining values of the model parameters.

Fig. 5 shows the comparison between experimental and calculated bond ratios S. As seen in Fig 5, the bonding model proposed in the present study predicts the various experimental S values. Therefore, let us discuss the Cu/Ni bonding based on the calculated results as an example of diffusion bonding between dissimilar materials.

Fig. 6 shows the mechanism maps for Cu/Ni bonding. As shown in Fig. 6(a), the creep deformation is more important in Cu/Ni bonding than in Ni/Ni bonding, i.e., a soft material of Cu can facilitate the deformation mechanisms. For the bonding pressure of P = 10 MPa, we can see the representative diffusion bonding process accepted generally in the wide temperature range (see Fig. 6(b)), in which the diffusion mechanism follows the creep deformation mechanism.

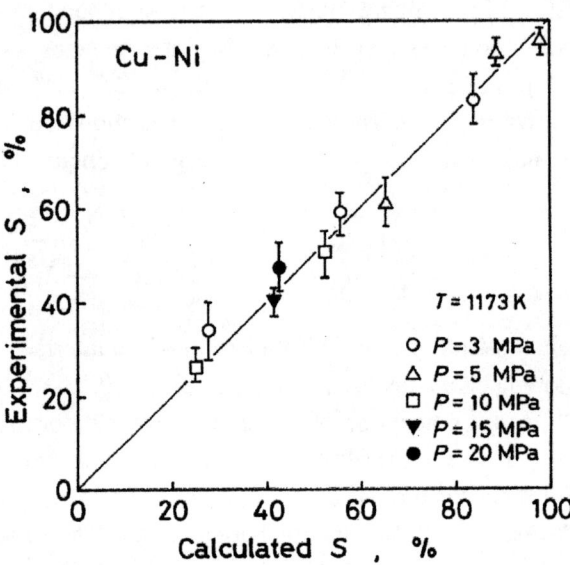

Fig. 5 Comparison between calculated and experimental results under various bonding conditions which are different from the conditions adopted for estimating the model parameters.

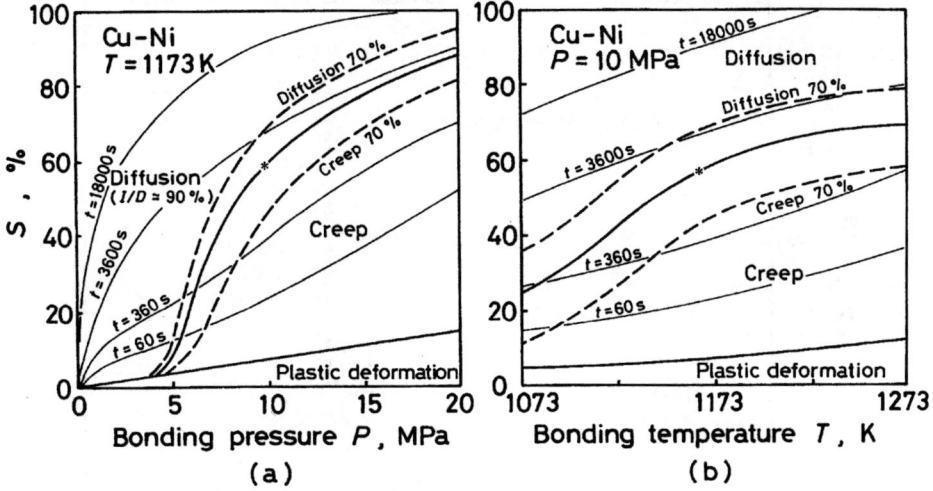

Fig. 6 Bonding mechanism maps for dissimilar metals (Cu/Ni). (a) S-P map and (b) S-T map.

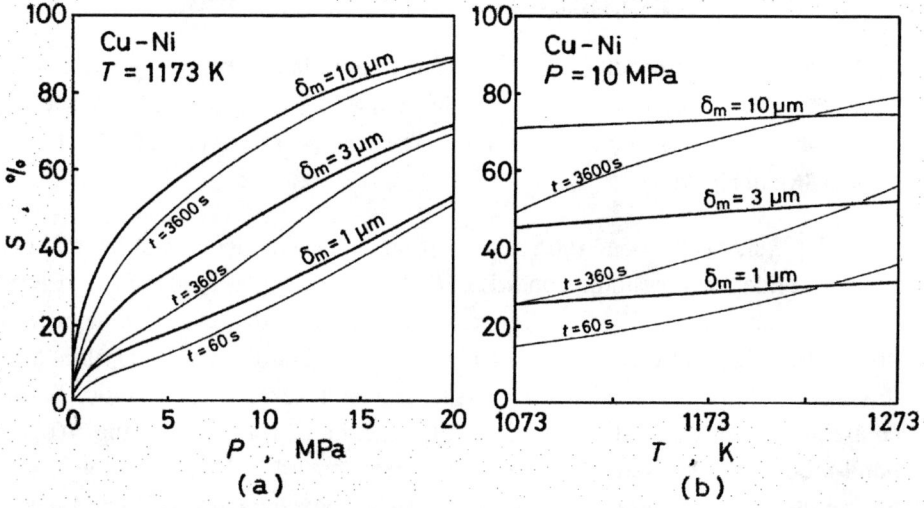

Fig. 7 Diagrams for thickness δ_m of interdiffusion layer and time contour curve in Cu/Ni bonding. (a) effect of bonding pressure on δ_m and (b) effect of bonding temperature on δ_m.

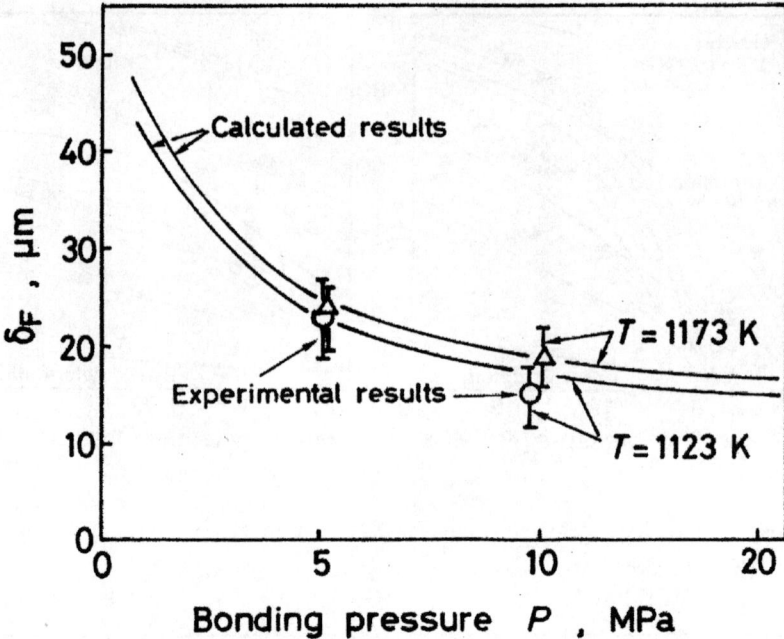

Fig. 8 Effect of bonding pressure on thickness of interdiffusion layer δ_F at $S = 100\%$ of Cu/Ni bonding. The void spacing at $S = 50\%$ is $L_{50\%} = 10.7$ μm and the surface roughness height is $h_{oo} = 1.4$ μm. The bonding time t_F taken for $S = 100\%$ is shown in Fig. 9.

Fig. 7 shows the bond ratio required to obtain each thickness of interdiffusion layer, δ_m, under each bonding condition (P, T). For example, in Fig. 7 (a), if $P = 10$ MPa, the bond-ratio of $S = 49\%$ is necessary to produce $\delta_m = 3$ μm. In other words, the diffusion layer of $\delta_m = 3$ μm is naturally produced during bonding, while $S = 49\%$ is achieved. If T is constant (Fig. 7(a)), as P increases, the bond-ratio S can increase under the same values of δ_m. On the other hand, if P is fixed (Fig. 7(b)), the bond-ratio S which gives the same δ_m does not depend so largely on the bonding temperature. Fig. 7 suggests that the deformation mechanisms facilitated with increasing P is useful for obtaining a larger S and a smaller δ_m. Because the interdiffusion is considered to be an accompanying phenomenon of the diffusion bonding, the diffusion layer produced should be limited by full contact (end of the void shrinkage). Fig. 8 shows the thickness of interdiffusion layer δ_F to obtain $S = 100\%$. It is

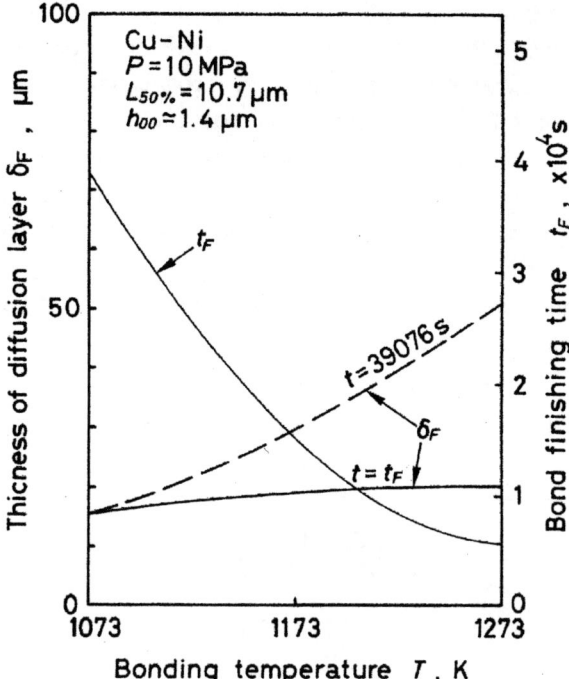

Fig. 9 Temperature dependence of the bond-finishing time t_F required to obtain $S = 100\%$ and the interdiffusion layer thickness δ_F which is produced for t_F. If the annealing time t is kept at about 39.1 ks, the interdiffusion layer thickness increases with T. The bonding time of $t = 39.1$ ks is equal to the bond-finishing time t_F at $T = 1073$ K. The difference between the dotted curve of $t = 39076$ s and the solid curve of $t = t_F$ for δ_F means the interdiffusion layer growth after the bonding process is over.

found that δ_F scarcely depends on T. This reason is explained in terms of the bonding time t_F taken to obtain $S = 100\%$. The time t_F decreases as T increases as shown in Fig. 9. If the annealing time is kept at $t = 39$ ks, the reaction layer δ_F increases with temperature T.

3) Ceramic/metal bonding

The interface reaction (atomistic reaction) is necessary to produce the chemical bond at the contacted area, which has been suggested by the observation of valence Auger peak across the bond interface [2,10]. Because titanium can easily reduce alumina surface under high temperature ($T \approx 1173$K), direct bonding is possible. An evidence that even copper can reduce silica surfaces was also given from valence Auger analysis [11], although the reaction is not so striking compared with titanium. Even Cu/silica bonding can be controlled by the intimate contacting step. This implies that the full contact with chemical bonds is very important for ceramic/metal bonding. If the bonding surfaces of alumina or other ceramics are properly metalized before bonding, the bonding process is naturally controlled by the contact process and ceramic/metal bonding can be equated to metal/metal bonding, although there remains the problem of the mismatch in thermal contraction produced in cooling the samples from bonding temperatures. If the full contact with chemical bonding attains, the excessive reaction layer is not necessary. As P increases, we can decrease the thickness of reaction layer produced before the full intimate contact, as suggested in Fig. 8. The necessary reaction layer depends on the system (kinds of ceramics and metals). Estimation and investigation for the necessary reaction is, therefore, essential to determine the optimal ceramic/metal joints but these may be complete in some methods, such as metallization, before the bonding.

In the present study, the necessary reaction layer has not been estimated but the dominant contacting mechanism was investigated for the Cu/silica bonding process. Fig. 10 shows the growth of intimate contact area S with the bonding time t, together with the calculated results of Cu/Cu bonding (assuming that L is constant

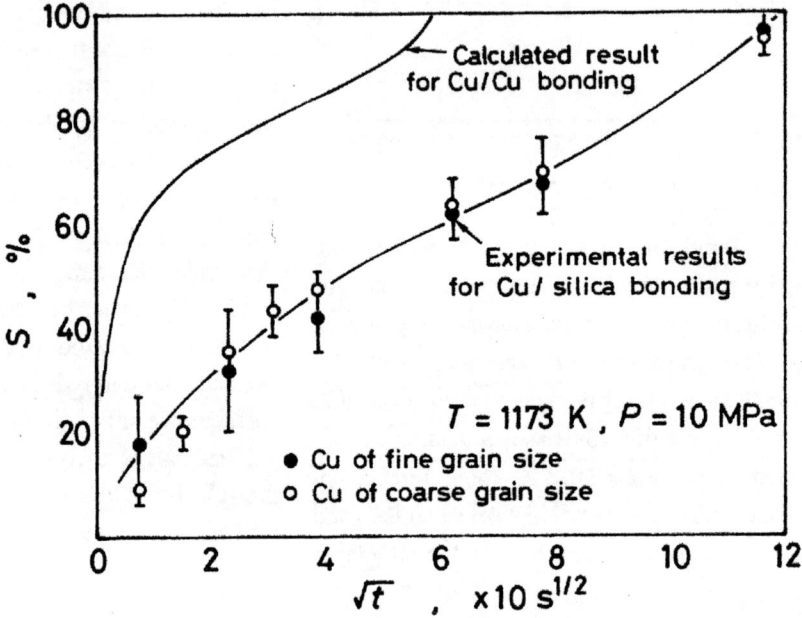

Fig. 10 Intimate contact process in Cu/silica bonding compared with Cu/Cu bonding calculated by the two dimensional model. $L = 12.5$ μm, $h_{oo} = 5$ μm was assumed to be kept constant. As the surface roughness of silica was much smaller than that of Cu, the silica surface was assumed to be flat. The fine grain size of Cu sample was $d_g \approx 25$ μm and the coarse grain size was $d_g \approx 175$ μm.

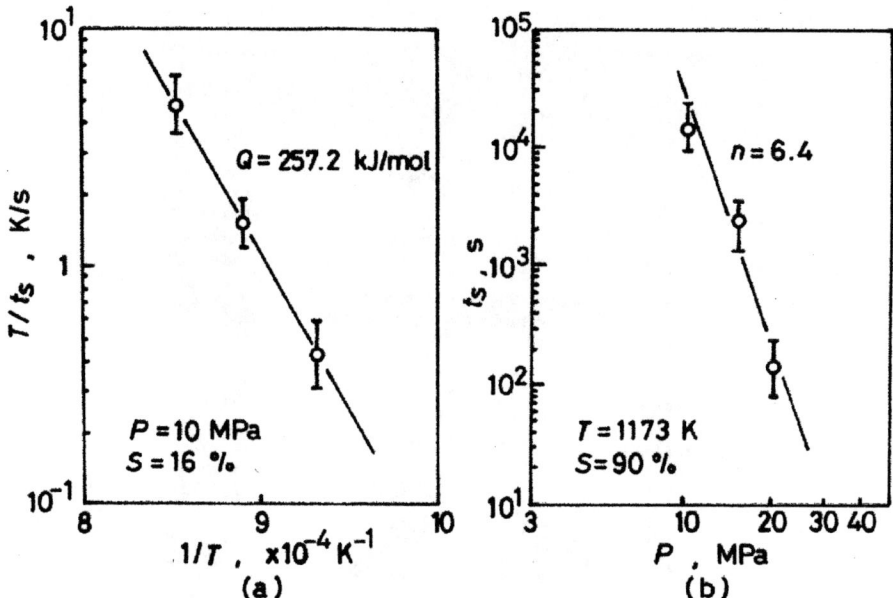

Fig. 11 Identification of the activation energy Q and stress exponent n of the bonding mechanism for Cu/silica bonding. (a) ln T/t_s - $(1/T)$, and (b) ln t_s - ln P, where t_s is the bonding time required to obtain a constant bond ratio S. In (a), t_s is for $S = 16$ % and in (b) t_s for $S = 90$ %. The bonding was assumed to be controlled by the contact process.

during bonding). L_{oo} and h_{oo} of Cu surface were about 12.5 μm and 5 μm, respectively. In experiments, it was very often that a crack was produced in the vicinity of the bond zone after bonding. The crack was due to the difference in the thermal expansion between silica and copper but the contacted area could be measured after fracturing the bond-interface.

As seen in Fig. 10, the contacting rate of Cu/SiO_2 bonding is smaller than that of Cu/Cu bonding and independent of the grain size of Cu. This is due to the constraint effect of bulk silica. It is found from Fig. 10 that the values of model parameters for simulating the bonding process are very different from those of Cu/Cu bonding.

According to ref. [9], the dominant void shrinkage (contact) mechanism can be identified from the two relationships of ln T/t_s-$1/T$ and ln t_s-ln P, i.e., the activation energy Q of the bonding mechanism is obtained from lnT/t_s-$1/T$ plots and the stress exponent n is given from ln t_s-ln P plots, where t_s is the time taken to obtain

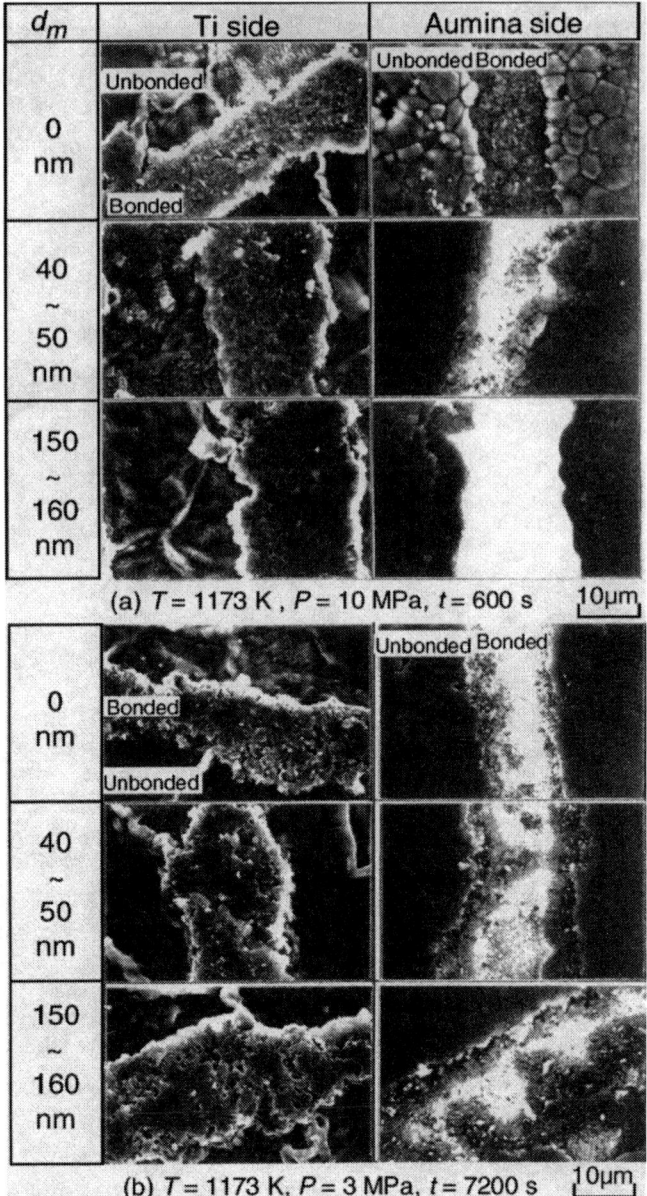

Fig. 12 Photographs of surfaces fractured after bonding between Al_2O_3 and Ti. (a) under high bonding pressure ($P = 10$ MPa) and (b) under low bonding pressure ($P = 3$ MPa). The fracture tests were carried out by a shear tensile test reported elsewhere [1].

the constant contact ratio S. If the bonding mechanism is diffusional, $n \approx 1$. On the other hand, if the creep deformation is dominant, $n > 4$.

Fig. 11 shows the relationships of $\ln T/t_s$-$1/T$ and $\ln t_s$-$\ln P$, from which $Q = 257$ kJ/mol and $n \approx 6.4$ are obtained, respectively. The value of $n = 6.4$ implies that the creep deformation mechanism is dominant by $S < 90\%$. In the present study, the diffusional contact mechanisms have not been identified but eq. (4) implies that a fine surface roughness with a small (L_{oo}, h_{oo}) promotes the diffusional contact mechanism and facilitates the void shrinkage. However, if the chemical interface reaction is easily produced or finished before bonding, the interfacial deformation mechanism is more important than the diffusional mechanism to prevent the excessive chemical reaction across the bond-interface [1] (because the creep mechanism becomes dominant as P increases.).

This was also suggested from Al_2O_3/Ti bonding as shown in Fig. 12 which shows photographs of fractured bond-interfaces of the joints between Al_2O_3 with flat surface and Ti of $L_{oo} \approx 25$ μm and $h_{oo} = 4$ μm. Fig. 12 shows different morphologies at the fractured surfaces influenced by the thickness d_m of deposited Ti film. The bond ratio S was not so affected by the amount of d_m if $d_m < 160$ nm, and was about 39~43% in all specimens[***]. All fractures occurred at the interface between deposited Ti film and alumina or often at the base alumina as the shear strength increased (at $d_m = 150$~160 nm). If the bonding was carried out under $t = 600$ s, $P = 10$ MPa and $T = 1173$ K, the bond-strength increases with d_m and became constant at $d_m = 50$~160 nm. On the other hand, if the bonding was done under $t = 7.2$ ks, $P = 3$ MPa and $T = 1173$ K, the bond strength was much lower than that of the specimens under $t = 600$ s, $P = 10$ MPa and $T = 1173$ K [1]. This suggests that the short bonding time is better from the viewpoint of bondability [1], if the necessary interface reaction (proper metallization) is established. In other words, plastic and creep (viscoplastic) deformation mechanisms are more useful than diffusional mechanism if the necessary reaction is obtained in advance. In the field of electronics, the disimilar

---

[***] If titanium was deposited on alumina surface, the mean value of S increased slightly but the increment ΔS due to Ti deposited layer of $d_m < 160$ nm was not so large ($\Delta S \approx 3$~5 % at $d_m = 160$ nm) and the value of ΔS became smaller as P decreased. The reason has not been made clear, but it was assumed that the creep mechanism was dominant under $P = 10$ MPa. The creep mechanism is thus easily influenced by the Ti deposited layer. Also, the bonding tests for fine surface roughness needs to be carried out.

material bonding in which the deformation mechanism are dominant is very often carried out to avoid the excessive interface reaction[12]. It will be the most important that the bonding mechanism breaks down the hindrance factors and suppresses the excessive accompanying phenomenon.

CONCLUSION

As mentioned above, the comprehension of the necessary interface reaction (chemical bonding) and the contact area growth is important to obtain optimal bond interfaces for dissimilar materials. In ceramic/metal bonding, many workers have discussed the interface reactions (or growth behaviors of reaction phase) and residual stresses due to mismach in thermal expansion. Surely, these matters are problems which should not be avoided, when the interface design is considered. An adequate insert material is chosen, and the interfacial reaction is very often noticed. However, it should be recognized that the excessive interfacial reaction is a secondary phenomenon after the necessary bonding process. The numerical examination presented in the present study seems to be useful for discussing the necessary bonding process between ceramics and metals.

If the effective model parameters are estimated and an adequate modification for reaction diffusion is carried out, the prediction of the bonding for complex dissimilar materials are possible, using the method described. The deformation mechanisms are more important to obtain the good joints. Comprehension of fundamental mechanisms for ceramic bonding is always important. Discussion about Cu/Ni bonding mechanism map is helpful for understanding dissimilar material bonding. The essential bonding process is universal, regardless of materials.

REFERENCES

1) Y. Takahashi and H. Ishii, "Interface Reaction and Bondability of Alumina to Titanium," Materials Science Forum, **207-209**, 777-780 (1996).
2) K. Takahashi, H. Ishii, Y. Takahashi and K. Nishiguchi, "Valence Auger Analysis of the Annealing Effect on Atomic Interaction at Titanium-sapphire, Titanium-silica and Silver-silica Interface," Thin Solid Films, **221**, 98-103 (1992).
3) Y. Takahashi, T. Nakamura, and K. Nishiguchi, " Dissolution Process of Surface Oxide Film During Diffusion Bonding of Metals," J. Mater. Sci., **27**, 485-498(1992).
4) Y. Takahashi, and K. Inoue, "Recent Void Shrinkage Models and Their Applica-

bility to Diffusion Bonding," J. Mater. Sci. Technol., **8**, 953-964 (1992).
5) Y. Takahashi and K. Nishiguchi, "Determination of Optimum Process Conditions in Solid Phase Bonding by a Numerical Model," Welding in the World, (Trans. IIW), **27**,[3/4],100-113(1989).
6) Y. Takahashi, S. Aono, T. Kamitani, K. Inoue, and K. Nishiguchi, " Development of Estimation Method of Void Spacing Distribution during Bonding and Modelling Interface Contact Process," Quarterly J. JPN Weld. Soc., **14** [4], 666-673 (1996).
7) Y. Takahashi, K. Miki and K. Inoue, " Prediction Algorithm of Solid State Diffusion Bonding in the Case When Material Constants Are Unknown," Transaction of JWRI, **24**, [2], 27-36 (1995).
8) Luiz, C. Correa da Silva and R. F. Mehl, " Interface and Marker Movements in Diffusion in Solid Solution of Metals," Trans. AIME, J. Metal, **191**, 155-173 (1951).
9) Y. Takahashi, K. Inoue and K. Nishiguchi, " Identification of Void Shrinkage Mechanisms," Acta Mater., **41** [11], 3077-3084 (1993).
10) K. Takahashi, H. Ishii, Y. Takahashi and K. Nishiguchi, "A Valence Auger Analysis Across the Annealed Interface Between a Deposited Titanium Film and Sapphire," Thin Solid Film, **216**, 239-243 (1992).
11) K. Nishiguchi, Y. Takahashi and K. Takahashi, "Auger Analysis of the Interface Between 3D Metals and Silica," J. JPN Weld. Soc., **9** [4], 544-549(1991).
12) Y. Takahashi, M. Inoue, "Numerical Study of Wire Bonding---Analysis of Interfacial Deformation Between Wire and Pad," ASME J. Electronic Packaging, **124**, 27-36 (2002).

DESIGNING JOINTS WITH GRADED LAYERS

J. Stamile, I. E. Reimanis
Metallurgical and Materials Engineering Department
Colorado School of Mines
Golden, Colorado 80401
USA

J. Chapa-Cabrera
Caterpillar Inc.
Technical Center-E854
P.O. Box 1875
Peoria, Illinois 61656-1875

ABSTRACT

Finite element modeling has been used to examine cracking behavior in elastic, discretely layered, graded joints. The present study focuses on how architectural parameters, specifically, the number of interlayers, and the interlayer thickness, effect cracking from a notch contained in a layer contained within a joint. A multilayered composite joint graded in elastic modulus and thermal expansion coefficient was first cooled from elevated temperature to room temperature to simulate thermal residual stresses, and then it was loaded by applying tension at the ends of the sample, parallel to the direction of gradation. The mode mixity and driving force for a preexisting edge crack contained within one of the layers was then determined for different architectural parameters and for varying elastic modulus gradient. It is shown that crack paths in joints with graded properties depend strongly on the interlayer thickness and the total number of layers. The results are discussed in the context of joint design.

INTRODUCTION

It is well established that the introduction of layers between components to be joined may improve joint strength through the reduction of residual stresses that arise from thermal expansion coefficient mismatch. Interlayers used in brazing relieve residual stresses through yielding. Interlayers may also be employed by grading the thermal expansion coefficient from one side of the joint to the other. Various studies have indicated that the maximum thermal residual stress may be reduced by such compositional gradation[1-3], and the architectural parameters for controlling this stress are fairly well characterized for a variety of graded

To the extent authorized under the laws of the United States of America, all copyright interests in this publication are the property of The American Ceramic Society. Any duplication, reproduction, or republication of this publication or any part thereof, without the express written consent of The American Ceramic Society or fee paid to the Copyright Clearance Center, is prohibited.

geometries. For example, it has been shown that the maximum stress occurring in a joint with discrete, compositionally graded layers is independent of the number of layers, but does depend on the overall thickness in relation to other joint dimensions.

When the maximum tensile stress occurs within the weakest end member of the joint, as previous studies have shown[4], then joint design should focus on reducing that maximum stress. However, in situations where failure may initiate within the interlayer region, it becomes essential to evaluate the stress distribution within the interlayers. The problem of predicting failure then becomes more complex because flaws within the graded region may have a wide range of spatial distribution, size and orientation, and they are loaded by the imposed residual and applied stresses whose distribution may be difficult to predict. If the design is driven simply by a reduction in the maximum tensile stress anywhere in the joint, it is likely to be overly conservative, since failure may not initiate from that location. Alterations in the joint design may alter the entire stress distribution, and this alteration may occur nonuniformly across the joint. Furthermore, the stress at the tip of a crack-like flaw is likely to be mixed shear and opening mode, and thus, the crack will be driven to kink in a direction of maximum tensile stress. The issue of crack path becomes important in developing a predictive failure model. The present study examines how certain architectural parameters and elastic modulus variation affect the direction of crack kinking from the base of a crack embedded in one of the layers of a discretely layered graded composite.

The study is based on a finite element based model developed previously[5] in which a maximum stress criterion is used to predict the fracture direction. Specifically, crack tip stress fields are obtained in an annular region around the crack tip, and the direction in which the tensile stresses are maximum is assumed to be the direction of crack kinking. The model has been shown to effectively predict macroscopically measured crack deflection angles in elastic/plastic Cu-W graded composites[6]. In this paper, the model is extended to examine how the crack kink angle is effected by the interlayer thickness, number of interlayers, elastic modulus gradation, and the fracture toughness of the interlayer containing the crack. The material properties used are identical to those of Cu, and Cu-W particulate composites, except that plasticity has been excluded so that the study applies primarily to ceramic-ceramic joints. Fully plastic models have been discussed elsewhere[6].

MODEL DESCRIPTION

The ABAQUS finite element code[7] was employed to develop and execute the model for the current study. The overall geometry is illustrated in Figure 1. All of the materials are either pure Cu or Cu-W composites; relative percentages in the composition are listed as volume percent. The ends of the joint comprise the same material in every model: the right side of the bar in Figure 1 is 80W/20Cu, and the left side is pure Cu. The interlayer region, is partitioned into a number of different layers, either 5, 3 or 1, as shown in a), b) and c), so that each could be assigned a unique set of material properties. In this way it was possible to vary the number of interlayers, the interlayer thickness, and the total joint thickness. The composition of the interlayers changes when the total number and/or thickness of the interlayers is altered, but the initial crack is always situated within a 40W/60Cu layer. The total specimen length (25.4 mm) always remains the same. A constant displacement loading condition was used on the edge of the single edge notch in tension (SENT) specimen, to simulate a fixed grips experiment. It was previously shown that this specimen geometry is very similar to a four point bending geometry in terms of the crack kink angles predicted[5].

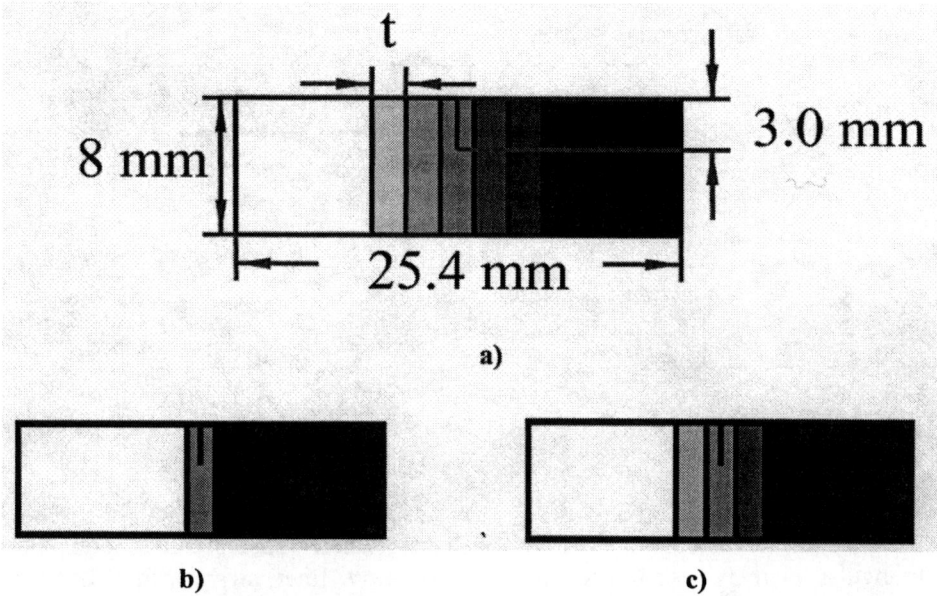

Figure 1. Several specimen configurations are examined. All specimens are 25.4 mm in length, 8 mm tall and contain a 3 mm deep pre-crack. The end members of all configurations are the same: the left side is pure Cu, the right side is 80W/20Cu. Three main specimen types with varying total number of layers (7, 5, 3), are shown in a), b) and c). The layer thickness, t, is varied systematically, as shown in Table I.

Table I illustrates the different types of configurations analyzed. The model was executed in two stages. In the first, the residual stresses were obtained by applying an initial temperature of 300°C to all the nodes and subsequently cooling down uniformly over the whole model to 25°C. 300°C was chosen as part of another study in which the plastic properties of the copper are also considered[6]. In the second stage of the model, a constant displacement load was applied to the ends of the specimen. Loading was such that the applied stresses were 10 MPa, 20 MPa, 40 MPa, 80 MPa and 160 MPa. The equivalent stress intensity factor at a kinked crack tip for each of these loads was calculated, as described below.

Table I. Joint Configurations Analyzed

Total Number of Layers	Interlayer Thickness (mm)	Total Interlayer Thickness (mm)	Joint Profile (vol. % W)
7	3	15	0,13,26,40,53,67,80
	2	10	0,13,26,40,53,67,80
	1	5	0,13,26,40,53,67,80
5	1	3	0,20,40,60,80
	2	6	0,20,40,60,80
	3	9	0,20,40,60,80
	4	12	0,20,40,60,80
	5	15	0,20,40,60,80
3	3	3	0,40,80
	6	6	0,40,80
	9	9	0,40,80
	12	12	0,40,80
	15	15	0,40,80

Plane-strain quad second order elements were used throughout the model except close to the top and bottom surfaces, where plane-strain second order triangular elements were used to transition to a finer mesh with 0.125 mm elements. Quad second order elements with three nodes collapsed on the crack tip were used. The midside node immediately away from the tip was positioned to a ¼ of the element length to make the element square root singular[7]. Earlier convergence studies determined the level of mesh refinement necessary; the current model was benchmarked with these earlier studies by reproducing the results of the earlier model.

The method used to obtain the crack kink angle and the equivalent stress intensity factor has been described elsewhere[5], and will only be briefly repeated here. The tangential stress in an annular region 12.5 μm from the crack tip was plotted as a function of angle from the crack tip, and the angle at which the maximum tangential stress occurs was recorded. The latter angle is termed the crack kink angle, θ_m. It is zero for a crack kink that is along the line of the initial crack, and positive if it is towards the right side in Figure 1 (towards the 80W composition end). The equivalent stress intensity factor for a kink crack with that kink angle, K_{IE}, was determined by relating K_{IE} to θ_m and the mode I and mode II stress intensity factors for the parent crack[8]. The latter were determined from the applied stresses. It is noted that for each configuration, there is a unique relationship between the applied stresses and the equivalent stress intensity factor.

MATERIAL PROPERTIES

Table II shows the properties of the end members, Cu and W, used in the model. These values were obtained from an earlier study[6]. It is recognized that these are somewhat arbitrary since the plasticity that would normally be active in Cu has been removed, and the specific results do not apply to any real material. A linear rule of mixtures was used to determine the intermediate properties of Cu-W composites employed as the interlayers. The various compositions are shown in Table II. The elastic modulus and thermal expansion coefficients employed were input as functions of temperature, but since the property changes up to 300°C, the highest temperature of the current model, were not substantial, the properties are not listed here as a function of temperature.

Table II. Room Temperature Material Properties of End Members

Material	Young's Elastic Modulus (GPa)	Poisson's Ratio	Thermal Expansion Coefficient (x 10^{-6}/°C)
Cu	124	0.3	17
80W-20Cu	280	0.3	6

RESULTS AND DISCUSSION

Figure 2 shows the crack kink angle, θ_m, as a function of the equivalent stress intensity factor, K_{IE}, in a 5-layer joint for different interlayer thicknesses. Note that K_{IE} is the result of superposing the applied and residual stress intensity factors at the crack tip, and determining the effective stress intensity factor for a kinked crack. It is a measure of the driving force at the crack tip, assuming the crack will propagate in the direction θ_m, which is the direction of maximum tensile stress. Thus, crack extension will occur in the direction θ_m when K_{IE} has exceeded the toughness of the interlayer, K_{IC}. It is immediately obvious from Figure 2 that the direction of crack propagation not only depends strongly on the various geometrical parameters, but also depends on the toughness of the interlayer K_{IC}. For smaller layer thickness (1 and 2 mm) the crack kink angle is either positive (deflection away from the Cu-rich side of the composite) or near zero. For thicker layers (3, 4, and 5 mm), the crack kink angle is negative (deflection towards the Cu-rich side). For lower applied loads, where residual stress dominates the stress fields, and where the equivalent K_I is smaller, the differences between the two sets of curves becomes pronounced, and all curves seem to converge towards very high absolute values of kink angle. The result is that low toughness joints exhibit high crack deflection angles. Further, a relatively small change in layer thickness, for example from 2 mm to 3 mm, for a material of toughness of about 4 MPam$^{1/2}$ results in a change in a large crack kink

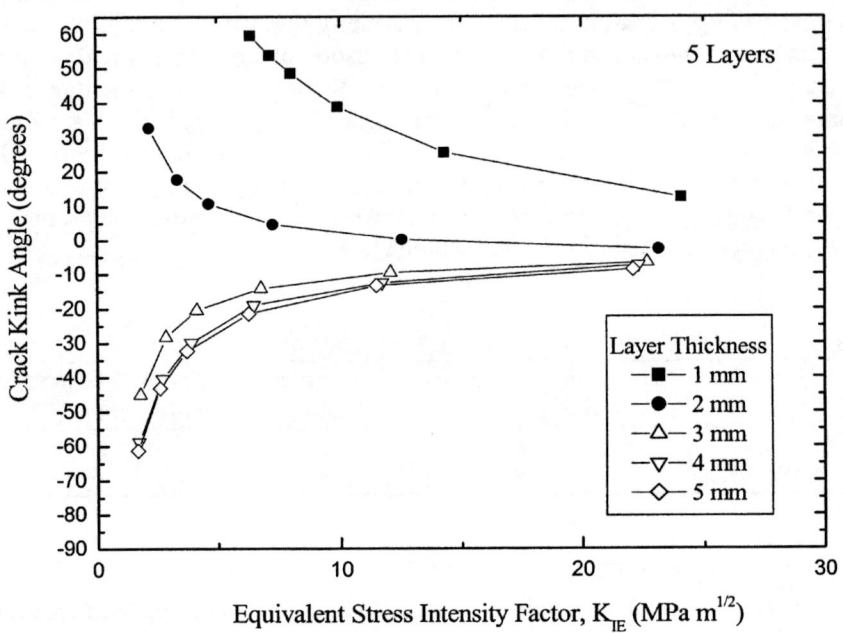

Figure 2. The crack kink angle is shown as a function of equivalent stress intensity factor for a 5-layer joint, for 5 different layer thicknesses. It is apparent that a dramatic transition in behavior occurs for layer thicknesses between 2 and 3 mm.

angle from approximately -25° to +15°. This high sensitivity of cracking direction to layer thickness should have a big impact on reliability. For example, if the crack deflected towards a tougher region of the joint, then it may actually arrest, whereas if it deflected towards the other side of the joint, instability and final failure would be expected to ensue. Very different behavior is expected for small geometric changes.

Figure 3 shows the crack kink angle as a function of equivalent K_I for different total number of layers where the layer thickness is fixed at 3mm. In this case, the 5- and 7-layer configurations lead to negative crack kink angles, whereas the 3-layer configuration is always positive for the equivalent K_I shown. Once again, the differences between the configurations that produce positive and negative crack kink angles become magnified at low applied loads. For thermal residual stress loading alone (the lowest K_{IE} for each curve), the difference in crack kink angle between the two curves is approximately 80°. As with varying layer thickness, a relatively small architectural change, for example, from 3 to 5 layers, may have a tremendous change on the type of failure behavior.

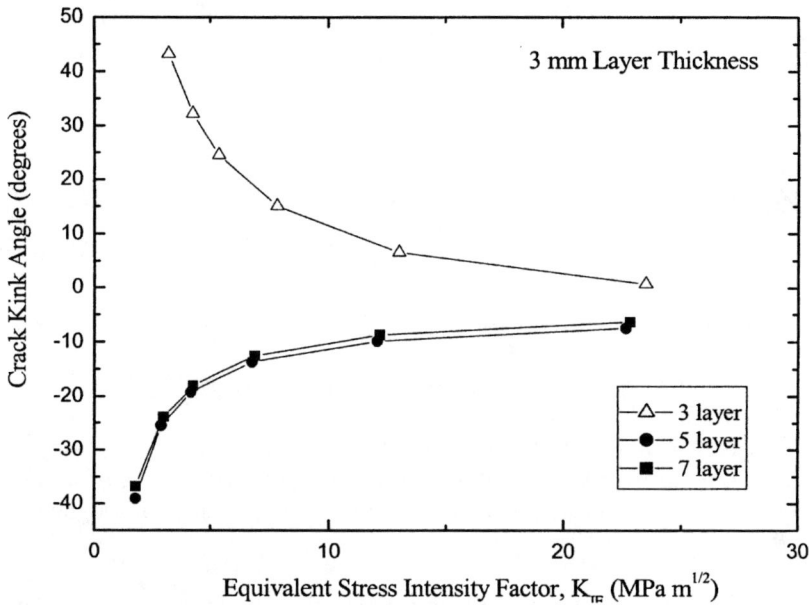

Figure 3. The crack kink angle is plotted as a function of equivalent stress intensity factor for a joint with 3 mm layer thicknesses, for 3-layer, 5-layer and 7-layer joints.

It is insightful to assume that the toughness of the layer that contains the crack is fixed, and to examine how the crack kink angle depends the various parameters when toughness is constant. Figure 4 shows the crack kink angle as a function of layer thickness for three values of toughness for the 5-layer configuration. It is apparent that for a thickness of approximately 2.5 mm, the kink angle appears not to depend strongly on toughness and is close to zero. Toughness only becomes important in controlling kink angle when the layer thickness is greater than or less than about 2.5 mm. It is also clear that the dependence of crack kink angle on layer thickness is much stronger for the less tough layer. The weaker material will exhibit higher crack deflection angles.

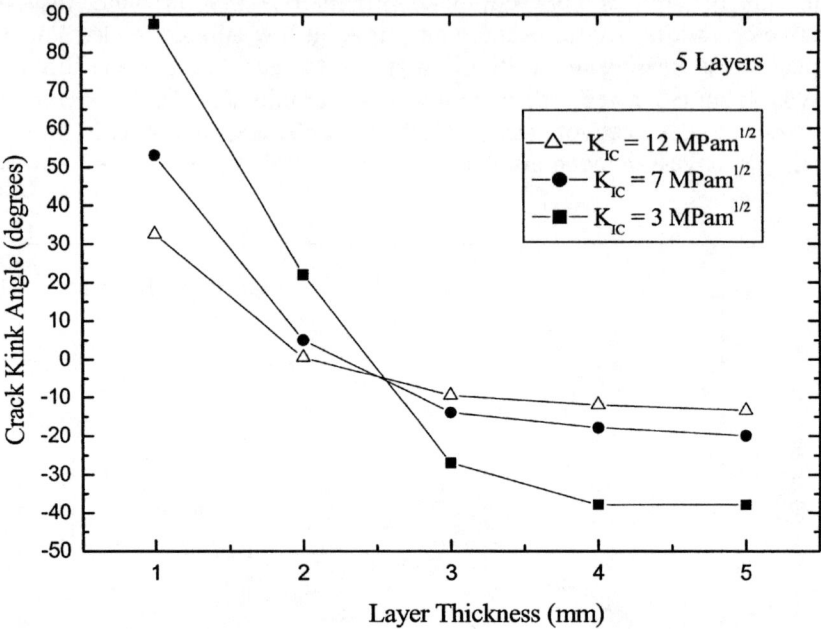

Figure 4. Crack kink angle as a function of joint layer thickness for 5-layer joint. The crack is always contained within the 40W layer. The effect of altering the toughness of that layer is studied, and is shown for three values of toughness.

The effect of the elastic modulus on crack kink angle is shown in Figure 5. E_1/E_2 is the ratio of elastic moduli of the end members, where E_1 is the modulus of the left end member of the joint in Figure 1 (the pure Cu composition), and E_2 is the modulus of the right end member. The configuration is a 5-layer joint with

2 mm layer thickness. At low loads, the crack kink angle is dominated by the residual stress field, but is not influenced substantially by the elastic modulus ratio, as revealed by the relative proximity of the three curves. At higher applied loads, the curves diverge because the elastic modulus ratio becomes more important in determining the symmetry of the applied load on the crack tip. At these higher loads, the crack kinks towards the more compliant side, but the differences in crack kink angle between the different curves is not very high. When the moduli of the end members are the same, then at very high applied loads, one would expect the crack to exhibit a crack kink angle of zero since the only asymmetry at the crack tip is due to the residual stress the magnitude of which is negligible compared to the applied stress. The model was not executed at these very high loads, but it does appear that this iso-elastic modulus curve is converging towards zero kink angle. Earlier studies have revealed that in the presence of elastic mismatch, at very high applied loads, the crack shows a tendency to kink towards the more compliant side of the joint, at a value that becomes independent of applied load[5].

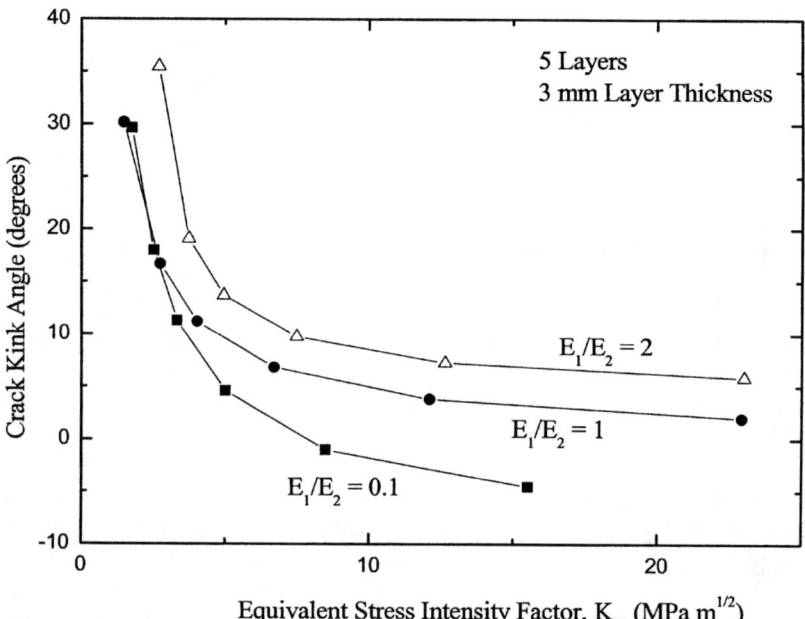

Figure 5. Crack kink angle shown as a function of equivalent stress intensity factor, for the 5-layer geometry with 3mm layer thickness. Different elastic moduli ratios are shown. E_1 is the modulus of the left end member of the joint in Figure 1 (the 80W composition), and E_2 is the modulus of the right end member.

CONCLUSIONS
In graded joint design it is clear that one must account for both applied and residual stresses, and that very different failure modes obtain for joints with different toughness. Furthermore, the stress fields present in the absence of cracks, as one might obtain by finite element analysis, may not reveal the type of failure expected when flaws are present in the interlayers. The current work has shown that the type of failure within a graded joint may depend strongly on the architectural parameters and the toughness of the interlayer containing the critical flaw. Generally, the tougher the layer containing the crack, the straighter will be the crack trajectory under an applied tensile load. Elastic modulus variation only perturbs the crack trajectory slightly, compared with the architectural effects.

ACKNOWLEDGEMENTS
The authors would like to acknowledge the U.S. Department of Energy, Office of Basic Energy Sciences for funding this research under contract DE-FG03-96ER45575.

REFERENCES
[1] R. L. Williamson, B. H. Rabin and J. T. Drake. "Finite Element Analysis of Thermal Residual Stresses at Graded Ceramic-Metal Interfaces. Part 1. Model Description and Geometrical Effects", *J. Appl. Phys.* 74 (2) p. 1310 (1993).

[2] J. T. Drake, R. L. Williamson and B. H. Rabin. "Finite Element Analysis of Thermal Residual Stresses at Graded Ceramic-Metal Interfaces. Part 2. Interface Optimization for Residual Stress Reduction", *J. Appl. Phys.* 74 (2) p. 1321 (1993).

[3] R. D. Torres, I. E. Reimanis, J. J. Moore, and G. W. Mustoe. "Design and Synthesis of Functionally Graded Composites: The $TiB_2/NiAl$ System", in Processing & Design Issues in High Temperature Materials, edited by N. S. Stolloff and R. H. Jones, The Minerals, Metals & Materials Society, Warrendale, PA (1997).

[4] A. N. Winter, B. A. Corff, I. E. Reimanis and B. H. Rabin. "Fabrication of Graded Nickel-Alumina Composites with a Thermal-Behavior-Matching Process," *Journal of the American Ceramic Society* 83 [9] 2147-54 (2000).

[5] J. Chapa-Cabrera and I. E. Reimanis. "Effects of Residual Stress and Geometry on Crack Kink Angles in Graded Composites", (invited paper) *International Journal of Engineering Fracture Mechanics,* Vol. 69, Issues 14-16, pp 1667-1678, (2002).

[6]J. Chapa-Cabrera and I. Reimanis, "Crack Deflection in Compositionally Graded Cu/W Composites", accepted for publication in *Philosophical Magazine A*, (2002).

[7]ABAQUS/Online reference manuals Version 6.2. Hibbit, Karlsson & Sorensen Inc., 2002.

[8]Erdogan F. and Sih G.C. On the crack extension in plates under plane loading and transverse shear. J Basic Eng 1963; 85:519-527.

Engineering High-Quality Ceramic-Metal Bonds

Victor A. Greenhut and Thomas R. Chapman
Ceramic & Materials Engineering
Rutgers University
Piscataway, NJ 08854-8065

Introduction

Stringent demands are being made of material properties for both traditional and advanced applications. Such demands frequently cannot be met by any single material. Metals, although ductile with high thermal and electrical conductivity, often cannot withstand high temperatures or corrosion, and expand significantly with increasing temperature (1). , Alternatively, ceramics, are brittle insulators, refractory, hard, and wear-resistant, with excellent hot properties and relatively low thermal expansion. Composite components can be manufactured by joining ceramics and metals that employ the desired properties of each material to meet these increasing requirements. The technology required bonding ceramics and metals, very dissimilar materials, effectively, reliably, and economically is in high demand. Several joining technologies have proven effective (2,3,4,5), but high processing costs limit penetration into potential markets. Direct joining requires few processing steps and therefore significantly reduces cost and eliminates insertion of an interfacial joining material such as an adhesive that may compromise properties (6,7,8,9).

The first section of this review is a treatment of those general principles, which are common to most (if not all) joining methods. Factors affecting bond strength--both intrinsic and extrinsic--as well as the methods used in bond evaluation are provided. The second section provides an overview of the processes employed in joining ceramics and metals in an effort to define their technological niches. Liquid phase joining methods are stressed because of their frequency of use and strength of bond. Alternative bonding methods are also presented. A flow chart of the logic followed in this review is shown in figure 1

1.   Contributions to Adhesion

Physical, mechanical, and chemical contributions to bond strength can be identified in many systems (3). However, assessment of their relative impact on bond strength is not trivial. This is because in almost every material system, multiple factors (both intrinsic and extrinsic) contribute to adhesion. Intrinsic factors affecting adhesion are designated here as those which are fundamental to the bond. These factors are independent of geometry, size, or quality of preparation. While these factors may indicate potential bond strength, actual performance depends strongly on extrinsic factors.

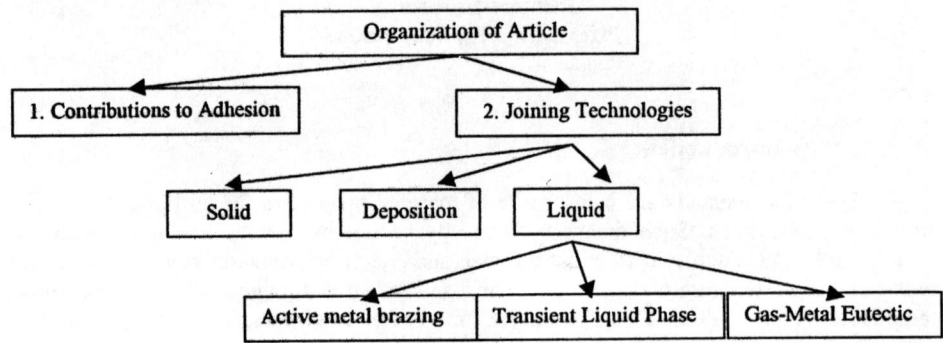

Figure 1   Literature survey logic flow chart

1.1. Intrinsic Contributions to Bonding

1.1.1. Physical Adhesion

Physical bonding results from interactions between surfaces in intimate contact on the atomic level. The system can reach a lower energy state by replacing two surfaces with one interface. Physical adhesion increases with un-bonded surface energy and decreases with increasing interfacial energy. The work of adhesion (10) of a ceramic metal bond (W_{ad}) is related to the surface free energy of the interface (γ_{12}) and of the individual surfaces (γ_1, γ_2) in the unbonded state by the Dupre Equation:

$$W_{ad} = (\gamma_1 + \gamma_2) - \gamma_{12}$$

These physical forces are generally much weaker than primary chemical bonds but can provide significant adhesion over a large area. If the interfacial contact area is increased through roughness, physical adhesion will increase, but only if complete contact is maintained. Because full contact is rarely achieved and the energies of each surface are reduced through the adsorption of foreign materials such as gases, measured physical adhesion is lower than predicted by theory.

Physical adhesion accounts for the adhesion strength of PVD films on polished substrates. Because the deposition occurs on an atomic level, intimate contact can occur. Surfaces should be clean and have high surface energies (which can be achieved by reverse sputtering). Another way to demonstrate this increase in surface energy is by reactive plasma cleaning. The wetting of water on electronic grade, 96% alumina substrates compared before and after oxygen plasma cleaning showed a 40° decrease in the contact angle (11). Over time, the surface relaxes and foreign material re-adsorb.

1.1.2. Chemical Adhesion

Chemical bonding, in the form of oxidation/reduction, dissolution, or diffusional reactions between the two components at the interface may occur (3). Such reactions can occur with sharp discontinuity, where the critical parameters are the degree of lattice mismatch and the strength of the oxide components (12). Alternately, bulk macroscopic reactions that create wide diffusional interfaces with gradients in properties between the ceramic and metal components are possible (13). In either case, localized equilibrium is a common characteristic of strong, reliable bonds (14) as in the case of protective oxides grown on aluminum or stainless steel (15). One model (16) suggests that adhesion is proportional to electron transfer between the metal and ceramic. The author shows a direct relationship between the work of adhesion between metals and alumina and the surface electron density of the metal. Because in all cases, the amount of reaction area is a direct consequence of interface area, roughness will again improve bonding. Extensive studies of ceramic metal reactions were performed by Yeomans and Page (17) and also by O'Bannon (18). They discuss the impact of more complex galvanic reactions that may occur (e.g. in porcelain enameling of low carbon steel).

1.1.3. Thermoelastic Properties

Heterogeneous joints produced at elevated temperature generate stress on cooling as the constituent materials contract at different rates (19). Large differences in thermal expansion as a function of temperature curves between ceramics and metals, combined with high elastic moduli, can result in detrimental residual thermal stresses (20,21). Plastic deformation accommodates some stress in certain cases but depends on joint design (3,22). Stress levels in particular joints depend on extrinsic factors (Sect. 1.2.2) such as the joint design, geometry, and size, but thermal expansion is an intrinsic property as is the mismatch between two materials. Stresses due to thermal cycling are eliminated for materials with equivalent expansion behavior.

Elastic modulus mismatch can also be considered for both intrinsic and extrinsic factors. When two materials having different elastic moduli (an intrinsic property) are strained to the same extent, higher stress occurs in the higher modulus material. This is usually the ceramic in a ceramic-to-metal bond. Again, extrinsic factors and joint design may be used to manipulate properties and performance of a specific joint with a fixed mismatch and will be discussed below.

Another form of mismatch generating interfacial stress results from differences in crystal lattice parameter or structure (20,23). In the $Ni-Al_2O_3$ system, an interfacial spinel layer forms at elevated temperature in the presence of oxygen. The lattice parameter mismatch between Al_2O_3 and $NiAl_2O_4$ is small and bonds are strong (24). The mismatch in $Ni-NiAl_2O_4$ is large and consequently failure occurs at this metal-spinel interface (24,25,26). In some systems, the ability of the material to accommodate lattice strains through misfit dislocations (23) and preferred interfacial orientations (26) can limit the effect.

1.2. Extrinsic Contributions to Bonding

Joint design variations, size effects, surface or interfacial modifications, as well as defects can dramatically affect bond performance. In ceramic-to-metal joining, lack of contact, contamination, blisters, impurities, brittle interfacial compounds, and other factors can limit strength and performance. Material processing operations may result in many undesirable surface properties: e.g. surface stresses from forming, grinding marks, contamination by machining oils, etc. Surface topography achieved through grinding, polishing, lapping, sand blasting etching etc. may effect the mechanical interlocking of surface features affecting mechanical adhesion. However, extrinsic factors such as induced damage, true contact area, and surface chemistry must be considered in design and will be discussed below.

1.2.1. Surface Roughness

Surface roughness relates to the surface area of the materials to be bonded and in turn affects the amount of physically and/or chemically bonded area, as well as the degree of mechanical adhesion through interlocking of surface features. These factors, as well as the potential for surface and sub-surface damage which can be sources of detrimental flaws, must be considered. Cutting, grinding, lapping, polishing, sand or grit blasting, etching, and thermal treatment are all used to modify surface roughness. Each of the above treatments provides a specific surface texture, which may also vary between materials. For example, electrical discharge machining of metals produces a pitted surface while saw cutting results in elongated scratches. As-formed surfaces also have unique characteristics; surfaces differ when the materials are plated, sputtered, pressed, cast, rolled, etc. In addition to variations in roughness for the above examples, surface stress, damage, and contamination, or other defects may also be significant factors determining strength. Basic understanding, characterization, measurement, and control of surface roughness are essential to attain optimal bond performance.

1.2.2. Mechanical Adhesion

Mechanical adhesion results from frictional interactions of surface topographic features. Two solids may join strongly when pressed together if plastic flow and diffusion allow surface asperities to interlock. One example for which mechanical effects dominate adhesive strength is the case of electroplated printed circuit boards. Copper, when plated onto as-formed ceramic circuit boards, has little or no adhesion. However, etching the ceramic material to form a fine, roughened structure provides surface relief that leads to sufficient bond strength. The same principles are also applied when etching the copper layer to maximize solder mask adhesion (27). Liquids and vapors reacting with a rough solid can readily flow or diffuse thereby penetrating into surface features under favorable wetting conditions. When these liquid or vapor phases solidify, strong mechanical interlocks may form which resist both shear and tensile stresses. Although mechanical adhesion increases with surface roughness, surface abrasion can induce damage both on and below the surface. When flaws are introduced above a critical size, catastrophic failure will result from increased local stress intensity.

1.2.3. Roughness Measurement

Surfaces contain short-range roughness, long-range waviness, errors of form, pits, and asperities. The combination of surface features can be quantified (28). Several parameters are used; the most common is the roughness average (Ra). Ra is defined as the mean height calculated over the measured surface:

$$\mathbf{Ra} = \frac{1}{MN} \sum_{i=1}^{M} \sum_{j=1}^{N} |Z_{ij}|$$

Measurements (often reported in µm) are made perpendicular to the surface direction. Ra values are obtained by adding individual height values (without regard to sign) and dividing the sum by the number of data points (N and M) in each direction on the sample.

The Ra value is selected to describe machined surfaces because of its reproducibility and ease of determination. The value describes general variations in overall profile height characteristics and is effective as a quality control measure (29). However, Ra represents the mean roughness, and as such, limits the impact of a single asperity or pit, which could be a catastrophic flaw. Also, harmless sample contamination can generate spurious results by functioning as apparent asperities. Ra does not account for the shape of irregularities or spatial separation. As a result, samples with equal Ra may have different surface profiles.

Root mean square (rms) roughness (Rq) for measured height deviations is:

$$\mathbf{Rq} = \sqrt{\frac{1}{MN} \sum_{k=1}^{M} \sum_{j=1}^{N} Z_{jk}^2}$$

Because Rq is obtained by squaring each value over the evaluation length or area, the impact of deep pits and tall asperities is enhanced. As a consequence, this parameter is often more sensitive to surface contamination than Ra.

One measurement of particular importance in ceramics is the maximum profile valley depth (Rv), which is the distance between the lowest point of the surface and the mean line within the evaluation length, or area. This value and its complimentary peak measurement (maximum profile peak height, Rp) vary from one location to the next requiring large sample sizes for reproducibility. The valleys in a surface profile provide information about how a part might retain a lubricant, contaminant, etc. In addition, this value is important for ceramics because it relates to the deepest surface flaw, which may indicate defects reducing potential strength. However, actual results obtained will vary depending on the depth resolution of the measurement technique.

Surface roughness measurement by stylus profilometer is most commonly used because of simplicity, availability, and low cost. In this technique, a sharp (3-15 µm) diamond stylus collects surface line profiles in contact mode. Vertical and lateral resolution reaches 5nm and 1µm respectively. This method is particularly useful in measuring large step heights and may cover large lengths of the surface. Interferometers are more expensive but provide 3-D measurements. Vertical and lateral resolution reaches 0.5nm and 1µm, respectively. Operation is more complex because there is no contact; optical effects can give spurious results (e.g. different refractive index of different grains). Interferometers are not effective on high roughness surfaces or vertical steps, and large scan areas come at a cost of height resolution. Atomic Force Microscopy can also give 3-D information, but only for small areas (typically 10µm x 10 µm). The vertical and lateral resolution can reach 0.02 nm and 10 nm, respectively, but the technique requires much greater operator skill. SEM stereoscopy, adsorption techniques, and others are also used but are more difficult to perform, require expertise and may less accuracy.

1.2.4. Cleaning

Contamination is one important factor affecting joint quality. Often, a small fingerprint or a monolayer of adsorbed organic is enough to produce failure at a ceramic-metal interface. Surfaces need to be free from water vapor and adsorbed organics that can out-gas during the bonding process, resulting in interfacial defects such as pores, blisters, or loss of surface contact. Oxide films grown on metal surfaces change the nature of surface interactions and are detrimental when the oxide is poorly bonded to the substrate (e.g. hydrated, rusted iron). Organic solvents including acetone and ethanol are often used in conjunction with distilled, de-ionized water to clean ceramic and metal surfaces. Ultrasonics, agitation, and heat are often used to increase chemical reactivity and improve cleaning. However, many preparation procedures leave residues behind which are only removed through heat treatment exceeding 600°C. In particular, organic solvents will bond to a ceramic or oxidized metal surface. Such films are not commonly removed by water. Vacuum during cleaning and joining processes promotes desorption and ensures that cleanliness is maintained. It is also possible, particularly for fired ceramics, that clean, damage free, ready-to-bond surfaces can be attained with the as-manufactured surface.

Common industrial cleaning practices include: vapor degreasing, ultrasonic-vapor degreasing, ultrasonic cleaning with a liquid rinse, and immersing, spraying, or wiping (30,31). Vapor degreasing is used for the removal of soluble oils, waxes, greases and any particulate material adhering to such contamination. In this process, the part is exposed to hot solvent vapors that rapidly condense on the part and drip off in a continuous flow.

Effective solvents such as methyl chloroform, methylene chloride, or trichloroethylene are now being replaced with less hazardous substitutes which are frequently less effective. Common properties of such solvents include, high solvency of solids, non-flammability, low vapor pressure, high vapor density, low diffusivity in air (prevents loss), low heat of vaporization, chemical stability, and safety (31). Degreasing chamber design and maintenance can also have a strong impact on cleaning effectiveness. Advantages over straight immersion processes stem from efficient re-use of a limited solvent supply allowing only clean solvent to make contact with the parts (thus limiting re-deposition of contaminants).

Immersion into a solvent bath with active ultrasonic transducers (either during vapor degreasing or otherwise), adds mechanical scrubbing action to the process. The formation of small bubbles in the solvent, and their subsequent collapse, produces high energy acoustic waves that impact the parts and any soils or particulates adsorbed on their surfaces. This process is effective for insoluble contaminants and remote features such as holes and can be used with most solvents including soaps and surfactants, acids, bases, or even rinses. The main requirement is that the solvent must cavitate. Cavitation (and hence effectiveness) in water drops dramatically when the temperature falls below 60°C. Ultrasonic cleaning in acetone (as well as some high density alkaline cleaners) is fruitless because it does not cavitate. Also, the solvent should not attack containers or foam excessively (31).

Final immersion, spraying, or wiping is used to eliminate any loose soils. The major consideration is that new contaminants (e.g. cloth lint) not be introduced to the part. Many industrial applications introduce fresh, unused solvent in the final rinse or spray process and then cycle them to earlier cleaning steps such as vapor degreasing.

Additional methods cleaning methods including acidic, alkaline, plasma and electrolytic cleaning may also be used, but all techniques are both material and contamination specific. Organics are removed by oxidizing processes: peroxide, chromic acid, oxygen plasma, or a high temperature bake. Typically oxide scales are removed under reducing conditions (e.g. Ar plasma for wire bonding surfaces, hydrogen firing of metal). In general, cleaning is considered to include only those processes that do not alter the topography or chemistry of the substrate (30). Aggressive acids and bases (for ceramics: hydrofluoric acid, ammonium fluoride, NaOH, etc.) will etch as well as clean. These may leave pitted surfaces and can remove certain chemical components. Many ceramics are known to have a surface enrichment in their grain boundary glassy phase that contributes to adhesion, but is easily removed by the above etch solutions.

1.2.5. Surface and Interfacial Modification

When material surfaces provide inadequate intrinsic adhesion, it may be necessary to modify or even create a different surface entirely (32). In the $Cu-Al_2O_3$ system, it has been demonstrated that ion beam bombardment of the substrate can promote both wetting and adhesion of copper on alumina (33,34). While ion milling/mixing, plasma etching, and sputtering, have found application in surface modification of high value-added products, large capital investments required to install these systems (coupled with low capacity and throughput) limits their use. More recently, lasers have also been used for surface preparation in specific applications (35). Such procedures are now being used for area selective surface enhancement (36). It has even been observed that when nickel is machined by wire electrical discharge machining EDM, traces of yttrium from the cutting wire deposit in the surface (20 μm) of the metal and enhance fracture toughness of solid-state joints (37).

As mentioned above, some systems demand an entire new surface for bonding. Alumina is grown on the surface of aluminum nitride through oxidation at high temperature (~1300 °C) in order to improve both wetting and bonding by utilizing oxide adherence mechanisms (38,39,40,41). Success in glass-metal sealing requires adherence oxides that dissolve in the molten glass and bring the interface into chemical equilibrium (42,43). Active metals such as titanium are vacuum deposited to promote adherence of metals to many ceramics (44,45). In sputtering metals to alumina, success has been achieved through first sputtering a thin (50 Å) layer of aluminum onto the ceramic surface followed by oxidation at high temperature (46). This new alumina layer has a different structure and is free of impurities and contaminants. In addition to adhesion benefits, high frequency signals traveling along this interface experience reduced attenuation. While the examples listed above illustrate methods of chemical interfacial modification, interlayers have also been used for their mechanical properties such as ductility, elasticity, thermal expansion, etc.

1.2.6. Stresses in Ceramic-Metal Bonds

Because residual stresses, either alone or in conjunction with applied stress, can cause failure in a component, thermal expansion behavior, elastic moduli, and ductility must all be considered during material selection. Stresses between reaction phases and interlayers, as well as the major bond constituents, need to be included. Intrinsic issues of stress management were discussed earlier, but selecting materials with matched thermal expansions and elastic moduli--an ideal solution--is rarely feasible. Even in cases where thermal expansions are matched the response to and distribution of applied stress are still critical.

There are considerable opportunities in joint design, material selection and processing variables to accommodate large mismatches in coefficient of thermal expansion (CTE) between ceramic and metal (21). Low temperature processing is an approach with an economic advantage. Interface design that incorporates a gradient in thermal expansion, instead of a discontinuous change, will distribute stress more evenly. One approach involves a composite interface of the two constituents, which creates a gradient in bonding and thermal expansion (21,47, 48). However a third component placed between the surfaces with an intermediate thermal expansion or with ductility (21,48,49) divides and reduces the stress between both interfaces. The "lamellar" interlayer method consisting of multiple components is an extension of this approach.

Whenever possible, placing the ceramic in compression is advantageous (3) as these brittle materials usually fail in tension. Designs that expose the component to applied stress that opposes and negates thermal stress are also preferred. Size reduction (50) on any scale will minimize stress. Other design considerations that minimize stress at discontinuities such as edges and corners may be as simple as rounding off sharp edges or adding fillets (50). Advances in finite element modeling have helped to identify and minimize these potential stress concentrators (48). Each of these techniques, used alone or in combination is successful in specific applications, but none are universally applicable.

Relief of residual stresses is possible through the use of specialized designs such as "Housekeeper seals" (3,43) for which a ductile metal is "feathered down" to a thickness that will deform under moderate stress. Only the thinnest, most ductile metals (typically with a low melting point or operating near the melting point) can alleviate significant stresses through plastic deformation. Thus, this relief mechanism is limited in application.

Other system-specific stress relief mechanisms have been identified (51): fine TiN particles formed at the interface of an active metal brazed silicon nitride reduce stress concentration at corners and at the interface; misfit dislocations in some metals can slide along the interface; interfacial ledges have some mobility at high temperatures. These stress relief mechanisms are not available for many material systems, but can be quite effective.

Management of applied stress is equally important. One significant difference between most metals and ceramics is the elastic modulus (3,19,21), which presents a problem in ceramic-metal joining as applied stresses are not equally distributed. The ceramic usually has a much higher modulus (stiffness) than the metal. For a bond to remain intact the strain at the interface must be equal for ceramic and metal. This means that there is a much higher stress for the near-interface ceramic or interface which may be regarded as ceramic with defects. As a result failure can occur at a seemingly low applied stress and/or residual stress in the metal. The ceramic or interface may experience much higher stress and bear the bulk of the load as is the principle in ceramic reinforcement of metal matrix composites. There are solutions to this problem such as use of ductile metal that deforms relaxing residual interfacial stresses or design of a bond so that the ceramic and interface experience compressive stresses.

In applications for which a bending strain will occur, and a high modulus coating must be placed in tension, one simple solution is to minimize the overall thickness (substrate and coating). Porcelain enamel fails on thick steel sheets when flexed, while equally stiff (but thin) coatings deposited on thin substrates can be flexed to a tight radius of curvature (e.g. wear resistant CVD glass coatings on thin polycarbonate sheets). Another variation is to make the metal substrate so thick that it resists flexure forces. Porcelain enamel on a thick steel plate or cast iron will remain bonded because of the metal's resistance to bending. Designs which account for modulus mismatch or place the ceramic in compression can be quite successful.

1.2.6.1. Joint Design

Several basic principles of joint design are considered briefly because the relative impact of joint design can be the dominating factor in a strong, failure-resistant bond. For simplicity, a simple lap joint is considered below as an example. These fabrication variations were considered and compared by (50) with respect to the strength and reliability of the adhesive layer in the joint. This example is simplified in that cohesive failures, shear stresses, and other factors are not considered. Dissimilar material properties, complex loading schemes, etc. increase the effect of bond geometry on overall performance and reliability.

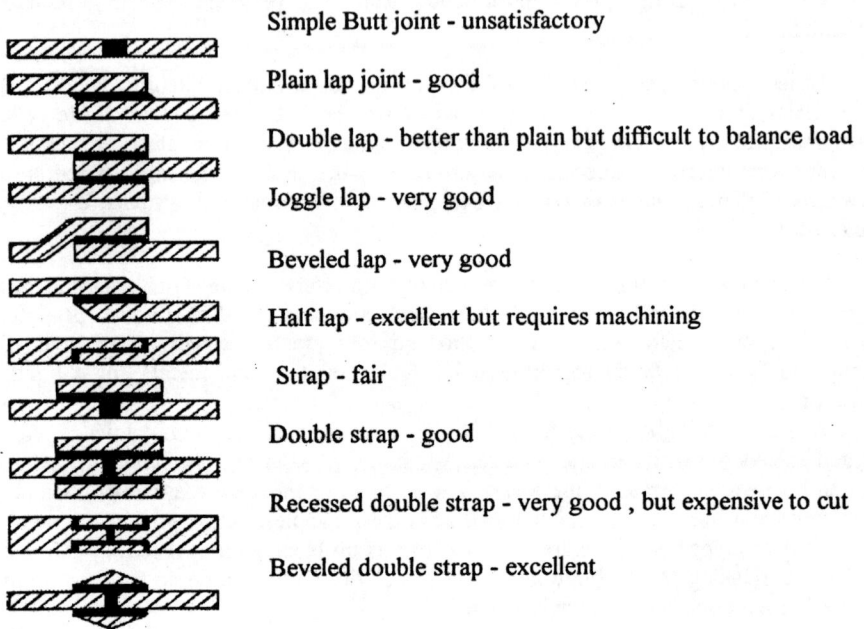

Figure 2   Comparison of adhesive joint designs

1.3 Bond Properties

Mechanical performance is of primary concern in ceramic joining because it often determines the reliability of the joint. Corrosion resistance, thermal conductivity, electronic properties, hermeticity etc. may also be critical parameters in certain specific applications, but adhesion and strength are a pre-requisite. Additional properties will depend on application and will not be considered in depth.

1.3.1 Adhesion Measurement.

The ideal adhesion test should be quantitative, reproducible, applicable to all materials, insensitive to operator experience, inexpensive and independent of other strength parameters such as cohesive strength (52). Such tests do not exist. The mechanical behavior of brittle materials depends on two factors: strength as dictated by the flaw distribution in the material, and fracture toughness, the energy required to propagate a crack a given distance through a material. The fundamental difficulty with adhesion measurement is that both factors contribute to the observed parameter. For this reason, multiple tests must be combined for a complete understanding: one which measures the stress required for catastrophic failure (a measure of the largest flaw), and a second test measuring the force required for stable crack propagation.

Numerous quality control procedures have been developed for both highly specific applications and for basic research. A bibliography of adhesion measurements of films and coatings by Mittal (53) contains over 300 references for different methods of adhesion measurement. The wide variety of common techniques makes comparison of adhesion results difficult.

1.3.2. Tensile and Bend Testing

Because ceramic materials predominantly fail in tension, the most appropriate strength test to perform is one that measures a pure, tensile failure stress. Although apparently simple, the test is sensitive to alignment, surface flaws, machining damage, clamping stress, and sample volume. As alignment varies, stress concentration along a particular edge may cause the material to fail under reduced stress. Surface and sub-surface scratches from machining must be avoided and sample design must consider clamping stresses. Because failure stresses may have a wide distribution of values, a large number of samples must be considered for each test. For these reasons, as well as the high costs for specimen preparation (particularly for ceramics), total cost and effort can be very high. However, this is the only method appropriate when comparing different materials: e.g. correlating the strength of polymer to that of a ceramic or metal.

Sample volume effects (mentioned above) result because tensile testing measures the largest flaw in the stressed volume of material. The probability of having a large flaw will always be higher for a larger amount of otherwise equivalent, material (54). In the case of ceramic-metal joints, unless failure occurs at the interface, the test will only give a threshold value. Although the stressed region of a joint is a planar interface, the theory is equivalent because stress is a force per unit area, not volume. Adjustments must be made to correct for samples of different cross sectional area (instead of volume) if they are to be compared.

Bend testing allows for mathematical extraction of a tensile failure stress using less expensive sample preparation due to the more robust nature of the test. Clamping stress, end effects and back surface (compressive side) flaws do not affect strength.

Although the method does not give a uniform stress distribution, and that stress distribution varies with strain, the method is quite popular for ceramics for which the strain to failure from plasticity is insignificant (54). Both 3-point and 4-point methods are used in practice but and each is valid for bonds that fail at a central point, at their interface.

While standard tension and flexure tests are widely accepted, sensitivity to flaw size requires that numerous measurements be made. Precise machining of multiple test samples increases testing costs such that inexpensive alternatives are often sought. In addition, intrinsic bond strengths cannot be determined because the failure stresses are derived from a combination of adhesion strength and the flaw size distribution.

1.3.3   Peel Adhesion Testing

Peel testing has been used with success for: brittle, and ductile coatings; ceramics, metals, and polymers; thick films and thin films; high strength and low strength interfaces. Sample preparation, operator training, and testing costs are minimal. The major difficulty has been comparison among different cases. Values presented in the literature are in units of force, force per unit length, and force per unit area, with some tests accounting for deformation of the peeled film and some not. There is no simple means of compensating for the difference between the plastic work of deforming a thick metal foil and the elastic bending of scotch tape. Several attempts have been made to calculate the energy or work of film deformation and subtract this value from the peel measurement to obtain true adhesion. While these calculations may provide some understanding of the mechanics involved in select cases, the results are not relevant to cases involving different substrates, or films of different geometries. However, there has been some progress in tests that experimentally determine the contribution to peel strength from film deformation. When determined properly, this value can be used to standardize a range of test data.

One advantage of peel testing is that the stress is concentrated at the interface. The potential for cohesion failure (where only a threshold value is obtained) is low when compared to other techniques. However, it is possible that failure can occur outside of the interface for all or part of the peel. Often in testing ceramics small areas of ceramic or individual grains are peeled with the film or a film residue remains on the ceramic surface. Although these phenomena are not separately considered in peel strength determination, the information is valuable in itself for bond optimization, process control, and defect elimination especially in the case of reacted or multilayer interfaces where the weakest link must be identified.

Peel adhesion tests can be classified into two basic types: first, peeling around a mandrel, where the foil curvature is fixed; second, free peeling, where the foil curvature is defined by the properties of the foil and the bond interface. Although angular variations are also used, 90° peeling is the most popular arrangement. In the extreme case where the peel angle is low, the test is more appropriately compared to lap shear. The mechanical properties of the constituents and the type of information required often dictate the test setup. For example, for quality control in mass production, the fastest, easiest, cheapest test is used and an empirically determined range of acceptable peel behavior is sufficient. More complex designs are employed only for fundamental research.

In addition to the energy required to debond an adherend per unit width, G, which is essentially the energy required to create two surfaces of the given area or propagate a crack along the interface, several other factors may contribute to the measured peel energy, P. Energy is dissipated in the plastic bending of the film as well as the unbending as peeling proceeds, $W_{plastic}$, and may also be stored elastically during bending, $W_{elastic}$. The relative amounts of each will depend on the properties of the foil as well as the foil thickness and radius of curvature during peeling. Elastic and plastic contributions may also appear along the line of force in the foil. There could be a linear extension which is either elastic, $L_{elastic}$, or plastic, $L_{plastic}$. These last contributions, usually negligible, increase as the peel angle decreases (55). Another plastic term, which is often ignored, is the crack tip plasticity, C. However, this term is accounted for by the fracture energy (56). In almost all cases it is assumed that the substrate is either rigid or elastic and so there is no energy contribution from the substrate. Other factors which may affect the peel value are the friction, F, and alignment weight, mg, in the case of peeling around a mandrel or roller (57). The total energy balance can be expressed as:

$$P = G + W_{plastic} + W_{elastic} + L_{elastic} + L_{plastic} + C + F + mg$$

In practice, many of these factors may vary widely in their relative contributions from insignificant to dominant and most material-specific models eliminate several of these terms.

1.3.3.1 Peeling Around a Mandrel

ASTM standard peel methods involve either a 1" diameter roller (58) or a 2" diameter mandrel (59). This method has been studied extensively by Troczynski, Sexsmith, Breslauer, et al (57,60,61,62,63) who have been able to account for the foil deformation term. The assembly is shown in figure 1.3 where the alignment weight ensures that the foil strain is fixed by the radius of the mandrel/roller (57). In their work, the additional terms for friction (F) and the alignment weight (mg) are included:

$$E = G + W_{plastic} + F + mg$$

The elastic energy stored in the foil is assumed negligible. The effect of this elastic energy would be seen in the residual stress of the foil. In order to determine peel contributions from the additional terms, a calibration sample which is not attached to the substrate (no adhesion) is pulled around the mandrel. Because the foil thickness, friction, and alignment weight are unchanged, this standard peel energy can be subtracted from that of the sample to give pure adhesion. It is possible to test any foils/adherends that fully conform to the mandrel either elastically or plastically.

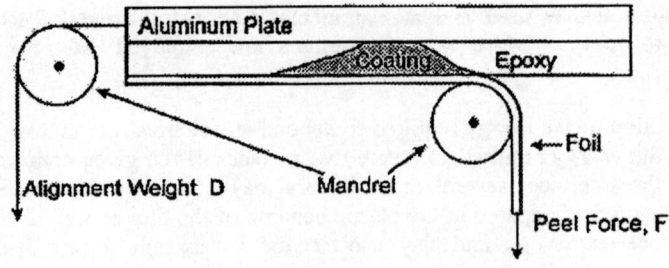

Figure 3 Mandrel assisted peel with alignment weight

Running a calibration standard eliminates much of the calculation and assumption. However, additional sources of error in the experimental work such as a difference in friction between the standard and test specimen may present a problem. Friction force must be treated as a function of tension (60). Sufficient alignment weight must be applied to ensure that, even with stiff foil, full conformance of the foil to the mandrel (fixed strain) is achieved in each case. The effects of the substrate cannot be considered because there is no interaction with the substrate in the calibration run. In testing lower elastic modulus substrates an effect may be present—as suggested previously—which will skew the measured peel strengths. Crack tip plasticity, may have the same effect.

1.3.3.2 Free Peeling

Free peel methods involve a less complicated test assembly and require little skill in operation and calibration as compared to mandrel assisted tests (64). For this reason, free peel tests have been used more extensively in industry for quality control. Fracture energy cannot ordinarily be extracted because the foil deformation energy is unknown. This energy, if measured, varies with interfacial strength. The radius of curvature during free peeling often decreases as the interface strength increases. Metal foil samples with low adhesion may fail without significant bending of the foil (thus causing weak bonds to register as even weaker). Strong bonds, in addition to a small radius of curvature for the foil, can also dissipate energy in the linear extension of the adherend.

While the data may not be standardized, free peeling is very effective for quantifying differences in adhesion and bond defects. Due to the popularity of this free peel test, several researchers have tried to model the behavior. Performing this test is trivial when compared to an analytical interpretation of the results.

Several polymers and extremely thin metal foils are either fully elastic or the plastic deformation is negligible; e.g. the scotch tape test (52). For the fully elastic case, energy dissipation through plastic bending as well as the mechanism for producing residual stress (plasticity) are excluded.

The peel test has been shown to be a direct measurement of interfacial toughness for copper films for cases where:

$$6 E p / \sigma_y^2 < t$$

E, σ_y, and t are the elastic modulus, yield stress, and film thickness of copper respectively and p is the peel force (56). This relation (although useful for low elastic modulus materials) corresponds to thickness of 1 cm or more for copper according to Kim and Kim (56). Their revised analysis (which accounts for plastic deformation) allows toughness measurement in the range of:

$$6 E p / \sigma_y^2 > t > p / \sigma_y \varepsilon_f$$

where ε_f = failure strain (0.55 for Cu). This range extends from 1 μm to 1 cm for copper films but depends on the elastic properties of the substrate and so is not universally applicable. An additional constraint is that the radius of curvature must not be less than 4-5 times the copper thickness. This was not an issue for their analysis but that same condition is often violated in peeling thick direct bonded copper where a bending moment should be considered. Experiments were conducted in parallel to the theoretical work showing that there exists an inverse effect of film thickness on measured peel strength, and a direct effect of substrate elasticity and film ductility (56). However, this analysis still does not cover the range of properties required for a universal peel test. There is still no way to compare the adhesion between rubber film and a plastic substrate to a metal foil on ceramic.

1.3.4. Quality Control Tests

1.3.4.1. Pin-Pull.

In the pin-pull adhesion test (34,65) a pin or button is glued to the film by epoxy and pulled off as the measured loads at failure are divided by actual contact area to obtain a tensile strength. The data from these experiments show a good fit to a Weibull distribution (65). Another test, useful in research, involves push-off of a solidified sessile drop (66,67). The resulting mode of failure is argued but the test does provide quantitative results for screening.

1.3.4.2 Pull-Peel.

Dupont and Motorola developed variations of a pull-peel test for the thick film industry. The "pull-peel" test setup (shown below in fig. 4) includes 2 mm square bond pads deposited on the ceramic substrate (115). A wire is then soldered to the bond pad and pulled normal to the substrate. The maximum failure stress and the failure mechanism (e.g. pad lift off, ceramic failure, etc.) are recorded. The test is termed "pull-peel" because the stress is higher on the leading edge of the pad and as a result will give a lower value than a direct tensile (nail-head) pull test where the force is evenly distributed.

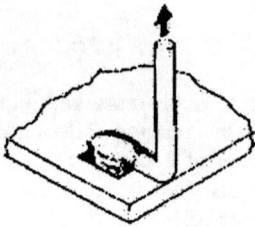

Figure 4   Pull-peel test sample configuration

Alignment is critical for this test. An off-angle pin (running from corner to corner) concentrates stress on a smaller area and results in reduced pull values. These samples are small enough that stresses are minimized but large solder balls can weaken the bonds. The solder reflow temperature is low to avoid altering the bond strength. Solder time/temperature can effect strengths of precious metal thick films because of their solubility in the liquid solder but does not effect direct bond copper or nickel bonds.

1.3.5   Thermo-Mechanical Performance

The performance of current ceramic-metal joints at elevated temperatures, under thermal shock, or thermal/mechanical cycling is inadequate. Alternative designs and extensive engineering have effectively circumvented these limitations thus far, but at significant cost. In contrast to homogeneous materials, joints between components differing in thermoelastic behavior can generate elevated stress when subjected to the above conditions. While estimates can be made of the thermo-mechanical performance of homogeneous materials based on responses to limited tests, extrapolation of ceramic metal joint performance to such conditions is risky. For these reasons, direct testing of bond performance is essential.

Elevated temperature testing in-situ is quite costly and usually reserved as a final trial prior to application. Elevated temperature exposure tests, where degradation is quantified using before and after performances, are more common because of their clear economic advantages. However, certain parameters such as creep resistance require that a combination of stress and temperature be considered. Using a dead load and measuring a time to failure can reduce the capital cost of test equipment. The strong dependency of joint design and application-specific parameters on thermo-mechanical performance limits acceptability of data collected on standard test coupons.

2. Methods of Bonding

Several methods of ceramic to metal bonding are successfully practiced in industry ranging from simple mechanical fastening or adhesive bonding to various types of reacted joints. Fastening, using bolts, screws, rivets, clamps, or other connections is by far the simplest of all joining technologies. A major advantage is that joining is reversible. However, the fact that a joint is supported at only a few points of contact leads to localized stress concentrations that may cause failure. Ceramics, being brittle materials, are generally not well suited for this type of joining because, for many components, drilled holes and other connections act as critical flaws. Compression (shrink fit) joints (3), which are widely used in joining ceramic turbine blades to metallic shafts, can be included in this category. Such compression bonds are particularly effective because they distribute stress more evenly. With correct design, the bond stress can be used to oppose applied stresses in service. Adhesive bonds (e.g. epoxy, etc.) can also prove very effective and economical. However, fastening and adhesive bonding, even when used in conjunction, have limitations. Numerous applications requiring high temperatures, hermeticity, corrosion resistance, high strength, and high reliability, demand ceramic-metal joints where the two constituent materials bond or are reacted (either with each other or with a third component) at all areas of contact.

These reacted bonds can be sub-divided into three groups by the method of fabrication: solid-state reaction, deposition, and liquid phase reaction. Specific methods of technological importance are discussed below with emphasis placed on the $Cu-Al_2O_3$ and $Ni-Al_2O_3$ systems. Properties, processing and structure are discussed and the advantages and disadvantages are highlighted.

2.1. Solid State Bonding

2.1.1. Pressure Bonding

Physical or diffusion bonding (more common for joining metals), has limited use for ceramic-metal systems (68,69,70) of limited geometries because the applied pressure is uniaxial. Although potential exists for very strong bonds, full contact is rarely achieved, and interfacial flaws (contamination, reactions generating stress, brittle compounds, etc.) further reduce the actual failure strength. The bonding process places two materials in contact under ultra-high vacuum at high temperature and pressure for extended periods of time to form a bond. When joining two bulk materials, atomically flat surfaces would be ideal as this would ensure full contact. However, real surfaces have roughness and in order to increase the contact area, pressure must be applied normal to the interface causing elastic and plastic deformation of surface asperities. Heating the assembly (below the melting temperature of the less refractory constituent) decreases the yield point and increases plastic flow of the material. Heating also enhances material transport by both evaporation/condensation and surface diffusion, which improves contact between the two surfaces. Finally, heat promotes chemical reaction and interdiffusion (across the interface). As a general rule 0.5 T_{melt} is considered a minimum temperature while 0.8 to 0.9 T_{melt} is optimal (71). Vacuum (or inert atmosphere) is used for cleanliness and to prevent gas adsorption.

Several researchers have used this method to join nickel and its alloys to alumina. Trumble and Ruhle bonded alumina to nickel at 1390°C (0.96 T_{melt}) under a pressure of 4 MPa for 2 hours in a vacuum of ~1 x 10^{-3} Pa (24). They investigated the effects of the dissolved oxygen content in the nickel on interfacial reactions and found that a micron scale spinel phase formed at a threshold oxygen level. The authors did not directly measure the strength but indicated that interfaces containing spinel failed when cross-sectioned while those without spinel withstood cutting, polishing, and dimpling. However, Calow et al (70), measured strengths for this system using samples bonded at 1100°C (0.75 T_{melt}) under 15 MPa of pressure in both reducing and neutral atmospheres. They found strengths of 5 MPa and 50 MPa respectively, thus indicating a beneficial impact of oxygen in the system.

2.1.2. Sintering Processes

High volume, low cost production of capacitors is achieved by co-firing both metal and ceramic layers of a green powder compact. The same bonding mechanisms employed in pressure bonding are used here (evaporation/condensation, diffusion, chemical reaction, etc.), however, the applied pressure is replaced by surface energy as the driving force for joining. The difficulty in this process lies in selecting an appropriate atmosphere and thermal schedule for the two fundamentally different materials. For example, oxygen is needed for spinel formation when joining nickel powder compacts to alumina (70) but obviously, excessive oxygen in the atmosphere for extended times will completely oxidize the metal (of particular concern when using fine powders).

Some ceramics and metals do not share an equilibrium atmosphere with respect to oxidation/reduction thermodynamics (e.g. some titanate materials and non-noble metals). Here, process control must be achieved by limiting reaction kinetics. Although solid-state reactions are slow, fine powders with high surface area can be very reactive (particularly when the particle size of one constituent must be very small to increase its sinterability). For this reason, the possible materials, reaction times, and temperatures are limited. Costly, refractory, noble metals such as platinum are often the only viable option for creating a join through a sintering process.

Another variation of the sintering process is thick-film metallization, where a paste of metal powder is screen printed onto a ceramic substrate and fired. Because the substrate is already sintered and the surface area is low, it is less reactive and more compatible with a reducing atmosphere if required.

Because most thick-film inks contain a glass frit that forms a viscous liquid during bonding, a distinction is made here to include only those materials that are termed "frit-less" in industry. Both copper and silver thick film inks are commercially available with copper oxide added instead of glass frit in order to promote adhesion to alumina. In typical production, the inks are fired onto the substrate in the range of 800°C-900°C for 10 to 20 minutes. In addition to thick film conductors, resistors are also regularly produced for screen-printing on alumina. Here, atmosphere control is particularly important because of the impact of oxidation/reduction reactions on resistance values.

2.1.3. Deposition onto a Solid

Deposition of a metal or ceramic either from solution or vapor is often used when thin layers are desired. Common applications include electronics where conductivity is desired on an insulator, or for coatings that improve the corrosion or abrasion resistance of a metal. Although numerous methods of application are available (spray, dip, spin, CVD, plasma spray, flame spray, etc.), sputtering, evaporation, and plating are most often used to generate pure, even coatings for metallization of ceramics. **These very thin layers may in themselves be regarded as a ceramic-metal join in which the metal or ceramic layer is very thin. This is often termed "metallization" when the metal is applied to the ceramic as a thin layer. The applied layer may be built up to create a thick material. In some cases a platinum layer has been vapor deposited onto alumina used to promote metal bonding. Metal salts have also been used and thermally decomposed to metallization or a bond metal. In electroforming a thin layer of metal, often copper, is vapor or electroless deposited to provide a conductive layer that is then built up by conventional electroplating. Titanium for active metal brazing may be deposited by physical vapor deposition or application and thermal decomposition of a metal salt solution applied to either a bonding layer or an intermediate. Ceramic protective layers are plasma sprayed onto nickel-based superalloy turbine blades to prevent high temperature oxidation and abrasion.**

2.1.3.1. Sputtering

Sputtering allows the low temperature deposition of almost any material and composition as thin (micron scale or less) films. A plasma is formed in a low pressure atmosphere (typically argon) causing ionized particles to collide with the target (cathode) where they can eject an atom that will deposit on the substrate. Advantages of sputtering include: wide compositional versatility, wide potential substrate temperature variation, very high purity, excellent adhesion, excellent surface finish (approaching that of the substrate), and a favorable stress condition which is typically low and compressive (72). Sputtering can also be used as a method of cleaning if the substrate is placed in the target position. Deposition rates are typically 1-10 microns/min. The substrate must be extremely clean, the process is capital intensive and, as a consequence, is not economically viable in many cases (73).

2.1.3.2. Evaporation

Vaporization of a metal at high temperature will allow its deposition on a substrate as it condenses. This process, like sputtering, is performed under vacuum which ensures a clean deposit. At common pressures (10^{-4} to 10^{-7} torr), the evaporated atoms arrive at the substrate without reactions, collisions, or energy loss. These atoms may reflect, adsorb (weak van der Waal's bond), chemically react, or associate with previously deposited atoms (72). For the case of most metals, vacuum is particularly important to prevent oxidation. As a simplified example, metals are placed inside a platinum pan or tungsten wire basket that is resistively heated. However, more complex versions of the process include Arc, electron beam, and laser evaporation coupled with a plasma or reactive gas which can provide more versatility. Like sputtering, deposition rates are in the range of microns/minute and high volume production is costly. In contrast to sputtering, evaporated coatings require substrate heating, usually crystallize, and typically have a tensile stress which can limit adhesion. In both methods of physical vapor deposition, characterization of the mechanical properties of the coatings is difficult because of the limited thickness.

2.1.3.3 Electroless Plating

Electroless deposition, also known as auto-catalytic or chemical deposition, involves the spontaneous growth of a coating from solution, onto a substrate. No voltage is applied in the process and uniform coatings can be applied to both conductors and activated non-conductors. A reducing agent is used to supply electrons to the dissolved metal ions, which converts them to the metallic state on the surface of the catalytic substrate (74). The first discovered, most common system for electroless deposition is Ni-P, which has been studied extensively since its invention in 1946 by Brenner and Riddel (75).

As an example, in the process invented by Brenner and Riddel, deposition of Ni-P involves reaction between an aqueous salt of nickel (usually $NiCl_2$) and sodium hypophosphite. Complexing ions, buffers, and other additives are used to modify the process. Temperature and pH control the rate of deposition, which has a strong effect on the deposit morphology. The amount of phosphorous that co-deposits is also highly dependent on the pH of the plating bath. Several metals can be deposited in the same manner using a metal salt and suitable reducing agent. Another important example utilizes hydrazene as a reducing agent for Ni, with the resulting deposit exceeding 99% purity (74,76).

Electroless deposition on ceramic substrates involves several pre-treatments including cleaning, etching, sensitizing, and activation (77). Etching of polycrystalline alumina removes the glassy grain boundary phase, which increases roughness and improves retention of activators and adhesion of the electroless deposit. Hydrofluoric acid is the most effective etchant for alumina and other ceramics, however sodium hydroxide (76) and ammonium fluoride (78) are more often used for safety reasons. Stannous chloride is the preferred sensitizer followed by a palladium chloride activator (78). The palladium (or other activator), which deposits on the substrate provides catalytic sites, and initiates electroless deposition. Both steps can be combined into one, but researchers have found that using separate baths improves adhesion to alumina by 30% to 50% (79). It was also discovered that more homogeneous nucleation was obtained with an intermediate immersion in a silver chloride solution. Using the above steps, electroless deposition of Ni (P) has also been demonstrated for SiC (80), AlN (81), and glass (82) and electroless copper deposition has been carried out on alumina (83).

Many deposits are x-ray amorphous; the nano-crystalline structure may only have short-range order resulting in a single broad peak in the x-ray diffraction pattern (84). Thermal treatments of electroless deposits may have a strong effect on deposit properties including hardness, ductility, stress at the interface, and ultimately adhesion (85). After heating, the crystallites coarsen and XRD peaks for both metals and any compounds are detected (86). These low temperature heat treatments may also be used for other types of deposits (e.g. sputtered) where the structure is amorphous or nano-crystalline.

2.1.3.4. Electrolytic Plating

Electroplating or electrodeposition refers to the formation of a relatively thin film whereby metallic ions move through a solution in an applied electric field and deposit on a substrate (cathode) as they gain electrons from that cathode following Faraday's law (72). One simple example, a "Watt's" bath, uses two Ni electrodes connected to a direct current source and immersed in an aqueous nickel sulfate solution. Positive nickel ions in solution are attracted to the negatively charged cathode where they accept electrons and deposit as a reduced metal. Oxidation occurs at the anode; metallic atoms lose electrons and dissolve in solution. Electrolytic plating is more appropriate for generating pure (99% to 99.99%) metal deposits than electroless processes (87). However, a major disadvantage of the technique is thickness variation, which often exceeds 100% on a single electronic circuit board due to current density variations. For this type of geometry, as an example, current density increases with radius from the center being highest at corners, and local maxima appear for thin traces and for features with sharp corners. Film properties depend on current density, solution concentration, agitation, temperature, electrode shape and structure, bath purity, and any bath additives such as brighteners or stabilizers (87).

2.2. Bonding via Liquid Phase

The following sections describing the various liquid-phase processes, which comprise the bulk of ceramic-metal joining technology. They are therefore the main emphasis of this review. Discussion of generic wetting principles is included because of the significant role that wetting behavior plays in bonding research, development, and fabrication.

Wetting behavior in ceramic-metal systems is perhaps the most important measure of compatibility for solid-liquid interfaces such as molten glass on solid metal and liquid metal on ceramic. Wetting insures intimate contact between the surfaces. Such full contact by the liquid is extremely important to guarantee hermetic joints. It also establishes maximum contact for bonding between surfaces. Once contact is achieved, the surface tension of the liquid can be used for the alignment of components. One example of this alignment function is in soldering devices to a circuit board. The accuracy of industrial pick-and-place equipment may not be sufficient for assembly but properly placed solder with good wetting will make parts self-align during re-flow.

While methods such as liquid flow into a capillary tube are popular for aqueous solutions, elevated temperature ceramic-metal systems are most often and effectively evaluated using the sessile drop technique (88,89). The degree to which a liquid drop spreads (or beads) on a solid surface results from a balance between the interfacial energies of the constituents and gravity. Figure 5 illustrates the sessile drop configuration and the components of the force balance.

$\gamma_{sv} - \gamma_{sl} = \gamma_{lv} \cos\theta$

γ_{sv} = solid surface energy

γ_{lv} = liquid surface energy

γ_{sl} = solid-liquid interface energy

θ = contact angle

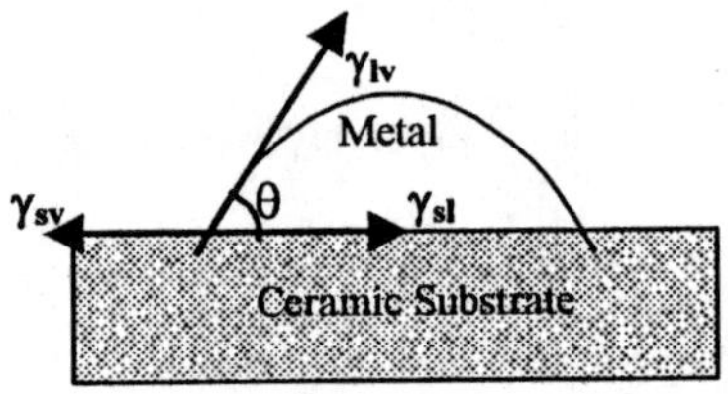

Figure 5   Sessile drop configuration

Contact angles less than 90° are termed "wetting" while those greater than 90° are "non-wetting." The special 0° case is known as "spreading" because the liquid spreads to a monolayer to maximize substrate coverage. When the sessile drop reaches equilibrium (becomes truly "sessile"), the contact angle can be measured and used to determine the surface tension. However, most wetting ceramic-metal systems are accompanied by interfacial reaction (90). In this case the system may form additional phases. Commonly such reactive systems are not carried to equilibrium. Thus, the simple wetting equation above may not be applicable (91). Because reaction occurs in many important ceramic-metal bonding systems, as well as variations in surface properties, atmosphere, and temperature, wetting behavior is dynamic and equilibrium is often not achieved in practice. Manipulation of process variables can alter wetting behavior (92) but cannot be expected to change a system from a non-wetting to a wetting case unless reactions occur (93). Changing the composition of the solid liquid or vapor can have a major effect and alter a non-wetting to wetting situation. Altering the gas environment is usually most effective and minimizes changes to the final solid components.

Commonly, wetting indicates that bonding will occur. A lower contact angle usually improves the bond quality, but may also relate to increased chemical interaction between materials. However, not all wetting systems bond and occasionally bonding can be achieved without wetting (3). Observing the dynamic behavior of the drop can be used to set production operating parameters (time, temperature, atmosphere) – particularly when equilibrium is not achieved. Cooled sessile drop can also be particularly valuable for evaluating bond strength because the force required to remove the solidified drop can be measured (66,67). This can provide a preliminary indication of bond strength but should be used with care because the small size of the drop minimizes the effect of residual thermoelastic stress.

2.2.1. Viscous Liquid

Sintered metal powder processing (SMPP) also known as the "moly-manganese" process or "refractory metallization" is one of the oldest joining techniques and is commonly used in the electronic industry for metallizing ceramic substrates (94). While this may appear to be a solid joining processes as discussed above, a distinction should be made. SMPP involves a viscous liquid although the metallization is apparently (macroscopically) sintered onto the ceramic surface. A paste is formed consisting of either tungsten or molybdenum particles (slightly oxidized), which is applied to the ceramic and sintered (~1500°C) under reducing conditions (95). The glassy phase of the ceramic infiltrates the metal particles near the interface creating the bond. Manganese oxide decreases the melting point and reduces the viscosity of the glassy phase while increasing its total volume to enhance bonding. When the ceramic will not provide sufficient glass, either glass frit or glass former (e.g. talc) is added to the SMPP formulation. This final structure of the SMPP joint provides a gradient in properties (bonding, thermal expansion, elastic modulus, etc.) between the two dissimilar materials, reducing local stress intensity. Molybdenum and tungsten are low expansion metals and provide a moderate expansion match to many ceramics. At the top surface, the metal particles are reduced and sinter to direct contact. The surface structure is virtually continuous metal. It can be used as a conductor but is usually plated either as metallization (a conductor circuit arrangement) or as a surface for conventional brazing or soldering to metal components. An additional advantage of this technique is that both tungsten and molybdenum sinter at temperatures similar to alumina, which facilitates co-firing (1).

Thick-film processes bond to ceramic in much the same way. A precious metal is mixed with a glass frit and this is fired onto the ceramic surface at approximately 850°C (3). In this case the liquid phase provided by the glass frit wets and bonds to the ceramic. A gradient from glass containing metal particles at the ceramic interface to sintered metal at the surface results. The glass may also penetrate the grain boundaries of the ceramic further promoting bonding. If precious metal such as silver, gold, platinum or their alloys is used a reducing environment is not needed. The surface may be used directly as metallization or joined to metal components by soldering or brazing.

2.2.2. Active Metal Brazing

Active metal brazing (96,97) is commonly used in industry for vacuum feed-through seals and other complex geometries where an appreciable amount of liquid must flow into a gap to ensure complete contact, and also in applications requiring high strength. Bond strengths have exceeded 200 MPa for alumina (97) and regularly fall in the range of 100-150 MPa. The braze, which is commercially available as foil or paste, is melted at the interface between the metal and ceramic where it wets the surfaces and promotes bonding. This brazing ordinarily takes place in inert atmospheres or good vacuum as the "active" metal (titanium or other group IV-B metal) readily oxidizes in air. Surfaces need to be clean and free of adsorbed material. Vacuum is preferred for this reason may increase production cost.

Braze alloys consist of titanium added to a filler metal at concentrations ranging from less than 1% to more than 30%. The filler metal alloy is selected primarily for its wetting and bond strength. This filler metal should also be ductile, to accommodate residual stresses, should not degrade the base metal, and should not exhibit blushing (surface flow) along the base metal or ceramic (2). If blushing does occur, a "stop-off" paint (often magnesia suspension) is required to prevent spreading. Additional benefits of the filler include tailored thermal expansion, melting point, oxidation resistance, and other properties. Typically copper and silver are used with approximately 2% titanium. Other elements such as indium are sometimes added to lower the melting point and/or improve wetting.

Bonding occurs in braze alloy systems because the active metal segregates to the interface and reacts with the ceramic to form a strong compound (TiO_2 for oxides, TiN for nitrides, etc.) at the interface. The active species of the braze alloy must have a higher affinity for the substrate anions than the do the substrate cations. One difficulty with this technique is that interfacial reaction products can cause embrittlement or debonding when excessively thick. For this reason, brazing time must be limited (typically minutes). Brazing temperatures are slightly above the liquidus temperature and depend on composition covering a wide range (typically between 500°C and 1200°C). Higher temperature braze alloys are required for bonds with elevated use temperature. Both fabrication and extended use at high temperatures greatly increases formation of excessive reaction phases which can lead to bond failure (71).

2.2.3. Gas-Metal Eutectic Bonding

Discovered by Burgess and Neugebauer at General Electric Company, the gas-metal eutectic process (98,99,100) involves the reaction of a gas, (e.g. oxygen), with the surface of a metal to form a eutectic surface composition. When the component is heated to a temperature between the melting point of the eutectic and that of the pure metal, the interface will melt. The two requirements are that the surface composition must melt below that of the pure metal and the liquid must wet the substrate. The "model" system for this technique (disclosed in the original patent and most often used in industry) is Cu-O for which the phase diagram (figure 6) is provided (101). Only 0.39 weight percent oxygen is required to reach the eutectic composition, as can be seen in the diagram, and the liquidus curves are steep on either side of the eutectic. Both atmosphere and temperature control is critical as small variations may either prevent melting or melt the entire copper thickness.

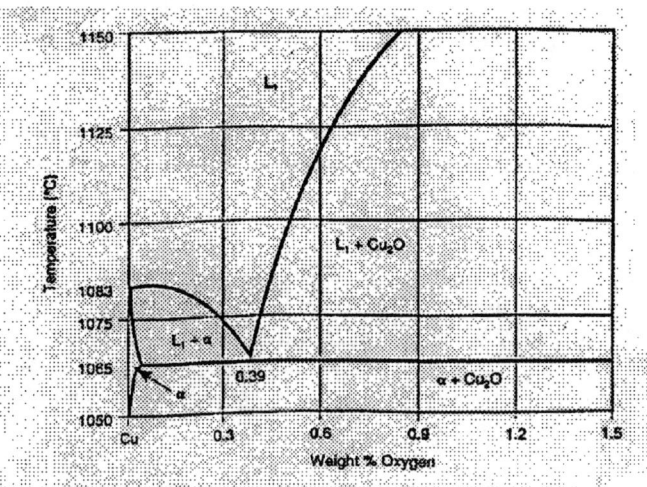

Figure 6   Cu-O binary phase diagram (*Ceramic Technology International*, 5, 37 (1997))

The Cu-O system is quite popular for metallizing alumina (102,103,104,105) and aluminum nitride (39,40,106) substrates for improved heat dissipation in high power electronic applications and for low loss at high frequencies. These attributes have caused the process in the form of both direct bond copper (DBC and plated/bonded copper to grow faster than any other metallization technology in recent years. The process has been used to bond to a variety of other substrates including: SiO_2, SiC, ZrO_2, BeO, and Si_3N_4. For Cu-O bonded to alumina, bond strengths exceed 100 MPa and often cause failure in the ceramic (9). This technique has also been demonstrated in other systems such as Ni-O (107). For the Ni-O system the process window is even tighter: T_{melt} = 1452°C and $T_{eutectic\ Ni-NiO}$ = 1440°C at 0.24 wt% oxygen.

Two basic processes are used in the formation of Cu-O eutectic bonds: pre-oxidation of the metal, and oxidation in-situ, at temperature. Pre-oxidation may achieved either thermally or chemically and both are successfully practiced in industry. For the case of metal pre-oxidation, a eutectic forms at the interface between the pure, bulk metal and the oxide-rich surface. This melt layer grows outward dissolving the metal and the oxide until one component is depleted or the temperature is reduced. In-situ oxidation occurs when the bond atmosphere exceeds the equilibrium gas partial pressure (~6 ppm O_2 for copper at T_{melt}). Again, the melt will eventually grow to consume the entire metal sample if the oxygen fugacity or the temperature is not reduced.

Although pure copper does not wet or bond with alumina, the copper oxide eutectic liquid will both wet and react to form a copper aluminate interfacial phase (108,109,110). Both $CuAl_2O_4$ ($CuO + Al_2O_3$) and $CuAlO_2$ (½Cu_2O + ½Al_2O_3) have been detected by several independent research groups but the impact of this reaction layer (aside from improved wetting) remains largely unknown. When the eutectic composition cools, both $Cu_{(\alpha)}$ and Cu_2O phases form from the melt (9,111). The morphology of the Cu_2O phase can be particulate or dendritic as shown in figure 7. The dendritic structure shows superior strength. The failure path follows the $Cu_{(\alpha)}$ phase intersection with either the ceramic or the oxide which preferentially bonds to it unless the particles become excessively large (111). Copper and its alloys are used principally for their electrical conductivity but high thermal conductivity, corrosion resistance, ease of forming, color, strength, and fatigue resistance all contribute in making it one of the most important and well-understood commercial metals (30).

The fact that copper is often used in high purity, as opposed to other metals which are mostly alloyed, is another significant contributing factor. Extensive research has been conducted in joining copper to alumina and numerous other ceramics using solid-state (118), gas-metal eutectic, thick-film (119), and brazing (97) methods. Although copper has a high thermal expansion, stresses in ceramic metal joints formed using copper are typically low because of the relatively low forming temperature, yield strength, and elastic modulus

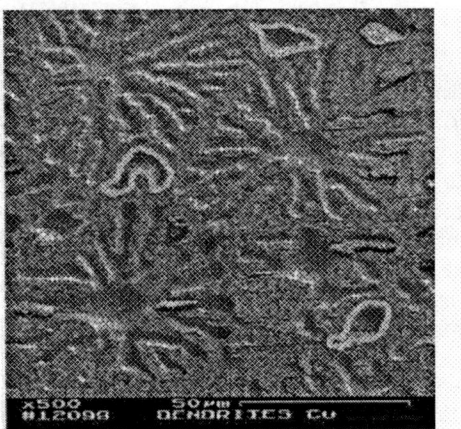 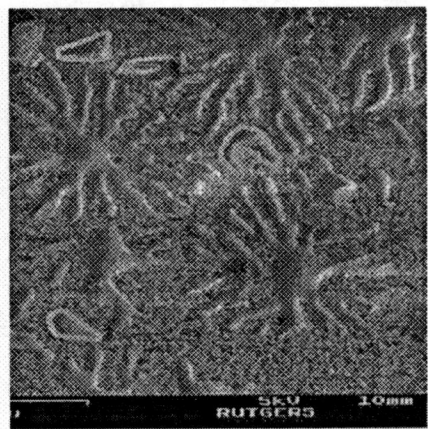

Figure 7   Metal (left) and ceramic (right) failure surfaces in direct bond copper with low-strength, particulate (top) and high-strength, dendritic (bottom) microstructures.

In the hyper-eutectic region of the diagram, wetting improves with oxygen content (120) as shown in Figure 8. The wetting angle and work of adhesion improve significantly from 0.001 to 3 wt. % oxygen. Within the region of liquid immiscibility (3-7.5 wt.%), the values are constant but improve slightly beyond 7.5 wt%. The effect of temperature was also considered (120) and from figure 9 it is clear that wetting behavior improves with temperature. While standard DBC prohibits using higher temperatures or larger oxygen additions, such limitations are eliminated by the transient gas-metal eutectic process (TEPP).

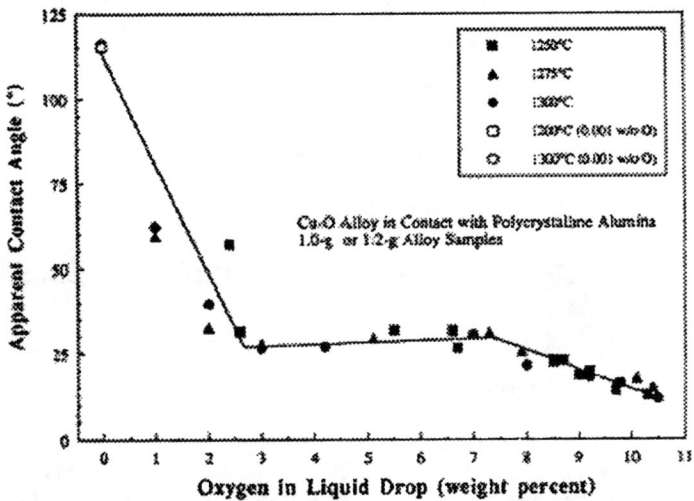

Figure 8   Contact angle vs. oxygen content for Cu on polycrystalline alumina

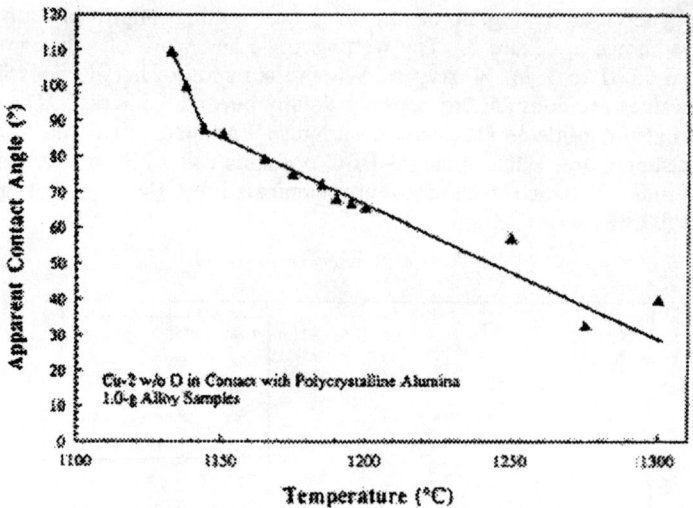

Figure 9   Contact angle vs. temperature for Cu-2 wt%O on polycrystalline alumina

2.2.4. Transient Liquid Phase Processes

Transient liquid phase processing requires liquid formation to promote contact, material transport, and bonding, but then through interactions with other components, the liquid will disappear. Subsequent heating above the formation temperature does not produce a liquid phase, allowing elevated temperature application. For example, two pieces of silver could be joined using a thin layer of liquid mercury at room temperature. The mercury and silver react to form a solid amalgam with an elevated melting point. In this particular case, a volume expansion during the reaction prohibits its use in geometries such as a butt joints. The method is quite successful in dental (ceramic-metal) applications using keyhole structures and several amalgam systems exist with limited applications.

In order for the liquid phase to be transient, one of the following methods must be available for its removal:

1. The liquid reacts with one or more of the components to form a stable compound as in the amalgam example above. These compounds can form from interactions with the ceramic, metal, or both.

2. The liquid alloys with another, more refractory component with which it exhibits extensive solid solubility such that the solidus temperature rises. This would be the case for two metals exhibiting complete solid solubility (e.g. Cu-Ni)

3. A localized concentration of a third component at the interface causes eutectic melting. Diffusion of this component into the bulk material reduces the local concentration resulting in isothermal solidification.

2.2.4.1. Reaction Method.

M. L. Shalz et al wrote the most complete review of TLP joining (71) in which they considered each case. The first case above, reaction to form a refractory phase, was considered in two ways. Thin layers of copper were deposited onto both sides of a niobium foil which was sandwiched between two pieces of alumina. Because the solubility of copper in niobium is limited (1.2% at 1080° C), and the equilibrium liquid phase contains only limited (few percent) niobium, the interdiffusion mechanism is deemed inoperable in this system (112). The authors suggest that the small Nb additions to the Cu liquid improve wetting (based on earlier sessile drop experiments) and that the liquid phase reacts with the ceramic to form a refractory ternary Cu-Al-O phase. The formation of copper aluminate (mentioned in the gas-metal eutectic section above) has only been observed in extremely thin layers (108,109). While the ternary phase thicknesses observed in DBC are much too thin to provide a viable means of removing the liquid, the bond temperatures are low and times are short for those reactions. Aside from the reaction kinetics, there is also a thermodynamic problem with the conclusion. Oxygen is required in order for copper to react with alumina (110) and is not provided under their experimental conditions (112). Confirmation of the isothermal solidification mechanism requires additional analytical work. Shalz, et al. also used tin instead of copper under parallel conditions. In this system, a refractory intermetallic phase (Nb_3Sn) forms above 1000°C (71).

2.2.4.2. Solid Solution Method

The second method of isothermal solidification listed above, solid solution with a refractory component, was investigated by Shalz et al using both the Cu-Ni (113) and Cu-Pt (114) systems. Again, thin layers of the low melting component were evaporated onto both sides of a more refractory foil, which was then sandwiched between ceramic and hot pressed. Due to the slow heating rate (4 hours to 1150°C), rapid interdiffusion, and the thin copper layer used (3 microns), a liquid could not actually form in this experiment. However, since an applied pressure of over 5 MPa was used in all of the cases (including the Nb-Cu, and Nb-Sn experiments) and the bonds were soaked at temperature for several hours, a strong bond should result from solid-state mechanisms. Each of these experiments was performed under vacuum with polished surfaces, suggesting that the oxygen essential for copper wetting and reaction was not available. However, the authors considered post bonding heat treatment as another factor in bonding. After heat treatment in air, the bond strength was significantly reduced. According to the authors, failure analysis revealed a blue spinel phase at the interface that led to failure.

Although the use of applied pressure, fast heating rates, vacuum processing, and polished surfaces makes the method impractical for industry, the results obtained were promising. For bonds made from a transient copper interlayer between either nickel or platinum and the alumina, four point bend strengths from 150 MPa to 250 MPa were obtained and in some cases ceramic failure resulted. The authors indicated that applied pressure in these studies was unavoidable due to equipment limitations. An isolated experiment using gold and platinum (where no oxidation occurs) was performed in air to demonstrate that much lower loads would suffice in providing adequate contact.

2.2.4.3. Transient Eutectic Phase Process (TEPP)

We have developed a new bonding technology termed the "transient eutectic phase process" (TEPP) which employs the second and/or third approaches. A broad process patent has been applied for. This new technology combines beneficial aspects of the gas-metal eutectic process with isothermal solidification by transient liquid phase technology. The gas metal eutectic process is used to form a liquid which wets the ceramic. This liquid then interacts with a more refractory metal and may then be solidified isothermally. The second metal may also be more active leading to enhanced bonding by the use of the active metal. A number of methods can be used to apply the metals and ceramic-metal composite materials can also be produced. The TEPP process provides a ceramic-metal bond with high strength, good wetting, a broad process window (relative to conventional gas-metal eutectic bonds), high thermal stability, and controlled thermo-elastic stress. The transport of a more active metal species to the ceramic interface can further improve adherence.

A simple model system was used to demonstrate the TEPP concept. Electronic grade alumina substrates had a foils of copper and nickel placed on top. The copper first formed a conventional gas-metal eutectic liquid which wet the alumina. Then nickel diffused into the copper metal or dissolved into liquid copper. The resulting alloy solidified isothermally. Nickel forms an enhanced ceramic-metal bond through the formation of a nickel aluminate layer at the ceramic interface. Preoxidation of the nickel prevents its premature diffusion or dissolution into the copper. Similar bonds could be produced by plating copper and nickel layers or combined plating and foils. During ordinary peel testing we often find failure of the ceramic before complete peeling occurs. The bonds are as strong as other high strength methods at room temperature. Peel tests conducted at elevated temperature showed that bond strength was retained to 800° C (1,508° F) - the furnace limit. Samples held in inert atmosphere for 100 hours at 1,000° C (1,832° F) retained the room temperature bond strength for the bonded interface.

3. Summary

An overview of important considerations for producing consistent strong, reliable ceramic metal joins has been provided. The condition and chemistry of material surfaces can aid or disrupt bonding. Surface contamination, even from organic cleaning solvents may cause defects and poor bond quality. Atmosphere control for wetting during bonding is vital to success. Composition and microstructure of the ceramic may affect bonding significantly. Special surface preparation and measurement methods may be required.

There are several strategies to avoid bond failure from thermo-elastic stresses and wetting observations are an important tool for determining probable bonding success.

A number of varied engineering methods may employed for successful ceramic-metal bonding and metallization. Those of major technological importance include: Metal Powder-Glass Frit, Moly-Manganese (SMPP), Active Metal, Non-Metallic (glass) Fusion, Gas-Metal Eutectic (DBC), Pressed Diffusion, Vapor Phase, Liquid Phase methods.

References

1. Intrater, James, "The Challenge of Bonding Metals to Ceramics" *Machine Design*, **61**, No. 24, November 23, 1989 pp 95-100.

2. Mizuhara, Howard, Huebel, E., Oyama, T., "High Reliability Joining of Ceramic to Metal" *Ceramic Bulletin*, **68** No. 9 1989, pp 1591-1599.

3. V. A. Greenhut, "Progress in Ceramic-Metal Joining and Metallization: an Overview of Techniques and Recent Advances," *Metal-Ceramic Joining*, P. Kumar and V. A. Greenhut Eds, p. 103-117, TMS, 1991.

4. Intrater, J. "Review of Some Processes for Ceramic to Metal Joining" *Materials and Manufacturing Processes*, **8** (3), pp. 353-373 (1993).

5. Elssner, Petzow G., "Metal/Ceramic Joining" *ISIJ International*, **30** (1990) NO. 12, pp. 1011-1032.

6. Greenhut, V. A. "Looking at Gas-Metal Eutectic Direct Bonding" Ceramic *Technology*, **3,** pp 37-40.

7. Martin W., Waibel, B., Laaser, W., "Thermal Resistance and Temperature Cycling Endurance of DBC Substrates" Hybrid *Circuits*, No. 22, May 1990, pp. 29-33.

8. J. F. Burgess and C. A. Neugebauer, "Direct Bonding of Metals with a Metal-Gas Eutectic," U.S. Patent No. 3,744,120, July 10 1973.

9. Chiang, Wan Lan, "Interfacial Structure, Process Control, and Adhesion Strength of Copper to Alumina and Aluminum Nitride Direct Bonds" Doctoral Dissertation, The Graduate School – New Brunswick Rutgers, The State University of New Jersey, October 1993.

10. Tabor, T. "Interaction Between Surfaces: Adhesion and Friction" *Surface Physics of Materials*, **11**, Academic Press, New York 1975 pp. 475-529.

11. T. Chapman, V. Greenhut, A. Williams "Wetting Analysis of Mercury Alloys on Al2O3 Substrates" Paper for Project SEED: Douglas College, Rutgers University, Sept. 2000.

12. R. E. Loehman, "Interfacial Reactions in Ceramic-Metal Systems" *American Ceramic Society Bulletin*, 68 [4] 891-896 (1989).

13. De Bruin, M.J., Moodie, A.F., Warble, C.E., "Ceramic-Metal Reaction Welding" *Journal of Material Science*, 7 (1972) pp. 909-918.

14. Pask, J.A., Tomsia, A., "Wetting, Spreading, and Reactions at Liquid/Solid Interfaces" Surfaces *and Interfaces in Ceramic and Ceramic Metal Systems*, J. Pask and A. Evans, eds., Plenum Press New York, NY (1981).

15. Peteves, S.D., et al, "Ceramic/Metal Reactions and Microstructures in Ceramic Joints" *Proceedings of the International Materials Conference on: Ceramic Microstructure '96: Control at the Atomic Level* (June 21-27, Berkely, CA), A.P. Tomsia and A. Glaeser, eds. (Plenum Publ.).

16. Li, Jian-Guo, "Wetting, Adhesion, and Electronic Structure of Metal/Ceramic Interfaces: a Comparison with Metal-Semiconductor Schottky Contacts" *Structural Ceramics Joining II*, Edited by Arthur J. Moorhead, 1993, The American Ceramic Society.

17. Yeomans, J.A., Page, T.F., *Studies of Ceramic-Liquid Metal Reaction Interfaces*, pp. 2312-2320 Copyright 1990 Chapman and Hall Ltd. New York, NY.

18. L.S. O'Bannon, "The Adherence of Enamels, Glass, and Ceramic Coatings to Metals- -a Review" Batelle Memorial Institute, Columbus Ohio, 1959.

19. He, M.Y., Evans, A.G., "The Strength and Fracture of Metal/Ceramic Bonds" *Acta Metall. Mater.* **39** No. 7 pp. 1587-1593, 1991.

20. Sheets, B.E., Kokini, K., "Thermal Stresses Under Engine Heat Flux-Part 1: Ceramic Coating on Metal Substrate" *Journal of Energy Resources Technology*, **114** December 1992 pp 291-297.

21. Suganuma, Katsuaki, et al. "Method for Preventing Thermal Expansion Mismatch Effect in Ceramic-Metal Joining." *Journal of Materials Science Letters*, **4** (1985) 648-650.

22. C. H. Hsueh and A. G. Evans, "Residual Stresses in Metal/Ceramic Bonded Strips," *Journal of the American Ceramic Society*, **68** [5] 241-248 (1985).

23. A.G. Evans, M. Ruhle, "Microstructure and Fracture Resistance of Metal/Ceramic Interfaces," *MRS Bulletin*, pp. 46-50, Oct. 1990

24. Trumble, K.P., M. Ruhle, "The Oxygen Activity Dependence of Spinel Interphase Formation During Ni/Al$_2$O$_3$ Diffusion Bonding"

25. Sun, X., Yeomans, J., "Optimization of a Ductile-Particle-Toughened Ceramic" *Journal of the American Ceramic Society*, **79** No. 10 pp. 2705-2717, 1996.

26. Betrabet, H.S., et al, "Spinel Formation in the Nickel-Alumina System" *Ceramic Engineering Society Proceedings*, **10**, No. 11-12, pp. 1531-1540, (1989).

27. N. Arabinick, "Microetch Comparisons", *Printed Circuit Fabrication*, **22**, No. 5, 1999, pp. 22-28.

28. Zygo Corporation, "MetroPro Surface Texture Parameters", Copyright 1997, SB-0291.

29. Digital Intruments, *Scanning Probe Microscopy Training Notebook*, 1998.

30. H. Boyer, T. Gall, *Metals Handbook, Desk Edition*, (1985), American Society for Metals, Metals Park, Ohio.

31. Richard C. Snogren, *Handbook of Surface Preparation*, (1974), Palmerton Publishing Co., Brattleboro Vermont.

32. G. Crosby, D. Shanefield, "Method for Bonding a Metal Pattern to a Substrate" United States Patent # 3,679,472, July 25, 1972.

33. G. Fuchs, et al, "Ion Beam mixing of Cu-Al$_2$O$_3$ interfaces for enhanced adhesion" *Materials Science and Engineering A*, **A109**, pp. 83-88, 1989.

34. Erck, R.A., "Pin-Pull Adhesion Measurement of Copper Films on Ion-Bombarded Alumina" *Thin Solid Films*, **253** (1994) pp. 362-366.

35. Kear, B.H., et al , "Surface Treatments Using Laser, Electron and Ion Beam Processing Methods" *Metall. Treatises*, 1981, pp. 321-342.

36. Shafeev, G.A., et al "Enhanced Adherence of Area Selective Electroless Metal Plating on Insulators" *Journal of Vacuum Science and Technology*, **A. 14** (2) March/April 1996.

37. Uno, Y., Takamori, Mohri, Saito, Suzuki, "Joining of Ceramic to Metal by Use of an Electrical Discharge Machined Surface" *Journal of Materials Science Letters*, **8** (1989) pp. 493-495.

38. W. L. Chiang, V. A. Greenhut, and D. J. Shanefield, "Effect of Substrate and Pretreatment on Cu to AlN Direct Bonds," *Ceramic Engineering Society Proceedings* 12 2105-2114 (1991).

39. Colaizzi, James W. "Effect of Thermal Cycling and Bonding on the Mechanical Properties of Direct Bonded Copper and Aluminum Nitride" Doctoral Dissertation, The Graduate School – New Brunswick Rutgers, The State University of New Jersey, October, 1996.

40. Entezarian, M., Drew, R.A.L., "Direct Bonding of Copper to Aluminum Nitride" *Materials Science and Engineering* **A212** (1996) pp. 206-212.

41. Y. Kuromitsu, et al., "Development of a surface-treatment method for AlN substrates to improve adhesion with thick-film conductors" *J. Adhesion Sci. Technology*, **12**, No. 1, pp. 105-119, 1998.

42. Borom, M.P., Pask, J.A., "Role of 'Adherence oxides' in the Development of Chemical Bonding at Glass-Metal Interfaces", *Journal of the American Ceramic Society*, **49** No. 1, January, 1966.

43. Kohl, "Glass-to-Metal Sealing" *Handbook of Materials and Techniques for Vacuum Devices*, pp 394-463.

44. Severin, J.W., et al, "The Adhesion of Electroless Ni(P) on Alumina Ceramic Using a Vacuum Deposited Ti-Pd Activator Layer" *Journal of the Electrochemical Society*, **140**, No. 6 June, 1993.

45. Howe, J.M., "Bonding, Structure, and Properties of Metal/Ceramic Interfaces: Part 1. Chemical Bonding, Chemical Reaction, and Interfacial Structure" *International Materials Review*, **38**, No. 5, 233, 1993.

46. Chapman, David, Vice President of R&D, MIC Technologies Corporation, Private Communication.

47. Lointier, P., Valin, F., Boncoer, M., "Diffusion Bonding of Inconel 600 to Alumina Without and With Intermediate Graded Layers" *Structural Ceramics Joining II*, Edited by Arthur J. Moorhead, © 1993, The American Ceramic Society.

48. Rabin, B.H., et al "Residual Strains in an Al_2O_3 – Ni Joint Bonded with a Composite Interlayer: Experimental Measurements and FEM Analysis" *Journal of the American Ceramic Society*.

49. Zhou, Ikeuchi, North, and Wang, "Effect of Plastic Deformation on Residual Stresses in Ceramic/Metal Interfaces" *Canadian Journal: Metallurgical Transactions A*, **22A** No. 11 pp. 2822-2825, Nov. 1991

50. K. Suganuma, T. Okamoto, and K Kamachi, "Influence of shape and size on residual stress in Ceramic/Metal Joining," *Journal of Material Science*, **22** 2702-2706 (1987).

51. Ishida, Yoichi, Suga, T., Wang, Jin-yeh "Chemical Relief of Thermal Stress at Metal/Ceramic Joined Interface" *Japan Society of Analytical Sciences*, **7** Supplement, (Proc. Int. Congr. Anal. Sci. 1991 Pt. 2) pp. 1231-1234

52. Hitch, T.T., "Adhesion Measurements on Thick Film Conductors" *Adhesion Measurements of Thin Films, Thick Films and Bulk Coatings*, ASTM STP 640, K.L. Mittal, Ed., American Society for Testing and Materials, 1978, pp.211-232.

53. Mittal, K.L., "Selected Bibliography on Adhesion Measurements of Films and Coatings" *Journal of Adhesion Science and Technology*, **1**, No. 3, pp. 247-259, 1987.

54. J. Wachtman, *Mechanical Properties of Ceramics* (1996) John Wiley and Sons, Inc., New York, NY.

55. K. Kendall, "Thin-film peeling—the elastic term," *J. Phys. D: Appl. Phys.*, **8**, 1449-1452 (1975).

56. K. Kim, J. Kim, "Elasto-Plastic Analysis of the Peel Test for Thin Film Adhesion" *Transactions of the ASME*, **110**, pp. 266-273, (July 1998)

57. M. Sexsmith, T. Troczynski, "Peel Adhesion Test for Thermal Spray Coatings" *J. Thermal Spray Technology*, **3**, No. 4, pp 404-411 (1994).

58. ASTM – D 3167 Standard test method for peel resistance of adhesives

59. ASTM – D 1781 Standard test method for climbing drum peel test of adhesives

60. M. Sexsmith, T. Troczynski, E. Breslauer, "Plastic work in the peeling of work hardening foils" *J. Adhesion Sci. Technology*, Vol. 11, No. 2, pp. 141-154 (1997).

61. H. Kurzweg, R. Heimann, T. Troczynski, "Adhesion of Thermally Sprayed Hydroxyapatite-Bond-Coat Systems Measured by a Novel Peel Test", *Journal of Materials Science: Materials in Medicine*, Vol. 9, pp. 9-16 (1998)

62. M. Sexsmith, T. Troczynski, "Development of peel adhesion test for thermal spray coatings" *Proceedings of ITSC '95*, pp. 897-901, Kobe (May 1995).

63. E. Breslauer, T. Troczynski, "Experimental Determination of the Peel Adhesion Strength for Metallic Foils", *J. Adhesion Sci. Technology*, **12**, No. 4, pp. 367-382, (1998).

64. Holowczack, "The effect of alumina composition on interfacial chemistry and strength of direct bonded copper-alumina" Masters Dissertation, The Graduate School – New Brunswick Rutgers, The State University of New Jersey, May 1989.

65. Erck, R.A., Nichols, F.A., Schult, D.L., "Weibull Analysis Applied to the Pull Adhesion Test and Fracture of a Metal-Ceramic Interface" *Tribology Transactions*, **37** (1994), 2 pp. 299-304.

66. Nicholas, M., Forgan, and Poole, "The Adhesion of Metal/Alumina Interfaces" *Journal of Materials Science*, **3**, pp. 9-14 (1968).

67. Nikolopoulos, Agathopoulos, and Tsoga, "A Method for the Calculation of Interfacial Energies in Al_2O_3 and ZrO_2/Liquid-Metal and Liquid Alloy Systems" *Journal of Materials Science*, **29**, pp. 4393-4398, (1994).

68. Suganuma, Katsuaki, et al. "New Method for Solid-State Bonding Between Ceramics and Metals" *Communications of the American Ceramic Society*, **C-117** (1983).

69. Wan, C., Dupeux, M., "Solid-State Bonding of Single-Crystals of $Ni_{(111)}/Al_2O_{3(0001)}$" *Journal of Materials Science*, **28** pp. 5079-5087, (1993).

70. Calow, C.A., Bayer, P.D., Porter, I.T., "The Solid State Bonding of Nickel, Chromium, and Nichrome Scheets to α - Al_2O_3", *Journal of Materials Science*, **6** pp. 150-155 (1971).

71. M.L. Shalz, et al "New approaches to joining ceramics for high temperature applications" *Structural Ceramics Joining II*, Edited by Arthur J. Moorhead (1993), The American Ceramic Society.

72. Berry, Hall, and Harris, *Thin Film Technology*, (1968) D. Van Nostrand Company, London England.

73. M.G.Hocking et al, *Metallic and Ceramic Coatings: Production, High Temperature Properties and Applications*, (1989), John Wiley and Sons, New York, New York.

74. Riedel, Wolfgang, *Electroless Nickel Plating*, Finishing Productions Ltd. (1991), Stevenage, England.

75. Brenner, A., Riddel, G.E., J. Res. Natl. Bur. Stan., (37), 31 (1946); *Proceedings of the American Electroplating Society*, (33), **23** (1946).

76. Bhatgadde, L.G., Mahapatra, S., "Pure Electroless Nickel Coating on Alumina" *Metal Finishing*, pp.31-32 (March 1988).

77. Ko, S., Chou, T., "Hydrogenation of (-) α Pinene Over Nickel Phosphorus / Aluminum Oxide Catalysts Prepared by Electroless Deposition", *The Canadian Journal of Chemical Engineering*, **72** (Oct. 1994), pp. 862-873.

78. Honma, H., Kanemitsu, K., "Electroless Nickel Plating on Alumina Ceramics" *Plating and Surface Finishing*, (Sept. 1987) pp. 62-67.

79. Severin, Hokke, van der Wel, and de With, "The Influence of Thermal Treatments on the Adhesion of Electrolessly Deposited Ni(P) Layers on Alumina Ceramic" *Journal of the Electrochemical Society*, **141**, No. 3, (March 1994) pp. 816-824.

80. Chung, W.S., Chang, S.Y., Lin, S.J., "Electroless Nickel Plating on SiC Powder with Hypophosphite as a Reducing Agent" *Plating and Surface Finishing* (March 1996), pp. 68-71.

81. Osaka, T. et al, "Metallization of AlN Ceramics by Electroless Ni-P Plating" *Journal of the Electrochemical Society*, **133**, No. 11, (1986) pp. 2345-2349.

82. Honma, H., et al. "Fabrication of Nickel Film on a Glass Disk by Electroless Nickel Plating" *Plating and Surface Finishing* (January 1995) pp. 60-62.

83. H. Honma, "Direct Electroless Copper Plating on Alumina Ceramics" *Plating And Surface Finishing* (June 1990) pp. 54-58.

84. Dietz, Laska, Schnieder, and Stein, "The Microstructure of Amorphous and Microcrystalline Electrodeposited Ni-P Alloys" *Journal of the Less Common Metals*, **145** (1988) pp. 573-580.

85. Aleksinas, M.J., Andre, R.C., "Stress of High Phosphorus Electroless Nickel Deposits" *Metal Finishing* (June 1992) pp. 103-107.

86. Criado, Millan, Conde, and Marquez, "Calorimetric and X-Ray Characterization of the Non-Isothermal Crystallization of the Metallic Glass $Ni_{89}P_{11}C$ (wt%)" *Materials Letters*, . **5**, No. 5,6 (May 1987) pp. 182-184.

87. Lowenheim, Frederick, A., *Modern Electroplating*, John Wiley & Sons, New York, NY (1974).

88. T. Young, *Trans. Royal Society*, 95 65 (1805)

89. J. A. Pask and A. P. Tomsia, "Wetting, Surface Energies, Adhesion and Interface Reaction Thermodynamics," *Engineered Materials Handbook*, **4**, 482-492, ASM International, OH, (1991).

90. Nakae, H., Fujii, H., Sato, K., "Reactive Wetting of Ceramics by Liquid Metals" *Materials Transactions, JIM*, **33**, No. 4 (1992) pp. 400-406.

91. Aksay, I.A., et al, *Journal of Physical Chemistry*, **78** (1974) 12, 1178.

92. H. Nakae, et al, "Effects of Surface Roughness on Wettability" *Acta Mater*. **46**, No. 7, pp. 2313-2318, (1998).

93. N. Eustathopoulos, " Dynamics of Wetting in Reactive Metal/Ceramic Systems" Acta Mater. **46**, No. 7, pp. 2319-2327 (1998).

94. R. M. Flurath and E. L. Hollar, Manganese Glass-Molybdenum Metallizing Ceramics," *American Ceramic Society Bulletin*, **47** [8] 493-497 (1968).

95. M. E. Twentyman, "High-Temperature Metallizing" *Journal of Materials Science*, **10**, pp. 765-776 (1975).

96. Y. S. Chung and T. Iseki, "Interfacial Phenomena in Joining of Ceramics by Active Metal Brazing Alloy," *Engineering Fracture Mechanics* , 40 [4-5] 941-949 (1991).

97. A. J. Moorhead, "Direct Brazing of Alumina Ceramics," *Advanced Ceramic Materials*, **2** [2] 159-166 (1987).

98. G. L Babcock, W. M. Bryant, C. A. Neugebauer, and J. F. Burgess, "Method of Direct Bonding Metals to Non-metallic Substrates," U.S. Patent No. 3,766,634, October 23, 1973.

99. G. L Babcock, W. M. Bryant, C. A. Neugebauer, and J. F. Burgess, "Bonds between Metal and a Non-metallic Substrate," U.S. Patent No. 3,993,411, November 23, 1976.

100. J. F. Burgess and C. A. Neugebauer, "Direct Bonding of Metals to Ceramics by the Gas-Metal Eutectic Method," *Journal of the Electrochemical Society*, **122** [5] 688-690 (1975).

101. J. P. Newmann, T. Zhong, and Y. A. Chang, "The Cu-O Binary," *Metal Progress*, **9**, 85-87 (1985).

102. Beraud, C., et al "Study of Copper-Alumina Bonding" *Journal of Material Science*, Vol. 24 (1989) pp. 4545-4554.

103. Yoshino, Yuichi, "Role of Oxygen in Bonding Copper to Alumina" *Journal of the American Ceramic Society*, **72**, No. 8 pp. 1322-1327 (1989).

104. Kim, S.T., Kim, C.H., "Interfacial Reaction Product and its Effect on the Strengh of Copper to Alumina Eutectic Bonding" *Journal of Material Science*, **27** (1992) pp. 2061-2066.

105. Sun, Y.S., Driscoll, J.C., "A New Hybrid Power Technique Utilizing a Direct Copper to Ceramic Bond" *IEEE Transactions on Electron Devices*, **ED-23**, No. 8 August (1976), pp. 961-967

106. Nakao, Y., et al "Bonding of Aluminum Nitride to Copper for Reducing Thermal Stress" pp. 910-916 (1994)

107. Wu, Y.C., Duh, J.G., "Eutectic Bonding of Nickel to Yttria-Stabilized Zirconia" *Journal of Material Science Letters*, **9** (1990) 583-586.

108. Ghetta, V., Fouletier, d., Chatain, D., "Oxygen Adsorption Isotherms at the Surfaces of Liquid Cu and Au-Cu Alloys and Their Interfaces with Al_2O_3 Detected by Wetting Experiments" *Acta Mater*, **44**, No..5 pp. 1927-1936, (1996).

109. Meier, A.M., Chidambaram, PR., Edwards, G.R., "A Comparison of the Wettability of Copper-Copper Oxide and Silver-Copper Oxide on Polycrystaline Alumina" *Journal of Material Science*, **30** (1995) pp. 4781-4786.

110. O'Brien, T.E., Chaklader, A.C.D., "Effect of Oxygen on the Reaction Between Copper and Sapphire" *Journal of the American Ceramic Society*, **57** No. 8 pp. 329-332, (1974).

111. T. Chapman, C. Delgado, V. Greenhut, "Direct Bonding Copper To Zirconia Via Gas-Metal Eutectic" presented and ceramographic poster at The American Ceramic Society 101st Annual Meeting, Indianapolis, IN, (May 1999).

112. M. Shalz, et al, "Ceramic Joining Part III: Partial transient liquid-phase bonding of alumina via Cu/Nb/Cu interlayers" *Journal of Materials Science*, **29**, No. 14, pp. 3678-3690 (July 15, 1994).

113. M. Shalz, et al, "Ceramic Joining Part II: Partial transient liquid-phase bonding of alumina via Cu/Ni/Cu multilayer interlayers" *Journal of Materials Science*, **29**, No. 12, pp. 3200-3208 (June 15, 1994).

114. M. Shalz, et al, "Ceramic Joining Part I: Partial transient liquid-phase bonding of alumina via Cu/Pt interlayers" *Journal of Materials Science*, **28**, pp. 1673-1684 (1993).

115. Duvall, Owczarski, and Paulonis, "TLP* Bonding: a New Method for Joining Heat Resistant Alloys" *Welding Journal*, (April, 1974) pp.203-214.

116. Saida, Zhou, and North, "The Influence of Base Metal Grain Size on Isothermal Solidification During Transient Liquid Phase Brazing of Nickel" *Journal of Materials Science*, **28**, pp. 6427-6432, (1993)

117. Y. Iino, "Partial transient liquid-phase metals layer technique of ceramic-metal bonding" *Journal of Materials Science*, Vol. 28, pp. 104-106 (1993).

118. D. Juve, et al., "Bonding of the Cu-Al_2O_3 interfaces. Mechanism, structure, and mechanical properties"

119. A. Kara-Slimane, et al., "Adhesion and reactivity in the copper-alumina system: influence of oxygen and silver" *J. Adhesion Sci. Technology*, **13**, No. 1, pp. 35-48, (1999).

120. A. Meier, M. Baldwin, P. Chidambaram, G. Edwards, "The effect of large oxygen additions on the wettability and work of adhesion of copper-oxygen alloys on polycrystalline alumina" *Materials Science and Engineering A*, **A196**, pp. 111-117, (1995).

121. T. Sakurai, et al., *Physics Review B*, **34** (1986), pp. 8379.

122. H. Matsumoto, et al., "Wettability of Al_2O_3 by Liquid Cu as Influenced by Additives and Partial Transient Liquid-Phase Bonding of Al_2O_3" *Materials Transaction, JIM*, **36**, No. 4, (1995), pp. 555-564.

Brazing

PARTICULATE LOADING OF HIGH TEMPERATURE BRAZES FOR JOINING ENGINEERING CERAMICS

K.M. Knowles*, D.R. Ormston*, D.B. Conquest*, L.J. Ecclestone[§] and J.A. Fernie[§]

* University of Cambridge, Department of Materials Science and Metallurgy, Pembroke Street, Cambridge CB2 3QZ, U.K.

[§] TWI, Granta Park, Great Abington, Cambridge, CB1 6AL, UK

ABSTRACT

Joint strengths and joint integrity can be improved significantly in SiC-SiC joints brazed with Ag-Cu-Ti in which titanium is an 'active element' by incorporating a small volume per cent (≤10 vol %) of micron size SiC particulates within Ticusil braze pastes. Analysis of the joints by a variety of microstructural characterisation techniques shows that the introduction of the SiC particulates enables the chemical reactions which occur within the joint to be controlled. The best joints were found to contain nanocrystalline reaction layers ~ 1 μm thick of TiC with low levels of secondary reaction products such as Ti_5Si_3 and γ-Cu_5Si. Progress in extending this particulate loaded active braze methodology to the joining of alumina for high temperature applications is also discussed.

INTRODUCTION

Joining technology is becoming increasingly important for the successful commercialisation and technical acceptance of engineering ceramics. The majority of applications require ceramics to be joined to themselves, or, more frequently, to a metal. Joining can be achieved through a number of routes, such as mechanical attachment, adhesives, brazing, diffusion bonding and, more recently, preceramic polymers.[1-9] Of these technologies, brazing using Ag-Cu based alloys is the most widely used. There are two basic variations: the use of pre-metallisation procedures, as in the Mo-Mn process for alumina, and active metal brazing, the latter of which has the advantage of being applicable to a wide range of ceramics.

It is therefore highly encouraging that, under favourable conditions, mechanically sound joints can be obtained with active metal brazing alloys, as in recent work using Ag-Cu-Ti active braze alloys to join partially stabilised zirconia to itself and to a Ni-based superalloy, Inconel 738, used for turbine components.[7,8]

Even though brazing is a proven technology, joint strength is governed not only by the chemistry at the interface, but by practical considerations, such as thermal expansion mismatch. While best practice in joint design is important,[5] there is always interest in developing methods of improving the inherent strength of a braze and developing alternative higher temperature compositions. Current brazes based on Ag-Cu-Ti have a useable temperature ceiling of ~ 450 °C.

In this work we have examined the effect on joint integrity of the incorporation of a ceramic phase into active braze alloys. Work by Chung and co-workers[10,11] has shown the beneficial effects arising from the incorporation into titanium-containing active braze alloys of ~ 10 vol% short carbon fibres. Here we have investigated the effects of particulate loading of high temperature braze alloys for joining engineering ceramics. For the joining of silicon carbide to itself, we have been able to show from a detailed and systematic study that the introduction of silicon carbide particulates into commercial Ag-Cu-Ti braze alloys can have beneficial effects on joint strengths by achieving control over chemical reactions and the phases formed in the joints during the brazing process.

We have extended this methodology to the joining of alumina. For this, we have used commercial Ni-Cr-Si braze alloys which we have modified by the introduction of titanium as an active element and silica as the particulate loading.

EXPERIMENTAL PROCEDURE

Simple butt-joints between hot pressed silicon carbide (HPSC) were made using two commercially available active braze alloys from Wesgo GTE: Cusil ABA® (Ag – 35.25 wt% Cu – 1.75 wt% Ti) and Ticusil® (Ag – 26.5 wt% Cu – 4.5 wt% Ti). Both brazes were reinforced with 1 – 7 μm diameter α-SiC particulates. Two methods were investigated for the incorporation of particulates into the braze. The first of these was an air spraying method where the particulates were held in an alcohol suspension and then air sprayed onto the braze foil. A small amount of acid was also added to the mixture to prevent agglomeration of the particulates in the solution. The second method involved the use of braze alloy powder rather than foil to make up a paste mixture. The particulates were added to the braze alloy powder (1 – 40 μm size) and mixed in a glass container. Organic binder was added to the mixture to form the paste. Modifications to the composition of the braze alloy powder were made by adding titanium hydride powder, thereby controlling the titanium content.

Brazing was carried out in a vacuum furnace at pressures below 10^{-2} Pa (10^{-4} mbar). A typical brazing cycle for the spraying preparation method consisted firstly of an initial ramp rate of 10° C min^{-1} to 750° C and holding for 15 minutes to allow the assembly to reach a uniform temperature. The samples were then heated at a rate of 5° C min^{-1} to the brazing temperature where they were held for up to 30 minutes. The brazing temperatures ranged from 850 – 950° C, the Ticusil braze alloy being brazed at the higher temperature because of its higher liquidus point. Brazing with the paste mixture required an initial ramp rate of 5 °C min^{-1} to 450 °C and holding for 10 minutes to allow the organic binder to burn off, and then allowing the normal brazing cycle to continue.

Simple butt joints were also made when joining the 99.7% purity alumina used for this work. The commercial Ni-Cr-Si braze alloy was received in the form of a powder and modified through the introduction of titanium, in the form of titanium hydride powder, and silica, in the form of 3 μm mean diameter particulates. Brazing was carried out at 1185 °C, some 50 °C higher than the liquidus temperature of the commercial braze (as stated by the manufacturer) in a vacuum furnace at pressures below 10^{-2} Pa. Heating and cooling times of 10 °C min^{-1} and braze times of 10 minutes were used.

Joint microstructures were examined using a range of techniques. Scanning electron microscopy (SEM) using a JEOL 5800LV scanning electron microscope equipped with energy dispersive X-ray analysis (EDX) facilities was used to examine joint integrity and the phases within the braze and at the braze-ceramic interfaces. Further information on the reaction products was gained from X-ray diffraction (XRD) and transmission electron microscopy (TEM).

The flexure strength of the joints was determined by four point bend testing at room temperature. The tests conformed to the procedure outlined in ASTM standard C1161 type C for the flexure testing of advanced ceramics.[12]

EXPERIMENTAL RESULTS ON JOINING SILICON CARBIDE

Joints produced using Cusil ABA braze foil

Initially, the Cusil ABA braze foil without the introduction of SiC particulates was investigated. The good wetting of this braze to the HPSC substrate is demonstrated in Fig. 1(a), which shows the microstructure through a joint containing no SiC particles. The ability to form a joint can be directly attributed to the 1.75 wt% titanium in the braze alloy. The braze microstructure consists of primary copper-rich dendrites and Ag-Cu eutectic.

In order to achieve void-free bonds when α-SiC particulates were incorporated into the Cusil ABA braze foil by air spraying, it was found necessary to sputter coat a ~ 1 μm thick coating of titanium onto the HPSC substrates.

Furthermore, for particulate loadings of greater than ~ 10 vol% it was necessary to increase the brazing temperature to 900 °C and to sputter coat the braze foil with titanium before deposition of the SiC particulates. An example of the microstructure of a successful joint formed in this way is shown in Fig. 1(b). It is apparent from this scanning electron micrograph that there is a preference for the SiC particulates to reside in the copper-rich regions of the braze. Maximum joint strengths in flexure testing of 175 MPa were achieved at 10 vol% SiC particulates for 50 μm thick joints, with these joints failing in the ceramic adjacent to the joint area. The highest amount of particulates that could be added to this system was found to be around 23 vol% SiC, for which the average joint strength in flexure testing was found to be only 28 MPa. By comparison, flexure strengths of ~ 125 MPa are quoted in the literature for SiC-SiC joints made with unreinforced Cusil ABA braze.[13]

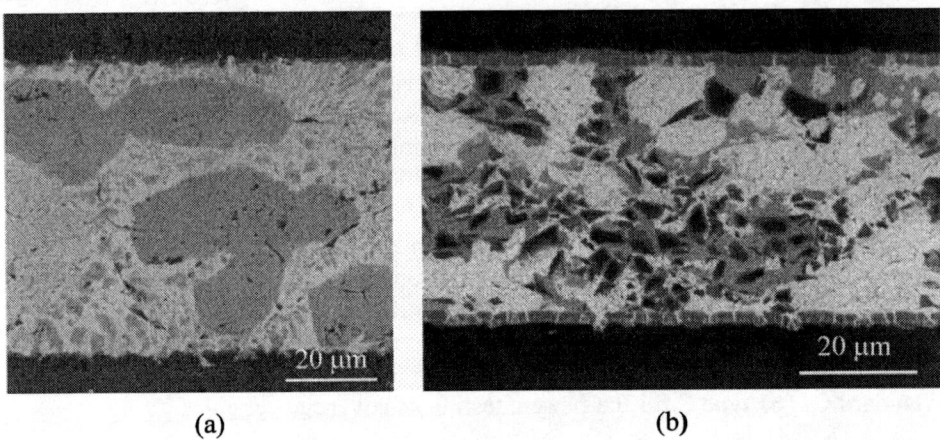

Figure 1. (a) Back-scattered scanning electron micrograph of an HPSC-HPSC joint brazed with Cusil ABA at 850 °C for 15 minutes, (b) Back-scattered scanning electron micrograph of an HPSC-HPSC joint brazed at 900 °C for 15 minutes with Cusil ABA and ~ 10 vol% SiC particulates. In (b) Ti coatings were deposited on each of the HPSC substrates and on the braze foil prior to spray deposition of the particulates and the subsequent brazing operation.

Joints produced using Ticusil braze foil

Using Ticusil active braze alloy foil simplified and improved the joining process considerably. No extra sputtering of titanium was required on either the

HPSC substrates or the braze foil because there was a sufficient amount of titanium available to wet both the substrates and the particulates. The micrograph in Fig. 2(a) shows the microstructure which developed when a 20 vol% SiC particulate loaded joint was brazed at 855° C for 15 minutes. The particulates show a strong interaction with the braze alloy. However, the particulates were not distributed evenly across the joint and 'banding' occurred, so that there was a preference for the particulates to collect in the middle of the joint. This banding arose from restriction of the movement of the particulates during brazing because of poor overall braze fluidity.

When brazing at 900° C for 30 minutes, the upper limit of reinforcement was found to be 20 vol% SiC particulates. Raising the brazing temperature to 950° C increased this upper limit to 30 vol% SiC particulates (Fig. 2(b)). Interestingly, this relatively high volume fraction of particulates did not show evidence of banding, but it was apparent from a visual examination of the substrate-braze and particulate-braze interfaces that the reaction layers were noticeably thinner than in joints prepared with lower volume fractions of particulates.

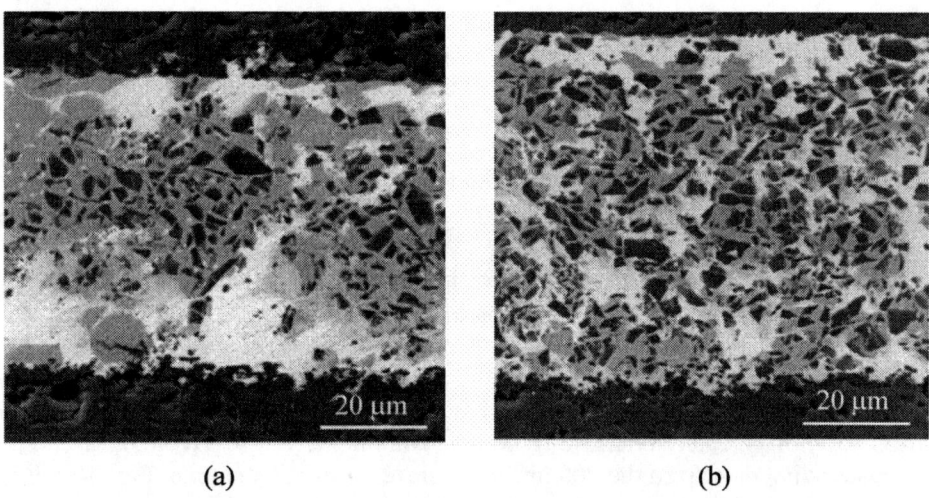

Figure 2   (a) Back-scattered scanning electron micrograph of an HPSC-HPSC joint brazed with Ticusil foil and 20 vol% SiC particulates at 855 °C for 15 minutes, (b) Back-scattered scanning electron micrograph of an HPSC-HPSC joint brazed with Ticusil foil and 30 vol% SiC particulates at 950 °C for 30 minutes. In both (a) and (b) the direction of spray deposition was from the top.

Despite the inhomogeneous nature of many of the joints produced using Ticusil braze foil loaded with SiC particulates, strengths achieved in flexure testing were encouraging. Joints 50 μm thick prepared with 5 – 10 vol% SiC had average strengths of 220 MPa, failing mainly in the ceramic adjacent to the braze, with some evidence of interfacial failure and fracture through the braze. The highest loadings of 20 – 30 vol% SiC particulates had lower flexural strengths of ~ 100 MPa, failing mainly by interfacial fracture. The best average strengths of 350 MPa were obtained with relatively low levels (< 5 vol %) of SiC particulates.

Joints produced using Ticusil powder

In comparison with the spraying process, powder mixing was found to give much greater control over the quantities of particulates added to the braze. The brazing conditions used to produce a homogeneous microstructure, such as that shown in Fig. 3(a) of a 20 vol% reinforced joint, were 950° C for 30 mins. The homogeneous microstructure is retained at low vol% additions of SiC particulates, such as in the example in Fig. 3(b) taken from a joint with 10 vol% SiC particulates. The even distribution of particulates results in less variation in joint strengths. It was found that the optimum amount of binder added to make up the paste varied with the amount of particulates added to the mixture. Increasing the volume of particulates decreased the amount of binder which could be added to make a void-free joint. In practice, it was found that 10 wt% binder was required as a minimum amount of binder required to produce a workable paste for 20 – 30 vol% SiC particulates without producing large voids within the joint. This level of binder was subsequently used for joints containing < 20 vol% SiC particulates as well.

The greater degree of control over joint preparation offered by the powder mixing process allowed both 50 μm and 100 μm thick braze joints loaded with particulates to be usefully examined in flexure testing. Flexural data from the 50 μm thick braze joints prepared by the powder route are compared in Fig. 4(a) with the data from the joints prepared from air sprayed braze foil and also data from 50 μm Ticusil braze foil joints without any SiC particulates. The corresponding data from the 100 μm thick braze joints are shown in Fig. 4(b). It is apparent from a comparison of the flexural testing data that the optimum strength data are obtained from the 100 μm thick braze joints loaded with 5 vol% SiC particulates. An examination of the fracture surfaces from these strong samples showed that they failed by multiple ceramic failure and interface failure.

The effect of the level of titanium on the strength of joints loaded with 10 vol% SiC particulates was examined by adding titanium hydride, TiH_2, to the Ticusil braze composition. Increasing the level of titanium from 4.5 wt% to 9 wt%

(a)   (b)

Figure 3 Back-scattered scanning electron micrographs of HPSC-HPSC joints brazed at 950 °C for 30 minutes with Ticusil powder and (a) 20 vol% SiC and (b) 10 vol% SiC particulates. Both joints had 10 wt% binder in the braze paste.

in the braze increased the mean four point bend strength from 260 MPa to 340 MPa, with the joints failing by multiple matrix cracking and interfacial failure, in a manner similar to the 5 vol% particulate loaded joints without supplementary titanium. However, this improvement in strength was still not sufficient to improve upon the 100 μm Ticusil powder joints loaded with 5 vol% SiC particulates which were 50% stronger than the unreinforced 100 μm thick Ticusil joints produced by the powder route.

Microstructural analysis of the joints

The presence of the titanium in the braze causes reaction layers to be formed at both the HPSC-braze and SiC particulate-braze interfaces, as others have reported previously.[2,13] It is recognised that titanium and silicon carbide first react together to form titanium carbide and silicon. The silicon released from this chemical reaction is then able to produce secondary reaction products, such as various titanium silicides. In practice, the titanium silicide Ti_5Si_3 is found to be a frequently observed secondary reaction product.[2]

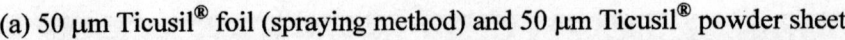
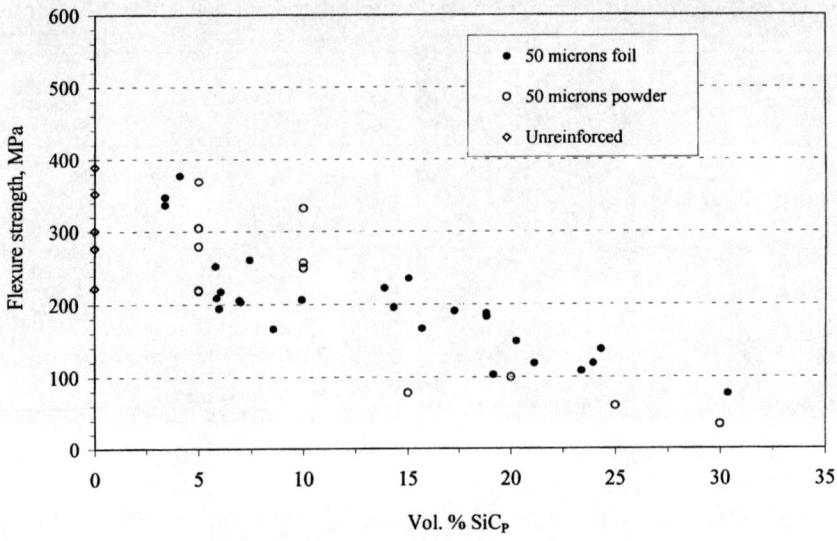
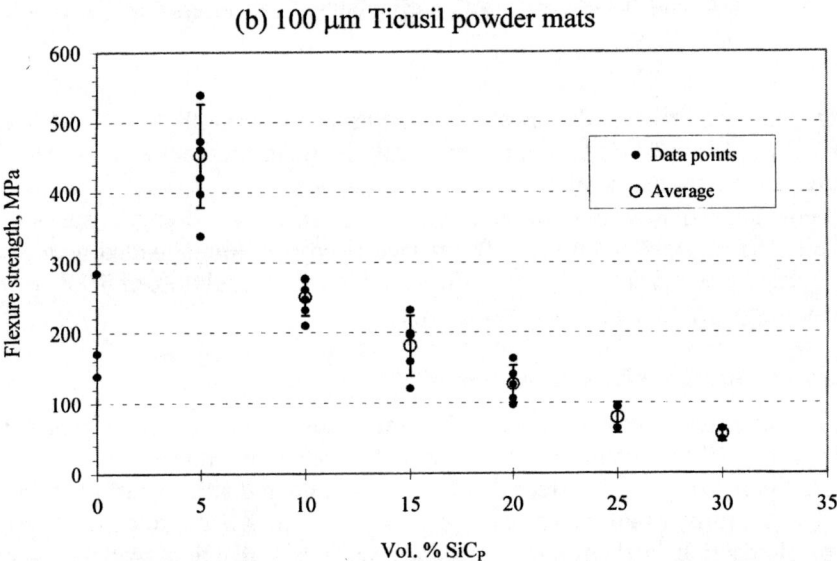

Figure 4 Four point bend strengths for SiC particulate reinforced Ticusil prepared with (a) 50 μm powder and 50 μm foil and (b) 100 μm powder. All the joints were brazed at 950 °C for 30 minutes.

Table I. Quantitative EDX analysis of Cu-rich and Ag-rich phases in 5 and 10 vol% SiC reinforced Ticusil powder joints, brazed at 950 °C for 30 minutes

Phase	SiC (vol%)	Ag (wt%)	Cu (wt%)	Ti (wt%)	Si (wt%)
Cu-rich phase	5	2.8	91.9	0.5	4.8
	10	3.9	87.8	0.4	8.0
Ag-rich phase	5	93.9	5.7	0	0.4
	10	94.2	5.5	0	0.3

Z-contrast in SEM images of the joints showed distinct reaction layers higher in mean atomic number than the SiC and lower than the copper-containing part of the braze. EDX mapping in of these reaction layers confirmed the presence of titanium in these reaction layers. Quantitative EDX analyses of the silver-rich and copper-rich phases in 5 and 10 vol% SiC particulate-loaded Ticusil joints clearly showed the occurrence of silicon in the copper-rich phases (Table I), with the level of silicon in the copper-rich phase increasing as the level of particulate loading increased. By comparison, the copper-rich phase in joints brazed with Ticusil alone contained less than 1 wt % silicon.

XRD spectra taken from the fracture surfaces of joints formed with Ticusil alone confirmed the presence of TiC and Ti_5Si_3 (Fig. 5). By comparison, joints made with SiC particulates showed significantly lower levels of Ti_5Si_3, to the extent that evidence for the formation of Ti_5Si_3 could only be found in 5 vol% loaded joints from electron diffraction patterns of a few precipitates by TEM. Instead, as the level of SiC loading increased, it was found that γ-Cu_5Si became the dominant reaction product in the braze, such as in the XRD spectrum from a 10 vol% SiC particulate loaded joint in Fig. 6, in which peaks attributable to copper alone were absent. Confirmatory evidence for this phase was found by TEM from electron diffraction patterns of copper-rich phases adjacent to TiC reaction layers in the particulate-loaded joints. Joints in which γ-Cu_5Si was identified showed evidence of braze fracture after bend testing, whereas joints in which this phase was absent did not show this mode of failure.

Increasing the titanium content of the joints through the introduction of titanium hydride into the braze paste reduced the amount of the γ-Cu_5Si and increased the level of Ti_5Si_3, so that at 9 wt% titanium and 10 vol% SiC particulates the 200 and 311 peaks from copper could be recovered.

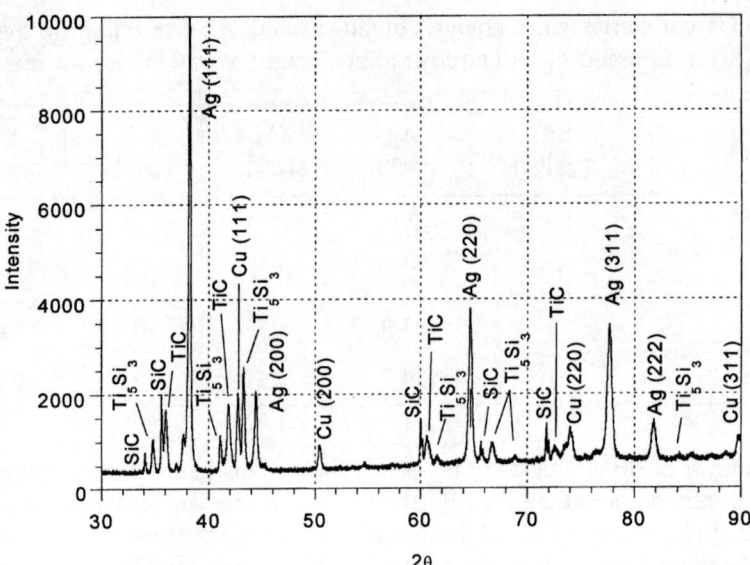

Figure 5 XRD spectrum of phases in the fracture surface of a joint prepared with Ticusil powder and brazed at 950 °C for 30 minutes.

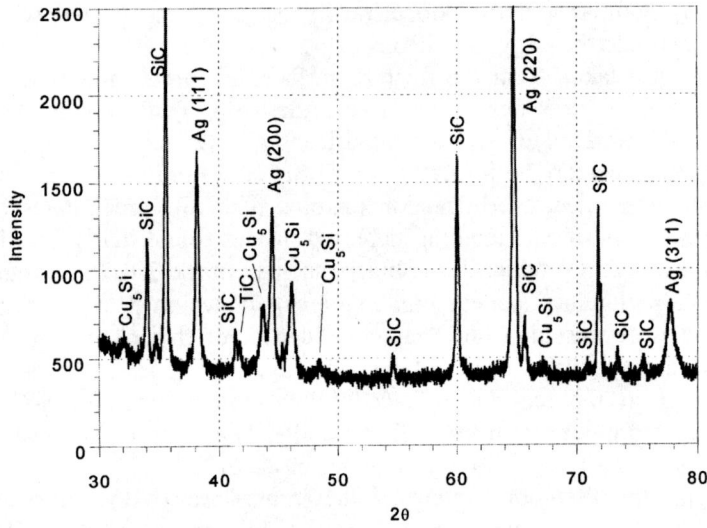

Figure 6 XRD spectrum of phases in the fracture surface of a joint prepared with Ticusil and 10 vol% SiC particulates.

An example of the microstructure found at the HPSC-braze interface in a joint prepared with Ticusil powder and 5 vol% SiC particulates is shown in Fig. 7. The nanocrystalline TiC reaction layer here is ~ 0.8 μm thick. Increasing the level of SiC particulates decreased the thickness of the TiC reaction layer at both the HPSC-braze and SiC particulate-braze interfaces, so that Ticusil joints with > 20 vol% SiC particulates brazed for 30 mins at 950 °C only had ~ 0.2 μm thick reaction layers.

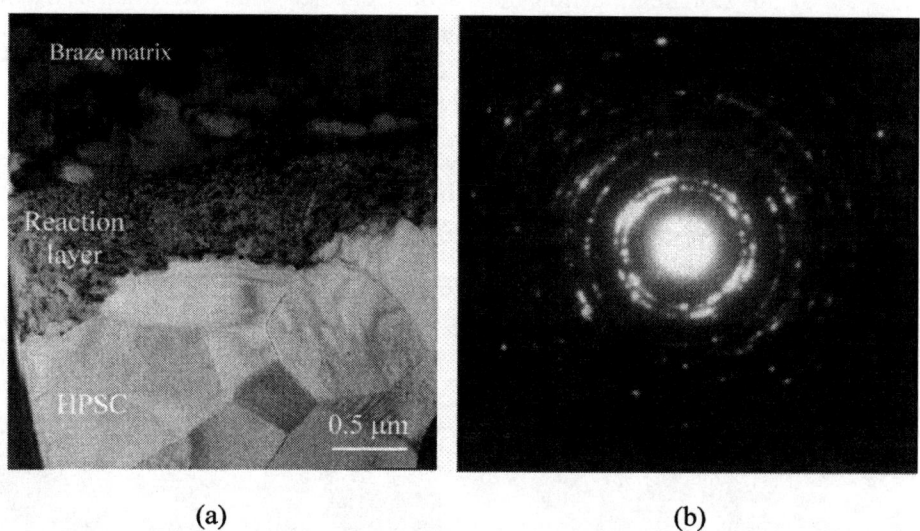

(a)   (b)

Figure 7   (a) Bright field TEM image of the nanocrystalline TiC reaction layer formed at the HPSC-Ticusil braze interface in a joint prepared with Ticusil powder and 5 vol% SiC particulates. (b) Selected area diffraction pattern from the TiC reaction layer. The two strong inner rings are the 111 and 200 rings (TiC: space group $Fm\bar{3}m$, $a = 0.4329$ nm).

EXPERIMENTAL RESULTS ON JOINING ALUMINA

Joints produced using experimental Ti-doped brazes

The primary objective of this work has been to select and develop an economically viable active braze system capable of joining alumina for use at service temperatures higher than those of the Ag-Cu-Ti brazes. Wetting trials on a variety of experimental brazes showed that the introduction of titanium in the form of titanium hydride powder into commercial braze powders in the range

0 – 16wt% titanium had the general effect of lowering contact angles.[14] Systems demonstrating bonding and low contact angles were selected as possible candidates for further development. Of these the best braze system was found to be a commercial Ni-Cr-Si braze alloy with 16 wt% Ti. Four point bend test samples had average failure stresses of 62 MPa in comparison with control samples brazed with Ticusil which had average failure stresses of 103 MPa.

A back-scattered image of the Ti-modified braze is shown in Fig. 8. EDX analysis in the scanning electron microscope together with XRD measurements showed that four phases occur in the braze. The bright phase in Fig. 8 with the highest average Z number is c.c.p. nickel containing chromium and titanium in solid solution. The grey block-like phase has a chemical composition of 57.0 at% Ni, 3.1 at% Cr, 20.8 at% Si and 19.1 at% Ti. XRD analysis identified this phase as Cr-doped $Ni_{16}Ti_6Si_7$. This ternary silicide G phase is cubic F with 116 atoms per unit cell and a unit cell side of 11.2Å.[15] It is reported to be softer than TiC with a Vickers microhardness of ~ 820.[16,17] The third major phase apparent in Fig. 8 is chromium-rich containing nickel in solid solution and is significantly darker than the other two major phases. Traces of a fourth titanium-rich phase appearing most dark of all in back-scattered images were also visible in parts of the braze microstructure.

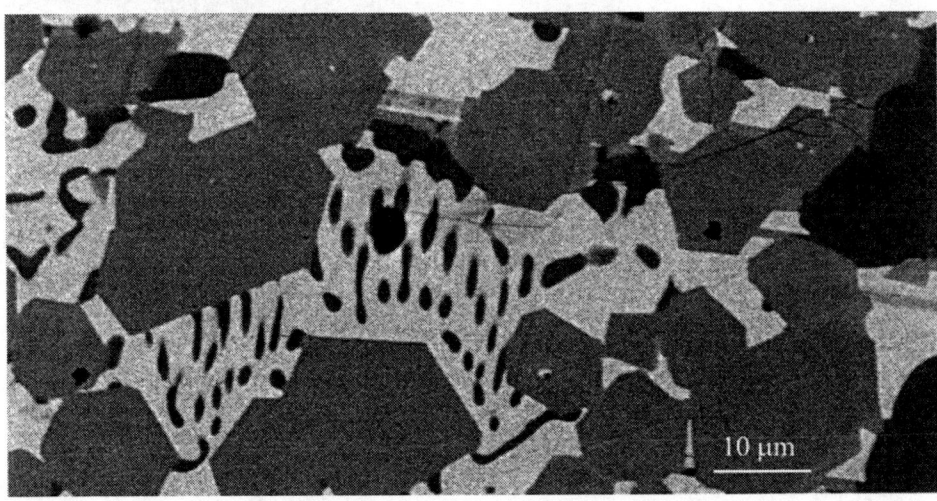

Figure 8. Back-scattered image of the experimental Ni-Cr-Si-Ti braze using for joining alumina.

Particulate loading

Preliminary work examining the effect of particulate loading has looked at the effect on flexural strength of additions of rutile, SiC and silica. Of these, silica showed the most promise at 2 vol% particulate additions to the Ni-Cr-Si braze alloy with 16 wt% Ti.

The effect of varying the titanium content on the strength of silica reinforced joints is shown in Fig. 9. At least 6 samples were tested for each datum point except for the sample doped with 20 wt% Ti, for which four samples were tested. The optimum composition was found to be Ni-Cr-Si + 24 wt% Ti + 2 vol% silica. Although further work is required to refine the reinforced compositions and brazing parameters to increase strength to levels in excess of the unreinforced brazes, it is encouraging that the Ti-modified braze loaded with 2 vol% silica and 24 wt% titanium has the same average failure stress as the Ti-modified braze with 16 wt% titanium and no silica, implying that there is the potential in this system to improve joint integrity further by optimising the braze microstructure.

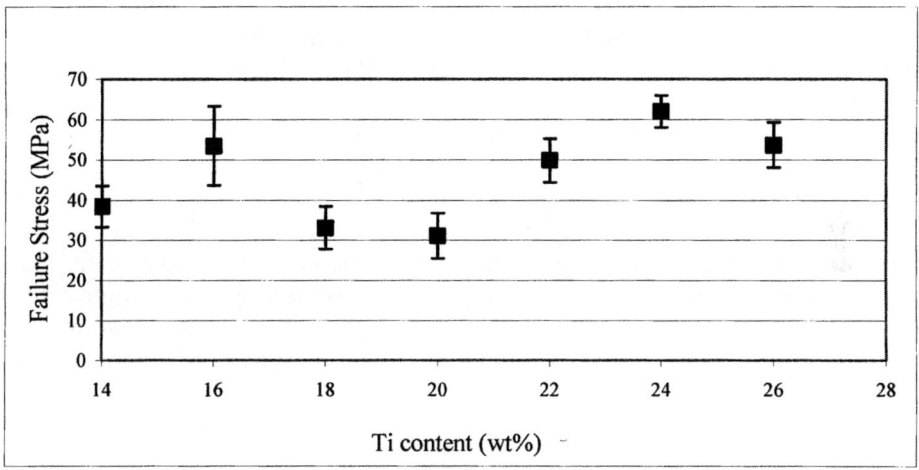

Figure 9. Effect of titanium content on the joint strength of Ni-Cr-Si brazes loaded with 2 vol% silica. Error bars represent standard deviation.

DISCUSSION

By controlling the levels of titanium and SiC particulates in Ag-Cu-Ti active braze alloys, it is apparent that together they allow control over the quantity and type of secondary reaction products formed. Silicon released from the primary chemical reaction between titanium and silicon carbide has a preference for reaction with free titanium to form titanium silicides, most notably Ti_5Si_3. However, as the surface area available for the primary chemical reaction between titanium and silicon carbide is increased through the introduction of particulates, the liberated silicon is unable to react with free titanium and instead dissolves into the copper-containing phase in the Ag-Cu-Ti braze. At sufficiently high volume fractions of silicon in the copper-rich phase, γ-Cu_5Si is formed.

The superior mechanical properties of the Ticusil joints loaded with 5 vol% SiC particulates can be attributed to the formation of a sufficiently thick (0.5 – 1 μm thick) TiC layer at the HPSC-braze and SiC particulate-braze interfaces and the relative suppression of secondary chemical reactions. The presence of SiC and TiC in the braze microstructure helps to reduce the coefficient of thermal expansion of the joints, but this reduction is relatively modest. In principle, higher volume fractions of SiC particulates, and thus joints with much lower coefficients of thermal expansion, could be introduced into joints by increasing the levels of titanium in the braze paste to help suppress the formation of γ-Cu_5Si, while preventing the formation of significant amounts of Ti_5Si_3. Such pastes would have to be brazed at higher temperatures because of the higher levels of titanium and the higher levels of SiC particulates, both of which reduce braze fluidity.

The extension of the active braze methodology to higher temperature brazes to bond alumina has already shown promise. The addition of titanium to commercial Ni-Cr-Si braze alloys has produced joints with acceptable mechanical integrity at room temperature. Preliminary experiments on loading Ti-doped brazes with silica particulates have produced four point bend test specimens which match the unreinforced braze in strength. There is clear scope for optimisation of the level of titanium and the level of particulate addition, and thus, control over the chemical reactions in the braze and at the braze-alumina interfaces, to produce strong joints.

CONCLUSIONS

Particulate loaded active braze alloys offer scope for an improved range of high strength ceramic joints. The effects of introducing SiC particulates into Ag-Cu-Ti brazes used for joining hot pressed silicon carbide are to control the thickness of the titanium carbide formed as the primary reaction product and the nature of the secondary reaction products. The strongest joints were formed when the silicon released when the titanium carbide is formed dissolves into the copper-rich phase of the eutectic in the braze, instead of forming Ti_5Si_3 when there is excess titanium or γ-Cu_5Si if there is too high a level of SiC particulates. Preliminary work in extending this particulate loading methodology to the joining of alumina for high temperature applications has shown promise with commercial Ni-Cr-Si braze alloys which we have modified by the introduction of titanium as an active element and silica as the particulate loading.

ACKNOWLEDGEMENTS

The authors wish to acknowledge support from The Department of Trade and Industry (DTI) through the Postgraduate Training Partnership (PTP) scheme between Cambridge University and TWI.

REFERENCES

[1] M.G. Nicholas, *Joining of Ceramics*. Chapman and Hall (1990).

[2] G. Elssner and G. Petzow, "Metal/Ceramic Joining," *ISIJ International*, **30** [12] 1011-32 (1990).

[3] O.M. Akselsen, "Advances in Brazing of Ceramics," *Journal of Materials Science* **27** [8] 1989-2000 (1992).

[4] G. Chaumat, B. Drevet and L. Vernier, "Reactive Brazing Study of a Silicon Nitride to Metal Joining," *Journal of the European Ceramic Society* **17** [15-16] 1925-27 (1997).

[5] J.A. Fernie and W.B. Hanson, "Best Practice for Producing Ceramic-Metal Bonds," *Industrial Ceramics* **19** [3] 172-75 (1999).

[6] S.H. Yang and S. Kang, "Fracture Behaviour and Reliability of Brazed Alumina Joints via Mo-Mn Process and Active Metal Brazing," *Journal of Materials Research* **15** [10] 2238-43 (2000).

[7] W.B. Hanson, K.I. Ironside and J.A. Fernie, "Active Metal Brazing of Zirconia," *Acta Materialia* **48** [18-19] 4673-76 (2000).

[8] D. Sciti, A. Bellosi and L. Esposito, Bonding of Zirconia to Super Alloy with the Active Brazing Technique," *Journal of the European Ceramic Society* **21** [1] 45-52 (2001).

[9] C.A. Lewinsohn, P. Colombo, I. Reimanis and Ö. Ünal, "Stresses Occurring during Joining of Ceramics Using Preceramic Polymers," *Journal of the American Ceramic Society* **84** [10] 2240-44 (2001).

[10] M. Zhu and D.D.L. Chung, "Active Brazing Alloy Containing Carbon Fibers for Metal-Ceramic Joining," *Journal of the American Ceramic Society* **77** [10] 2712-20 (1994).

[11] M. Zhu and D.D.L. Chung, "Improving the Strength of Brazed Joints to Alumina by Adding Carbon Fibres," *Journal of Materials Science* **32** [20] 5321-33 (1997).

[12] ASTM C1161-94, Standard Test Method for Flexural Strength of Advance Ceramics at Ambient Temperature (1996).

[13]T. Tamai and M. Naka, "Ti Effect on Microstructure and Strength of Si_3N_4–Si_3N_4 and SiC-SiC Joints Brazed with Cu-Ag-Ti Filler Metals," *Journal of Materials Science Letters* **15** [14] 1203-04 (1996).

[14]D.B. Conquest, K.M. Knowles, L.J. Ecclestone and J.A. Fernie, "Brazing of Alumina for High Temperature Applications," submitted to CIMTEC 2002: 10th International Ceramics Congress and 3rd Forum on New Materials, Florence, Italy (2002).

[15]F.X. Spiegel, D. Bardos and P.A. Beck, "Ternary G and E Silicides and Germanides of Transition Elements," *Transactions of the Metallurgical Society of AIME* **227** 575-79 (1963).

[16]H.J. Beattie and W.C. Hagel, "Intermetallic Compounds in Titanium-Hardened Alloys," *Transactions of the Metallurgical Society of AIME* **209** 911-17 (1957).

[17]K.J. Williams, "The 1000 °C (1273 K) Isotherm of the Ni-Si-Ti System from 0 to 16% Si and 0 to 16% Ti," *Journal of the Institute of Metals* **99** 310-315 (1971).

DEVELOPMENT OF A COPPER OXIDE-SILVER BRAZE FOR CERAMIC JOINING

Jin Yong Kim and K. Scott Weil
Pacific Northwest National Laboratory
P.O. Box 999
Richland, WA 99352

ABSTRACT

The joining of ceramic materials has become an increasingly important technology as the demand for high temperature structural ceramic components in gas turbines, combustion engines, heat exchangers, and burners has grown. One of the challenges in developing a useful ceramic joining technique is in forming a joint interface which can maintain its strength under a high temperature, oxidizing environment. A recently developed method of ceramic joining referred to as reactive air brazing (RAB) appears to be promising in this regard. The copper oxide-rich CuO/Ag RAB compositions investigated in the present study display excellent wettability with polycrystalline alumina. However, as will be discussed, an inverse relationship between wettability and four-point bend strength was observed.

INTRODUCTION

As the operating temperatures of advanced power generation equipment continue to be pushed upward by thermal efficiency considerations, there is an ever increasing need to develop materials suitable for these applications, particularly for use under oxidizing conditions. Ceramics are attractive because of their excellent high-temperature mechanical properties and their high level of wear and corrosion resistance. What limits their usefulness, however, is our current ability to economically manufacture large or complex-shaped ceramic components that exhibit reliable performance. One alternative is to fabricate small-sized, simple-shaped parts that can be assembled and joined to form a larger, more complex structure. Although a considerable amount of research effort has been directed towards developing various methods of ceramic joining, intrinsic to each technique is some form of trade-off in terms joint properties, ease of processing, and/or cost.

To the extent authorized under the laws of the United States of America, all copyright interests in this publication are the property of The American Ceramic Society. Any duplication, reproduction, or republication of this publication or any part thereof, without the express written consent of The American Ceramic Society or fee paid to the Copyright Clearance Center, is prohibited.

Glass joining, for example, is a cost-effective and relatively simple method of bonding ceramics. However, the maximum operating temperature that a glass joint may be exposed to is limited by the softening point of the glass. Additional complications arise if the glass undergoes devitrification during service, as its thermomechanical properties will begin to deviate from the original carefully engineered state [1]. Alternatively, diffusion bonded ceramic joints are formed at high temperatures and under high pressures. Because of the pressure requirement however, components fabricated by diffusion bonding are typically limited to simple shapes. Reaction bonding, also a high temperature joining process, often yields joints that contain residual porosity, unconverted reactants, and undesired secondary product phases, each of which can reduce joint strength by acting as sites for crack initiation [2]. Joints formed by converting a polymeric precursor to the final ceramic bonding phase often experience cracking during processing because of the large volumetric shrinkage that accompanies pyrolysis. The use of a ceramic filler material can partially mitigate this problem, but the joint often retains a significant amount of porosity, which reduces its strength and reliability [3]. Active metal brazing requires a stringent firing atmosphere, either high vacuum or reducing-gas conditions, to prevent the active species, typically titanium, from pre-oxidizing. This represents a high capital expense and higher operating costs relative to air-fired processes. In addition, recent studies on the oxidation behavior of active metal brazes have shown that they are unreliable at temperatures beyond 500°C, at which point they eventually oxidize completely, conferring little or no strength to the joint [4,5].

With the exception of diffusion bonding, all of these joining techniques rely on an intermediary material to bond the two faying surfaces. In order to deliver a high integrity joint, the intermediary and joining surfaces must achieve a chemical equilibrium; that is, form a chemical bond across the intermediary-to-ceramic interface. Otherwise, only weak Van der Waals bonding is possible. Thus, one of the conditions necessary for retaining joint integrity under operating conditions is that the reaction products formed at these interfaces must remain stable. In an effort to satisy these conditions and offer a joining technique which, like glass joining, could readily be carried out in air, an alternative reactive brazing approach was developed. The objective of the new technique, referred to as reactive air brazing or RAB, is to reactively modify one or both oxide faying surfaces with an oxide compound that has been at least partially dissolved in a noble metal solvent, e.g. silver, gold, or platinum, such that the newly formed surface is readily wetted by the remaining molten filler material. In many respects, this concept is similar to active metal brazing, except that the joining operation can be conducted in air and the final joint should be resistant to oxidation at moderate-to-high temperatures.

One system that appears to be readily suited to RAB is the CuO-Ag system. Equilibrium phase studies conducted by Shao et al. [6] have shown that there are two invariant points in the CuO-Ag phase diagram from which new braze compositions could be developed: a monotectic reaction at 964±3°C, where CuO and a liquid L_2 coexist with a second liquid phase L_1 at a composition of 30.65 mol.% Ag and 2) a eutectic reaction at 932±3°C, where CuO and Ag coexist with the liquid phase L_2 at a composition of 98.6 mol.% Ag. Extending between these three-phase reaction points is a two-phase liquid miscibility gap. In addition, Meier et al. [7] demonstrated in a series of sessile drop experiments conducted in inert atmosphere that the contact angle between silver and alumina is greatly reduced by small additions of CuO. The improvement in wetting apparently results because of: 1) an increase in the oxygen activity of the melt and 2) the formation of an interfacial compound, $CuAlO_2$ [8-10]. Based on these studies, Schüler et al. [11] recognized that the CuO-Ag system could be exploited to bond ceramics in air, reporting their findings on a 1 mol% CuO-Ag braze composition used to join alumina substrates for power semiconductor packaging. In the study described below, CuO-Ag compositions near the monotectic end of the phase diagram were used as a starting point for developing a reactive air braze for alumina. Three types of experiments were performed in this investigation: (1) sessile drop measurements to determine the wetting behavior of the different CuO-Ag braze compositions on polycrystalline alumina, (2) analysis of the braze/alumina interfacial regions within as-formed and exposure-tested joints to determine the nature of wetting and to identify changes in the braze due to high temperature oxidation, and (3) four-point bend testing of as-brazed joints to measure joint strength at room temperature.

EXPERIMENTAL
Materials

The polycrystalline alumina (Al-23, Alfa Aesar, Inc.) used in this study was approximately 98% dense and 99.7% pure, containing a small amount of silicate material. Alumina discs measuring 50 mm in diameter and 6 mm thick were employed in the wetting and initial joining experiments. The discs were polished on one face to a 10μm finish using successively finer grit diamond paste, cleaned with acetone and rinsed with propanol, air dried, and finally heated in static air to 600°C for four hours to burn off any residual organic contamination. The alumina used for four-point bend testing were plates measuring 100mm x 25mm x 4mm, which were joined along the long side using one of the experimental brazes to form a 100mm x 50mm x 4mm plate from which the bend specimens were cut.

As listed in Table I, four different braze compositions were formulated by dry mixing the appropriate amounts of copper powder (99%, 2.5μm average particle size; Alfa Aesar) and silver powder (99.9%, 0.75μm average particle diameter;

Alfa Aesar). The copper oxidizes in-situ forming CuO as the braze is heated. For the wetting studies, the mixtures were cold pressed into pellets measuring approximatley 7mm in diameter by 10mm thick. The pellet densities averaged roughly 65% of theoretical based on a rule of mixtures calculation for the dry starting materials. To prepare braze pastes for the joining experiments, a liquid binder (BX-18, Ferro Corp.) was added to the dry powder mixture in a 1:5 weight ratio. As formed, the paste was found to have acceptable thixotropic properties for the joining experiments.

Table I. Braze compositions employed in this study

Braze Identification	CuO Content (in mol%)		Ag Content (in mol%)
CA8020	80		20
CA6931	69.35	(monotectic composition)	30.65
CA6040	60		40
CA0199	1.4	(eutectic composition)	98.6

Testing and Characterization

Wetting experiments were performed in a static air box furnace furnished with a large quartz window on the front door through which the heated specimen could be observed. A high speed video camera equipped with a zoom lens was used to record the wetting specimen during an entire heating cycle. Each braze pellet was placed on the polished side of an alumina disc and heated at 30°C/min to 900°C, at which point the heating rate was reduced to 10°C/min for the subsequent heat treatment. The furnace temperature was raised to 1000°C, where the temperature remained for fifteen minutes, then increased again to 1100°C and held for fifteen minutes. In this way, the contact angle between the braze and alumina was allowed to stabilize for measurement at each temperature. Using Videum^{TM} software (Winnov, Inc.), select frames from the videotape were converted to computer images, from which the wetting angle between the braze and alumina substrate could be measured and correlated with the temperature log for the heating run.

Joining samples were prepared by spreading a thin amount of the braze paste on the faying surface of each alumina part. A bead of excess paste was allowed to remain along the side of the joint to flow back and fill in as the binder burned out and the powders melted. Disc samples were fixtured within a steel spring clip which kept the joint under compression partway through the heating cycle, up to ~500 - 600°C. The following heat treatment schedule was employed in fabricating all but one of the joining specimens: heat in static air at 5°C/min to 1000°C, hold at 1000°C for ½hr, and cool to room temperature at 5°C/min. CA8020 was heated to 1100°C, since it was determined that this braze does not melt completely at the lower temperature. Once joined, the discs were cut in half using a diamond blade saw and cleaned with acetone, followed by a propanol rinse and air drying. One half of each joining specimen was set aside for metallographic preparation and analysis and the other half was subjected to exposure testing. Testing was conducted in a static air muffle furnace held at 800°C for 100hrs to simulate prototypical service conditions. After exposure under these conditions, the samples were mounted and polished for comparative metallographic analysis.

Block samples were held together by the weight of one of the alumina blocks resting on the other. Spring steel side clips and refractory brick kept the arrangement from slipping or toppling during heating. The braze paste was applied to the faying surface of each piece and the parts were brought together and joined using the same procedure described above for the disc specimens. Once joined, each block was machined into rectangular bend bars measuring 4mm x 3mm x 50mm with the joint at the center of the bar. The tensile side of each bend specimen was polished to a 1μm diamond paste finish and chamfered to remove machining flaws that could intiate premature failure. Strength testing was conducted by four-point bending. The spans between the inner and outer contact points were 20 and 40mm, respectively, and testing was performed at a displacement rate of 0.5mm/min. Flexure strengths were calculated from the load at failure using standard relationships derived for monolithic elastic materials [12]:

$$\sigma_F = \frac{3 \cdot P \cdot L}{b \cdot d^2} \quad (1)$$

Where P is the applied load, L is the length of the outer span, and b and d are the respective width and height of the specimen. Five specimens, each cut from the same plate, were used to determine the room temperature joint strength for a given braze composition.

Microstructural analysis of the joints was performed on polished cross-sectioned samples using a scanning electron microscope (SEM, JEOL JSM-5900LV). The SEM is equipped with an Oxford energy dispersive X-ray analysis (EDX) system, which employs a windowless detector for quantitative detection of both light and heavy elements. To avoid electrical charging of the samples in the SEM, they were carbon coated and grounded. Elemental profiles were recorded across joint interfaces in the line-scan mode.

RESULTS AND DISCUSSION
Sessile Drop Experiments

As plotted in Figure 1(a), all four braze compositions displayed measurable wetting on the polished polycrystalline alumina substrates. Within a 10 - 20°C difference, melting of the binary braze compositions intitiated at the temperature

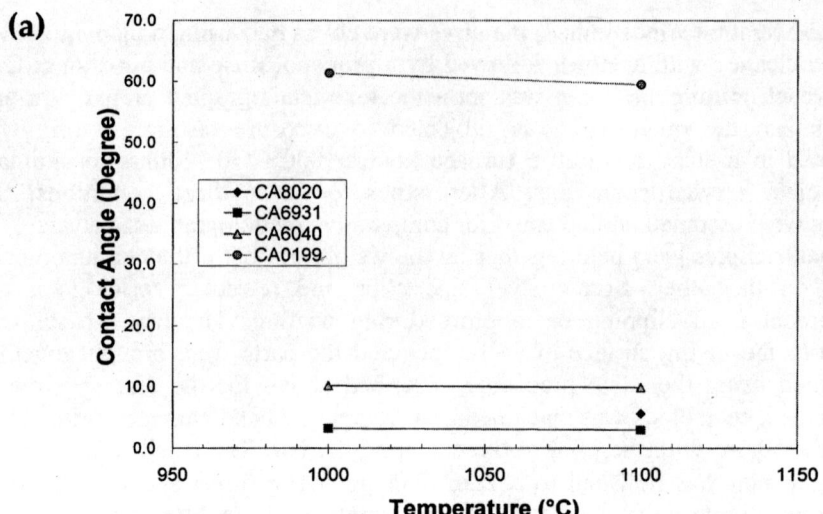

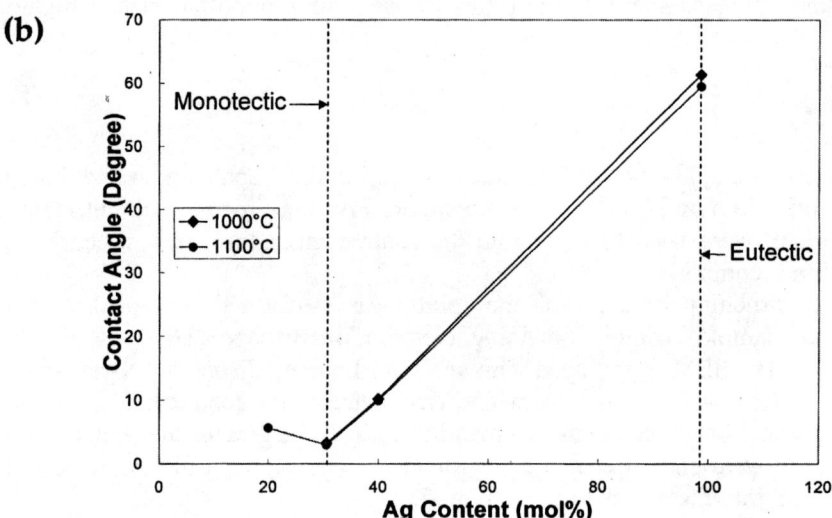

Figure 1. Contact angle as a function of (a) temperature and (b) composition for sessile drops of CA8020, CA6931, CA6040, and CA0199 on Al_2O_3 in ambient air. The hold time for each soak temperature was 15 min.

predicted by the CuO-Ag phase diagram, indicating that the CuO and Ag are not impeded from reaching equilibrium by diffusion or solid state reaction kinetics. The fifteen minute hold time used in taking the sessile drop measurements appeared to be long enough for interfacial equilibrium to be established; in all cases the contact angle reached its stable value within five minutes. With the exception of CA8020, each braze was completely molten at 1000°C or less. The CA8020 braze was not expected to melt fully until ~1027°C [6]. Shown in Figure 1(b) is a plot of contact angle as a function of braze composition for the two hold temperatures. Between the monotectic and eutectic compositions, the contact angle displays a monotonic increase with increasing Ag content, whereas the effect of temperature on contact angle, Figure 1(a), is marginal. This suggests that the wetting phenomena which take place on the braze/alumina interface are rapid and essentially complete by 1000°C, being unaffected by an increase in temperature, but may be hindered from reaching their maximum effect by the lack of reactant, i.e. too little CuO. As will be seen in the metallographic results, a likely reason for this is that a CuO-rich liquid phase interacts with and prewets the alumina surface. Thus, maximum surface coverage will be achieved when the braze contains greater than a critical concentration of CuO at the alumina faying surface.

Microstructural Analysis of As-Joined and As-Oxidized RAB Specimens

Back scattered electron images of the as-joined RAB specimens are shown in Figure 2. As seen in Figure 2(a), the sample that was joined using the CA8020 braze, which is hypermonotectic with respect to CuO composition, exhibits an extensive and continuous copper alumunium oxide, $CuAlO_2$, reaction zone adjacent to the braze/alumina interface. The composition of this reaction product is consistent with that predicted by the copper oxide (Cu_2O and CuO)-alumina phase diagrams [13]. Extending from the reaction zones toward the center of the braze is a region which consists of two blocky phases which compositionally are nearly pure CuO and nearly pure Ag. The CuO-Ag phase diagram indicates that at 1100°C, the braze is a single liquid phase which is rich in copper oxide; possibly Cu_2O since pure CuO will spontaneously reduce above 1020°C. The molten liquid reacts with the alumina at the joining surfaces to form a solid $CuAlO_2$ interfacial phase at 1100°C. A similar phenomenon has been observed previously at this temperature in the copper oxide-alumina system [14]. Given that the $CuAlO_2$ zones in Figure 2(a) are fairly extensive in comparison with the thickness of the braze region, the molten phase will become depleted in copper oxide. As this continues, the composition of the liquid could easily reach the miscibility boundary in the CuO-Ag phase diagram, and thus form two immiscible liquids which would have a tendency to segregate. The minor phase liquid would be silver-rich, containing on the order of 90 mol% Ag, whereas the major liquid phase would be silver-poor with a composition of approximately 35 mol% Ag. Liquid phase separation may account for the significant amount of silver segregation observed in Figure 2(a); virtually no silver is found in the CuO region of the braze. Upon further cooling, as the two liquids reach the monotectic temperature, the silver-poor liquid would become further depleted in silver and eventually CuO would precipitate out of solution. After the monotectic reaction, the remaining small amount of liquid would contain very little CuO, ~ 2 mol%. When it solidifies, it will form predominantly silver and a small amount of copper oxide.

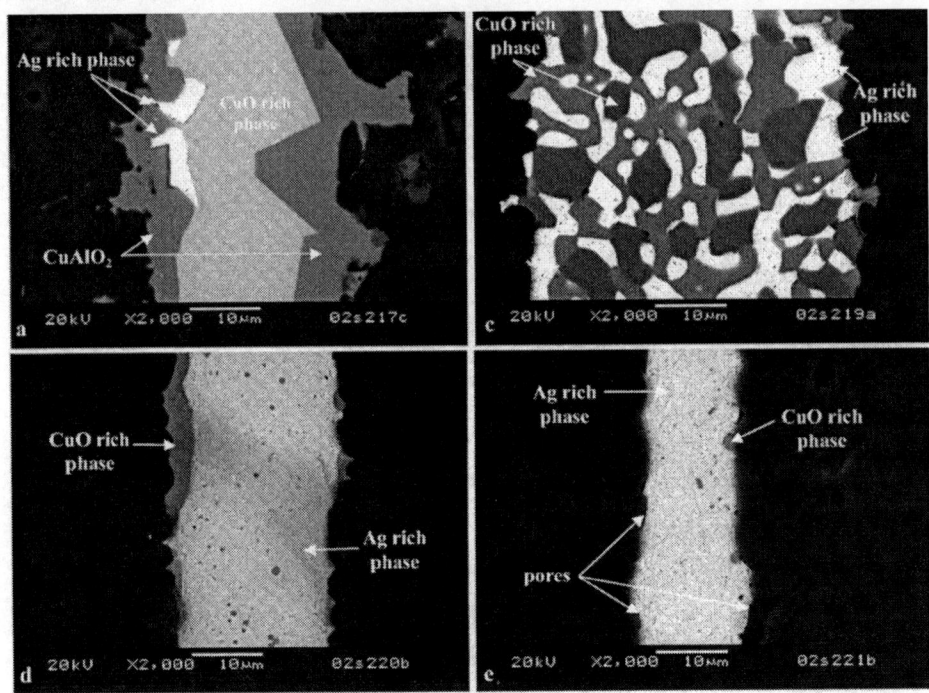

Figure 2 Cross-sectional SEM micrographs of braze/alumina interfaces: (a) CA8020, (b) CA6931, (c) CA6040, and (d) CA0199. Each specimen was heated in air at a final soak temperature of 1000°C, except for the joint containing the CA8020 braze which was heated to 1100°C.

As seen in Figure 2(b), the microstructure of the monotectic braze CA6931, which was heated to 1000°C, contains a random mixture of two phases, one which is nearly pure Ag and the other nearly pure CuO. This microstructure is typical for a monotectic reaction. At the monotectic temperature, solid CuO and a silver-rich liquid nucleate simultaneously from the silver-poor monotectic liquid.

Proportionally, CuO is the major product. As it forms and grows during the invariant reaction, the oxide precipitates will eventually impinge with each other trapping the still molten silver-rich phase within. Under further slow cooling, the liquid eliminates additional copper oxide, presumably at the interface with the proeutectic CuO. Eventually the eutectic liquid solidifies forming predominantly silver and a small amount of CuO. Unlike the CA8020 brazed joint, this sample does not contain an extensive reaction zone and no $CuAlO_2$ was found. However, the EDX analysis shown in Figure 3 suggests that a thin, <1μm thick $CuO-Al_2O_3$ diffusion zone (marked in the figure by the two asterisks) exists along the braze/alumina interfaces. This result is consistent with the $CuO-Al_2O_3$ phase diagram which displays complete solubility between CuO and Al_2O_3.

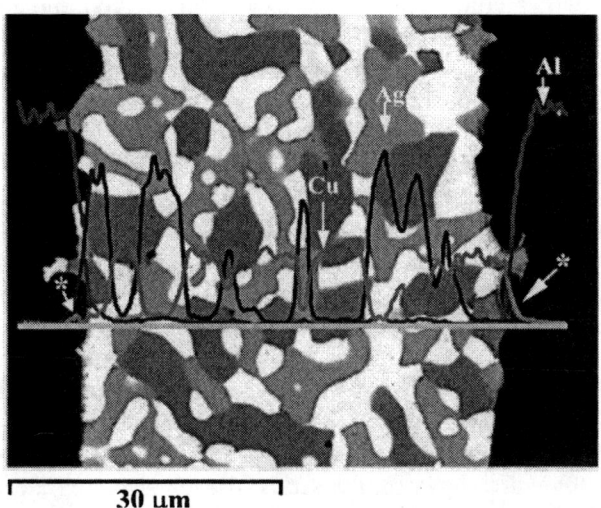

Figure 3   EDX analysis (line profiles) of Cu, Al, Ag obtained on the CA6931 braze: The regions indicated by '*' represent the presence of Cu in the alumina plates near the interface.

The CA6040 brazed joint, shown in Figure 2(c) also displays two phases, CuO and Ag, but the morphologies of each are quite different from that of CA6931. Most of the CuO in CA6040 is found in a nearly continuous layer along each interface with the alumina. When this braze is heated to 1000°C, two liquid phases form, one which is rich in silver (the minor phase) and the other silver-poor (the major phase). Because the phases are immiscible, it is expected they will segregate, with the silver-poor liquid preferentially migrating to and wetting the alumina surfaces because of its higher CuO content and therefore lower expected interfacial energy with alumina. Upon cooling to the monotectic temperature, CuO begins to precipitate from this liquid, nucleating along the boundary with alumina. As it does so, the silver-rich liquid becomes further enriched with silver. At the eutectic temperature, solid CuO and Ag will simultaneously nucleate from the remaining liquid, presumably heterogeneously on the surface of the previously formed CuO layers which coat the alumina faying surfaces. Because the eutectic liquid is predominantly silver, the central region of the braze is nearly free of CuO precipitates. Those that do exist within this region assume an equiaxed morphology.

The joint formed using the braze with the smallest CuO content, a eutectic composition of 1.4 mol% CuO and 98.6 mol% Ag, displays discrete CuO particles both within a nearly pure Ag central region and along the interface with alumina. At 1000°C, the CA0199 braze will form a single silver-rich liquid phase between the two alumina faying surfaces. Upon cooling to the eutectic temperature, solid Ag and CuO form simultaneously from the eutectic liquid. However, because the CuO concentration of the molten phase is very low, the CuO nucleates as fine, discrete particulates that decorate the interface with alumina and the interior of the braze. In addition, an occasional pore can be found along the braze/alumina interface, indicating the wettability of this braze is not as good as the others, even at the micro-scale level. As mentioned previously, the contact angles observed in Figure 1(a) can be directly related to the phenomena occuring at the braze/alumina interface. It is apparent that for the silver-rich eutectic liquid to wet the alumina appropriately, a nearly continuous $CuO-Al_2O_3$ diffusion zone and/or CuO interfacial layer is required. Obviously the discrete CuO particles that populate the interfaces in the CA0199 brazed joint are spaced closely enough to provide sufficient wetting with the alumina, but do not offer the type of wettability exhibited by the CA6931 and CA6040 brazes.

Microstructural changes within the brazed joints that underwent air oxidation at 800°C for 100hrs are shown in the series of back scattered electron images in Figures 4(a) – (d). It is immediately obvious from this set of micrographs that neither the bulk matrix nor the braze/alumina interfaces change significantly during exposure to high temperature air. As found in the as-joined samples, the exposure-tested CA8020 brazed joint still exhibits the $CuAlO_2$ reaction layer along each interface with alumina. This phase does not appear to thicken as a result of the 100hr thermal treatment. The other three joints also appear to retain their as-joined microstructural condition after exposure testing. There was no indication, for example, that the copper aluminate phase observed in CA8020 formed in any these joining specimens, suggesting that the RAB brazes potentially possess good oxidation resistance.

Strength of As-Joined RAB Specimens

The four-point bend strengths of each joint, as measured at room temperature, are plotted along with contact angle as a function of braze composition in Figure

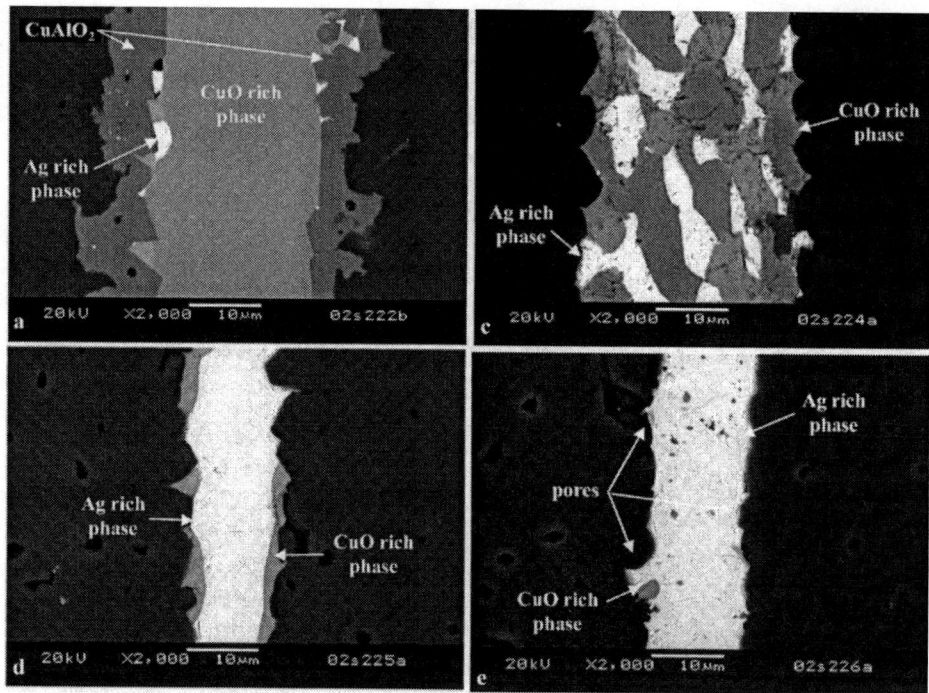

Figure 4 Cross-sectional SEM micrographs of the same four alumina/braze/alumina joints shown in Figures 2(a) – (d) after testing for 100hrs at 800°C in air: (a) CA8020, (b) CA6931, (c) CA6040, and (d) CA0199.

5. The results reveal that fracture strength improves significantly with increasing Ag content, whereas wettability, the inverse of contact angle, moves in the opposite direction. Thus, the specimen joined using the braze containing 80 mol% of CuO (CA8020) displays a bending strength of 84±20 MPa while the specimen brazed with the eutectic composition, 1.4 mol% of CuO (CA0199), exhibits a two-fold improvement in bending strength of 181±20 MPa. Although wetting is greatly meliorated by the addition of CuO to silver, it appears that the presence of a continuous phase of CuO either within the interior of the braze, as in the cases of CA8020 and CA6931, or along the braze/alumina interface (CA6040) is deleterious to the strength of the joint. Only when the CuO nucleates and grows as a discrete phase at the interface with the substrate are wetting behavior and joint strength enhanced simultaneously. Means of further improving the CuO-Ag RAB braze might include: (1) increasing the wettability of silver on the discrete interfacial CuO phase that was found to form in the CA0199 specimen, (2)

modifying the braze composition or processing conditions such that a finer size, more closely spaced dispersion of CuO particles nucleates on the surface of the alumina, and (3) investigating whether a CuO-Al_2O_3 diffusion zone is established in eutectic or near-eutectic braze compositions and what effect this might have on wetting behavior and bond strength.

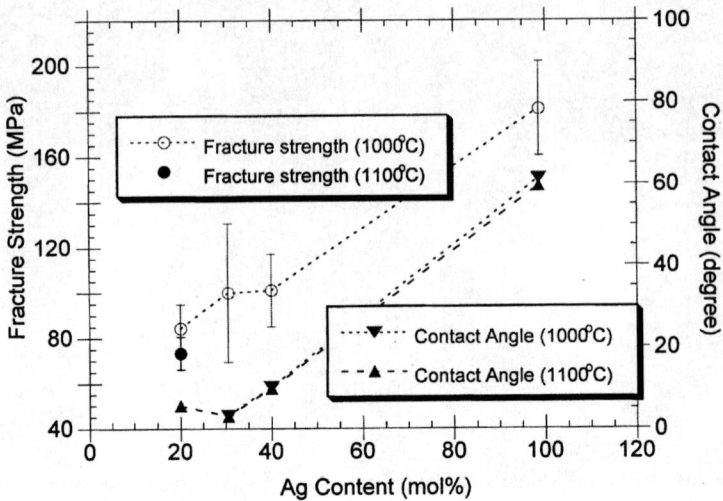

Figure 5 Room temperature four-point bend strength and contact angle as a function of Ag content. Note that all of the bend bar specimens were joined under the same conditions: heat in static air at 5°C/min to 1000°C (or 1100°C for CA8020), hold at the soak temperature for 30 min, and cool to room temperature at 5°C/min.

CONCLUSIONS

Reaction air brazing using CuO-Ag brazes was investigated as a potential method of developing an oxidation-resistant ceramic joint. It was found that the addition of copper oxide to silver significantly improves the wetting behavior of silver on alumina. In general, the observed decrease in contact angle is related to the formation of a nearly continuous CuO-Al_2O_3 diffusion zone and/or CuO layer along the braze/alumina interface. The effect of temperature on the wetting characteristics of these brazes was marginal. Despite the improvement in wetting due to the addition of CuO, the resulting bending strengths of these joints display an inverse relationship with copper oxide content. Microstructural results suggest that the presence of a continuous CuO phase within the braze or along the interface with alumina degrades joint strength. Only when the CuO forms as a discrete phase decorating the braze/alumina interface does the strength of the RAB joint approach that of monolithic alumina.

ACKNOWLEDGMENTS
The authors would like to thank Nat Saenz, Shelly Carlson, and Jim Coleman for their assistance in polishing the wetting samples and conducting the metallographic and SEM analysis work. This work was supported by the U. S. Department of Energy, Office of Fossil Energy, Advanced Research and Technology Development Program. The Pacific Northwest National Laboratory is operated by Battelle Memorial Institute for the United States Department of Energy (U.S. DOE) under Contract DE-AC06-76RLO 1830.

REFERENCES
[1] K. Eichler, G. Solow, P. Otschik, and W. Schaffrath, "Degradation Effects at Sealing Glasses for the SOFC"; pp. 899-906 in *Proceedings of the Fourth European Solid Oxide Fuel Cell Forum*. Edited by A.J. McEvoy. Oberrohrdorf, Switzerland (2000).
[2] C.A. Lewinsohn, M. Singh, T. Shibayama, T. Hinoki, M. Ando, Y. Katoh, and A. Kohyama, "Joining of Silicon Carbide Composites for Fusion Energy Applications," *Journal of Nuclear Materials*, 283-287B 1258-61 (2000).
[3] E. Pippel, J. Woltersdorf, P. Colombo, and A. Donato, "Structure and Composition of Interlayers in Joints between SiC Bodies," *Journal of the European Ceramic Society*, 17 [10] 1259-65 (1997).
[4] J-H Kim and Y-C Yoo, "Bonding of Alumina to Metals with Ag-Cu-Zr Brazing Alloy," *Journal of Materials Science Letters*, 16 [14] 1212-15 (1997).
[5] J.P. Rice, D.M. Paxton, and K.S. Weil, "Oxidation Behavior of a Commercial Gold-Based Braze Alloy for Ceramic-to-Metal Joining," Proceedings of the 26th Annual Conference on Composites, Advanced Ceramics, Materials, and Structures, in publication.
[6] Z.B. Shao, K.R. Liu, L.Q. Liu, H.K. Liu, S. Dou, "Equilibrium Phase Diagrams in the Systems PbO-Ag and CuO-Ag," *Journal of the American Ceramic Society*, 76 [10] 2663-4 (1993).
[7] A.M. Meier, P.R. Chidambaram, and G.R. Edwards, "A Comparison of the Wettability of Copper-Copper Oxide and Silver-Copper Oxide on Polycrystalline Alumina," *Journal of Materials Science*, 30 [19] 4781-6 (1995).
[8] Y. Yoshino, "Role of Oxygen in Bonding Copper to Alumina," *Journal of the American Ceramic Society*, 72 [8] 1322-7 (1989).
[9] C. Beraud, M. Courbiere, C. Esnouf, D. Juve, and D. Treheux, "Study of Copper-Alumina Bonding," *Journal of Materials Science*, 24 [12] 4545-54 (1989)
[10] Y. Yoshino and T. Shibata, "Structure and Bond Strength of a Copper-Alumina Interface," *Journal of the American Ceramic Society*, 75 [10] 2756-60 (1992).

[11]C.C. Shüler, A. Stuck, N. Beck, H. Keser, and U. Täck, "Direct Silver Bonding - An Alternative for Substrates in Power Semiconductor Packaging," *Journal of Materials Science: Materials in Electronics*, **11** [3] 389-96 (2000).

[12]M.R. Locatelli, A.P. Tomsia, K. Nakashima, B.J. Dalgleish, and A.M. Glaeser, "New Strategies for Joining Ceramics for High-Temperature Applications," *Key Engineering Materials*, **111-112** 157-90 (1995).

[13]S. K. Misra and A. C. D. Chaklader, *Journal of the American Ceramic Society*, **46** [10] 609- (1963).

[14]D.W. Sosnitzky and C.B. Carter, "The Formation of Copper Aluminate by Solid-State Reaction," *Journal of Materials Research*, **6** [9] 1958-63 (1991).

Biomedical Applications

A REVIEW OF RECENT INVESTIGATIONS ON ZIRCONIA JOINING FOR BIOMEDICAL APPLICATIONS

S. Agathopoulos, S. Pina and R.N. Correia
Ceramics and Glass Engineering Department
University of Aveiro
3810-193 Aveiro, Portugal

ABSTRACT

In this article, selected earlier and current research data have been gleaned in order to provide a general perspective on zirconia joining at high temperatures, specifically aimed for biomedical applications. Since non-reactive zirconia/metal systems result in low adhesion joints, this article addresses its interest on reactive systems which involve Ti, either as component of brazing fillers or as bulk material in form of Ti or TiAlV. The case of direct bonding of zirconia with Ti as well as the influence of Ag-Cu, Pt, Au, Ag and Zr as brazing agents in the joining process and the stability of the resulting joint are discussed in detail. The microstructure of the interfaces is presented with regard to biomedical applications and the anticipated mechanical performance of the joints.

INTRODUCTION

The use of inert bioceramics, such as alumina and zirconia, in medical implants [1-3], attracts particular interest since ceramics generally possess superior behavior compared with other materials (i.e. metals or plastics) in terms of long-term chemical stability and negligible degradation in the chemically aggressive environment of the human body as well as relatively low density and high electrical resistance, resulting potentially in implant devices reliable for a whole life-time.

In biomedicine, the joining of ceramics with metals is interesting because of two reasons:

(a) A ceramic/metal composite structure [4], featuring the coexistence of ceramic properties together with those of the metal, would eliminate the problem of the low fracture toughness of the ceramic, while in the particular case of Ti profiting from the known excellent mechanical properties and biocompatibility of the metal.

To the extent authorized under the laws of the United States of America, all copyright interests in this publication are the property of The American Ceramic Society. Any duplication, reproduction, or republication of this publication or any part thereof, without the express written consent of The American Ceramic Society or fee paid to the Copyright Clearance Center, is prohibited.

(b) Several electrical or electronic applications, such as intelligent sensing devices (so called biosensors) in which ceramics act as radiofrequency windows for metal encapsulated electronic circuits, require leak-tight ceramic/metal joints.

Ceramic/metal joining usually takes place at elevated temperatures [5]. A simple approach involves wetting of ceramics by liquid metals. In this case, wettability, measured by the contact angle (θ), or compiled in terms of work of adhesion (W_a), or interfacial energy (γ_{SL}), as defined by the Young and Young-Dupre equations [6-9], can be an index for the mechanical strength of the resulting ceramic/metal interface [10].

This article aims to outline the joining of zirconia ceramics particularly in biomedicine with regard to the involvement of Ti, with the aid of earlier and current experimental results and perspectives.

NON-REACTIVE SYSTEMS

Liquid metals or alloys which do not chemically react with zirconia [11], as proven by wetting experiments (a) because there is no evidence of bonding at the interface after removal of the solidified metallic drop from the ceramic surface and (b) because the equilibrium contact angle was instantly established as long as temperature reached a plateau, such as In, Sn, Bi, Pb, Ag, Cu, Ni, Co, Bi-Pb, Bi-Sn, Pb-Sn, Bi-Pb-Sn, Cu-Sn, Cu-Ni, do not wet (i.e. $\theta>90°$) ZrO_2 (5wt% CaO-stab.) within a wide temperature range in inert (i.e. 1 atm flowing Ar) atmosphere (Fig.1a) [12-15]. Among the models that successfully predict the W_a for alumina systems [8,11,16-19], only the model proposed by Sotoripoulou and Nikolopoulos satisfactorily interprets the poor interfacial adhesion in non-reactive ZrO_2/liquid-metal systems [18,19].

According to the equation proposed by Nikolopoulos et al. [15], good wetting conditions are not expected at the melting point of the metals in the case of non-reactive ZrO_2/metal systems (Fig.1a). Assuming that the entropy of these systems, represented by the term $d\gamma_{SL}/dT$, is practically constant within the investigated temperature range and therefore the γ_{SL} for each ZrO_2/liquid-metal system is a linear temperature function [15], Fig.1b theoretically anticipates a good wetting regime (i.e. $\theta<90°$ or $\gamma_{SL}<\gamma_{SV}$) only for few metals and at very high temperatures.

Consequently, poor adhesion is predicted between ZrO_2 and metals which do not chemically react with the ceramic.

REACTIVE SYSTEMS – THE CASE OF Ti

The strong affinity between Ti and oxygen is the driving force for chemical reactions between oxide ceramics and metal phases that contain Ti, resulting probably in stronger interfacial adhesion than that of the case of physical interfacial interactions. Ti, either pure or alloyed, can be used by two ways:

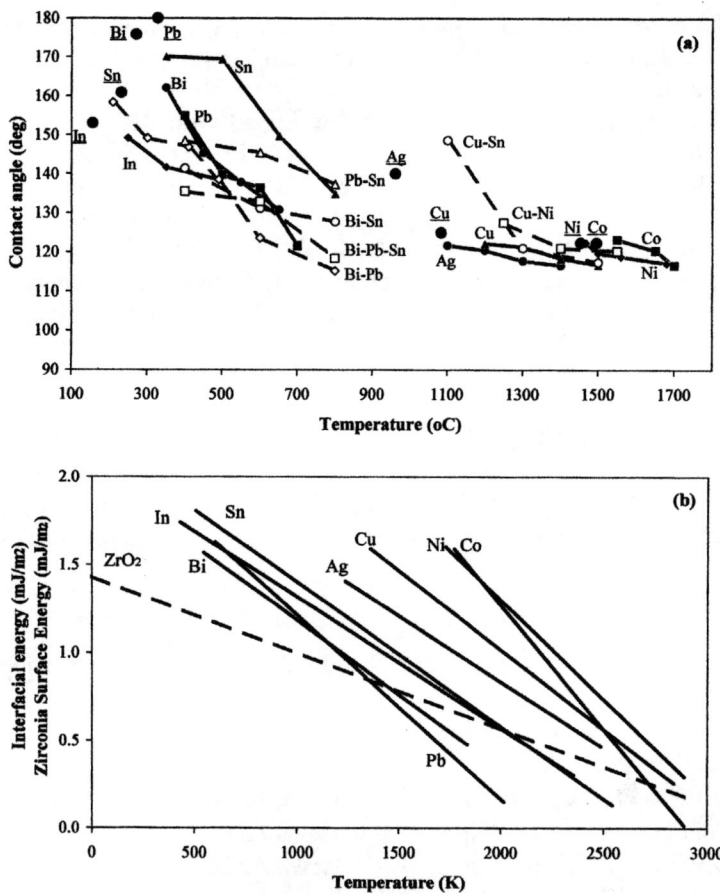

Fig.1: Non-reactive ZrO_2(CaO-stab.)/liquid-metal systems (Ar-atmosphere).
(a) Temperature dependence of contact angles (±10°) [12-15] and predicted contact angles for the pure metals (black circles – underlined elements) at their melting point according to Ref.15.
(b) Temperature dependence of interfacial energy (γ_{SL}) and comparison with the surface energy (γ_{SV}) of ZrO_2 (data available in Ref.15). The γ_{SL} lines have been drawn from the melting point of the metals until either the melting point of ZrO_2 or the boiling point of the metal assuming that that the entropic terms $d\gamma/dT$ are constant within the investigated temperature range. Good wetting regime (i.e. $\theta<90°$) is anticipated when $\gamma_{SL}<\gamma_{SV}$.

(a) As a component of a thin interlayer placed between ZrO_2 and another material block, either ceramic or metal that can facilitate the joining of the two parent blocks.

(b) As a block material, in order to be joined with ZrO_2, provided that no (initial or formed) interlayer hinders diffusion of Ti towards the ceramic.

In both cases, Ti and its principal alloy Ti6Al4V attract further interest since (a) they have similar thermal expansion coefficient with zirconia (TZP (i.e. tetragonal ZrO_2 3mol% Y_2O_3-stab.) $9.6 \times 10^{-6} K^{-1}$, Ti $9.0 \times 10^{-6} K^{-1}$, Ti6Al4V $9.4 \times 10^{-6} K^{-1}$) anticipating therefore interfaces almost free from residual stresses, (b) from clinical experience, they have well-documented biocompatibility and (c) they have moderately high Young's modulus (TZP 200 GPa, annealed Ti and Ti-alloys 110 GPa).

DIRECT BONDING WITH Ti

According to the previous statements, direct join of zirconia (TZP) and Ti (or its alloys) would sound promising since (a) it does not introduce foreign elements with doubtful biocompatibility and (b) Ti and Zr are mutually and completely miscible.

Diffusion Bonding

Experimental results for diffusion bonding are available for a wide range of temperatures:

(a) TZP/Ti, 1000°C, 5h, 50MPa, vacuum [20].
(b) TZP/TiAlV, 1000°C, 5h, 50MPa, vacuum [20].
(c) TZP/Ti, 1162°C, 1-180min, 5MPa, flown Ar [21].
(d) TZP/Ti, 1245°C, 1-180min, 5MPa, flown Ar [21].
(e) TZP/Ti, 1328°C, 1-180min, 5MPa, flown Ar [21].
(f) TZP/Ti, 1494°C, 1-180min, 5MPa, flown Ar [21].

The most important conclusions from these experiments are as follows:

In cases (a)-(d) the interfaces failed while no evidence of chemical reactions was observed except the zirconia blackened, which was attributed to ZrO_{2-x} [22-23]. The chemical composition across the interface changed steeply from the ceramic to the metallic phase (i.e there is no diffusion zone) [20]. The metal phase was assigned to α-Ti[O] (maximum O 33at% [24]), verifying therefore the partial reduction of zirconia.

Interfaces strong enough to survive ceramographic preparation were obtained in cases (e) (15-180 min) and (f) (1-180 min). In both cases, two new layers were detected between the blackened ZrO_{2-x} and α-Ti[O] (no traces of Zr were detected in the latter phase). In the ceramic matrix, a wide zone featured clear evidence of total ZrO_2 reduction (Zr-concentration remains constant while O-concentration decreases towards the interface, almost symmetrically over an increasing Ti-concentration), attributed therefore to $(Zr,Ti)O_2+(Zr,Ti)_2O$. At the metal side of the interface there is a metal-like thin zone assigned to $(Ti,Zr)_2O$ (the XRD patterns fit to Ti_2O) with a Ti/Zr ratio being increasing from 1 to 2 towards the metal. It is worth noting that both these new phases are not predicted from the relevant pseudobinary Ti-ZrO_2 phase diagram [25]. Despite the strong reaction, the joints featured negligible fracture strength probably due to the embrittlement of Ti caused by the enlargement of Ti-grains by two orders of magnitude [21].

Liquid Ti

The interactions between zirconia and liquid Ti were thoroughly investigated by Lin and Lin [26,27].

Direct contact of ZrO_2 (5mol% CaO-stab.) with liquid Ti at 1700°C for 7 minutes under Ar atmosphere resulted in strong reaction that featured almost the same general microstructure of the interfaces (i.e. the phase sequence) reported in high temperature diffusion bonding: ZrO_2/blackened ZrO_{2-x} ceramic matrix with dispersed α-Zr[O]/reaction zone/α-Ti[O]/Ti. The particular characteristics of the strong reaction were: (a) $CaZrO_3$ precipitated from the solid solution of ZrO_{2-x}. (b) The x was identified as 0.3. (c) TiO_2 formed at the reaction zone. (d) Small pores were attributed to oxygen of reduced ZrO_2 which has not been bound to Ti [26].

Further information of this reaction was obtained from a detailed study conducted at the same experimental conditions with TZP: The larger pores in ZrO_2 matrix were attributed to the Kirkendall effect resulting from the faster diffusion of Zr towards Ti than Ti to ZrO_2, whereas the smaller ones observed at the grain boundaries of Ti were assigned to oxygen of reduced ZrO_2. Ti_2ZrO was detected in α-Ti[O], suggesting that the metal phase should be rather correctly written as α-Ti[Zr,O]. The oxygen deficient area of the ceramic was assigned to $ZrO_{1.53}$ and contained dissolved 1.8at%Ti. Yttria was found being strongly reduced to $YO_{0.55}$ in the metal side containing also Ti (10.4at%) and Zr (5.9at%). Finally, Ti_3O was detected probably resulted from α-Ti[O] during cooling [27].

Generally, liquid Ti facilitates interfacial contact because it penetrates into the pores of the ceramic while elevated temperatures result in strong chemical reactions characterized by Ti-oxide formation, liberation of oxygen from the reduced ceramic and precipitation of phases related to the stabilizing oxides (CaO or Y_2O_3). However, since the microstructure is similar to that reported in high-temperature diffusion-bonding, no outstanding fracture strength would be expected for joints produced via this route.

BONDING FACILITATED BY METAL INTERLAYER

According to the aforementioned results, direct joining requires very high temperatures resulting however in weak bonding. Therefore, the use of metal interlayers has been investigated.

Ag-Cu-Ti brazing alloys

Commercial Ag-Cu-Ti brazing alloys, namely Cusil-ABA (Wesgo, Belmont, CA, USA, with 1.65wt%Ti) and CB4 (Degussa AG, Hanau, Germany, with 3wt% Ti), in the form of fillers (50 and 90 μm thickness, respectively) placed between the parent materials, can considerably reduce the joining temperature to as low as 815 and 805°C (liquidus temperatures), respectively. Experiments with such alloys have been already conducted at 900°C under vacuum [20,28]. According to the results of these investigations, chemical reaction occurs at the interfaces with the following features:

(a) Zirconia is partially reduced by Ti as indicated by its blackening and the recovering of its whiteness after heating in air. From the thickness of the blackened zone in TZP/TZP joints, where the amount of the available for reaction Ti (that could bind the oxygen of the blackened zirconia) was limited, the x value of ZrO_{2-x} was approximately estimated in the order of 10^{-3}.

(b) Brazing alloys greatly improve wettability, (compare the contact angles of Fig.1a for Ag and Cu with the contact angle shown in Fig.2), since the wetting now holds between the residue of the liquid alloy and the Ti-oxide resulted from the interfacial reaction.

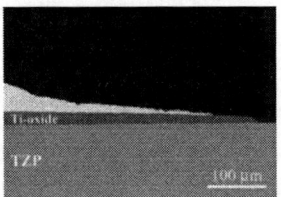

Fig.2: The TZP/Ag-Cu-Ti system shows very good wettability (900°C, vacuum) because of the formation of Ti-oxide layer resulted from the reaction between zirconia and Ti.

(c) In TZP/TZP joints, the limited amount of Ti from the brazing alloy is quickly exhausted forming Ti-oxide layer adjacent to the interface whose thickness is therefore independent of brazing time. The sequence of the layers across the interface is ZrO_{2-x}/δ-TiO/α-Ti[O]/Cu_3Ti_3O/Ag-Cu-eutectic-alloy. In the case of less available Ti in the brazing filler (e.g. Cusil-ABA), the zones of the α-Ti[O] and Cu_3Ti_3O might not been detected. In general, these findings are in a good agreement with similar studies conducted with brazed zirconia [29-31].

(d) In TZP/Ti joints, unlimited Ti migrates towards zirconia resulting in a reaction zone that generally thickens over brazing time and features the sequence $ZrO_{2-x}/Ti_2O/Cu_2Ti_4O/Ag[Cu]/TiCu/Ti_2Cu/\alpha\text{-}Ti[O]$ whereas other phases predicted from the Ti-Cu phase diagram, such as $TiCu_4$ and Ti_3Cu_4, have been occasionally detected. This sequence is consistence with thermodynamics and particularly the Ti and O activity diagrams of the Cu-Ti-O ternary system at 945°C [32]. No differences can be suggested when TiAlV-block is joined to TZP, that agrees with other literature [33,34], except that at short (1 min) brazing times the phase Cu_3Ti_3O was found next to Ti_2O zone whereas in prolonged heat treatment the zone of Cu_2Ti_4O consists of $Cu_2(Ti,Al,V)_4O$ with a Ti/Al/V ratio (in at%) 46/9/3. In the literature however, because of the important role of Al in the thermodynamics of these systems [32], there is some argument if Ti_2O or a compound of the general type M_6O forms adjacent to the ceramic [20,30,33,34]. It is noteworthy that the TZP/Ti joints produced at the shortest brazing time (i.e. 1min), resulted in the strongest flexural strength, namely 445MPa under 4-point bending loading [20,28] (i.e. ~62% of the ceramic strength and even stronger than TZP/TZP joints [29]), indicating in other words the thinner reaction zone the stronger joint.

The Ag-Cu-Ti alloys feature two particular characteristics: (a) a miscibility gap [35] and (b) extensive evaporation of Ag at >1.100°C under vacuum.

Although this method seems very promising in terms of interfacial strength, it might meet some reservations with regard to biomedical applications as far as the possible toxicity effect of Cu is concerned. Thus the use of noble metals, such as Pt, Au or Ag, has been investigated.

Platinum

Correia *et al.* have thoroughly investigated the potential use of Pt as interlayer (25μm) between TZP and Ti-containing blocks within a wide temperature range [21]. The results of that study are summarized as follows:

TZP/Ti joints produced after short time (<2h) diffusion bonding at <1100°C and 5MPa loading in Ar atmosphere using a Pt-filler between TZP and Ti blocks did not generally survive cutting.

At 1162°C and 1245°C, the microstructure of the interface indicated clear evidence of chemical reaction and total reduction of zirconia. The most characteristic feature was the formation of a Pt-rich phase, assigned to Pt[Zr,Ti] solid solution, adjacent to ZrO_{2-x} ceramic phase. This phase seemingly penetrated along grain boundaries of zirconia, which suggests an active role of Ti afterwards. This zone was followed by the phase sequence $TiPt_3/Ti_3Pt_5/TiPt/Ti_3Pt_2/Ti_3Pt/\alpha\text{-}Ti[O]$, which agrees fairly well with the Ti-Pt phase diagram, except the phase Ti_3Pt_2 that is not anticipated [36]. It is noteworthy that Zr was always found dissolved in small amounts (<10at%) in all these intermetallics, confirming the reduction of zirconia.

Liquid phase brazing at 1328°C and 1494°C in Ar did not considerably change the previous microstructure except a duplex layer formed between the TiPt and the Ti_3Pt_2 zones. However, prolonged heating and higher temperatures favour (a) the mixing of the zones of Pt[Zr,Ti] and $TiPt_3$ (or correctly $(Ti,Zr)Pt_3$) and (b) the formation of Ti_2O_3 that seemingly replace $TiPt_3$. The type of the Ti-oxide greatly depends on the Ti-block composition since in TZP/TiAlV joints, though the microstructure remains the same, TiO forms instead of the Ti_2O_3, likely attributed to the different Ti-activity due to the presence of Al and V.

Consequently, the particular chemistry of Zr-Pt-Ti-O system greatly determines the microstructure of these interfaces. However, though the chemical reaction is strong, the interfaces are rather weak, actually failing at the interface between TZP and the Pt-reach zone [21].

Gold

Our interest then shifted to gold. Since Au dissolves up to ~11at% Ti at 1115°C, a coating technique (i.e. sputtering) was employed to produce thin interlayers (<1μm) in the form of single or multi-layer coatings either on TZP or on Au thin (25μm) foils in order to retained Au/Ti atomic ratio between 99/1 – 92/8. These interlayers were used to investigate the possibility of production of TZP/TZP joints by brazing at 1065-1100°C under vacuum [37].

According to the results of these experiments, the ceramic/metal interfaces featured the phase sequence ZrO_{2-x}/Ti-oxide/Au. The Ti-oxide forms very rapidly. From the contrast of the micrographs under both secondary-emission and back-scattering modes just one type of oxide is suggested but its very small thickness did not allow to ascertain its composition.

The most characteristic problem in this system is the poor wettability (Fig.3a) resulting in an inadequate filling of the gap between the two ceramic work-pieces (Fig.3b) that is more pronounced if ceramic surfaces bear some surface curvature. Apparently, as long as the melting temperature of Au is reached (1064°C), Ti rapidly migrates from the alloy towards the interface, reacts with ZrO_2 forming Ti-oxide and then the Au depleted in Ti does not wet this oxide. Therefore, ionocovalent type Ti-oxide might be suggested rather than a metallic-type one [8].

In TZP/(Au-25μm)/Ti joints (under vacuum), the infinite supply of Ti to the interface through the liquid Au resulted in continuous interface without gaps, featuring the phase sequence $ZrO_{2-x}/TiO_2/TiAu_6/TiAu_2/TiAu/Ti_3Au/\alpha\text{-}Ti[O]$ (Fig.3c) that seems independent on temperature (within 1065 and 1100°C) but widens with brazing time. The Ti-Au intermetallics, which apparently do not hinder Ti-diffusion towards the ceramic, follow the sequence anticipated from the relevant phase diagram, although there is some argument with regard to the existence of $TiAu_6$ or $TiAu_4$ phase [37].

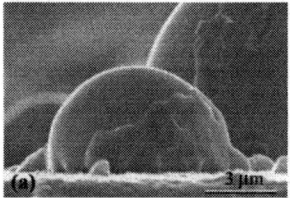 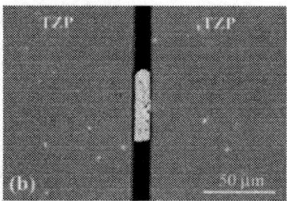 

Fig.3: Poor wetting was observed in TZP/Au/Ti systems in vacuum, (a) ~4at%Ti, 1175°C/15min, (b) ~7at%Ti, 1100°C/15min. (c) Interface microstructure after treatment of TZP/Au(25μm)/Ti at 1080°C/60min in vacuum.

Silver

Silver, which can further reduce brazing temperature due to its lower melting point (962°C), was also tested in the form of thin foil (35μm) for the production of TZP/Ti joints at 980°C under vacuum. The interfacial reaction (resulted also in blackening of TZP) seemed stronger than in Au case. A thick zone of a Ti-oxide (assigned to Ti_3O_2) formed at the interface featuring large holes (fig.4). Such images strongly recall micrographs of alumina/Ag/Ti joints that attributed to the increasing activity of Ti due the presence of Ag [38,39]. Therefore, similar action of Ag, in terms of increasing Ti-activity, is suggested also for the case of zirconia.

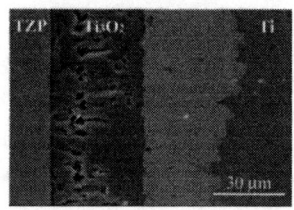

Fig.4: Interface microstructure after treatment of TZP/Ag(35μm)/Ti at 980°C/30min in vacuum.

Zirconium

In order to avoid the involvement of foreign elements, the diffusion of metallic zirconium in TZP/Ti couples was preliminarily attempted. Thin Zr-coatings (<1μm) on either TZP or Ti blocks were applied. The interfaces produced by low-pressure (~1MPa) diffusion bonding under vacuum at low temperatures (700-900°C) failed. Further investigation in this system at higher loadings is under way.

CONCLUDING REMARKS

Zirconia can be joined with metals only when chemical reaction takes place at the interface. Metals that develop merely physical interactions with it or low temperature (<1200°C) direct contact (by diffusion bonding) with reactive metals, such as titanium, result in poor adherence at interfaces.

Direct contact with Ti at very high temperatures, either by diffusion bonding (>1200°C) or with liquid titanium, results in strong chemical reaction and total reduction of zirconia.

The use of lower melting point metallic interlayers, liquidified during joining, reduces the processing temperature and generally results in benign chemical reactions, characterized by the blackening of zirconia due to the formation of ZrO_{2-x} while metallic-Zr was never detected. The reaction zones, formed parallel to the interface and being generally thickened with increasing heating time as long as unlimited Ti is provided, comprise Ti-oxides adjacent to ceramic, whose type depend on the metal used, followed by several zones of intermetallics predicted by each particular Ti-metal phase diagram. Platinum exhibits a peculiar behavior likely governed by the particular chemistry of the system.

Generally, active metal brazing techniques result in strong interfaces. However, with regard to biomedical applications, further research is needed in two areas: (a) improvement of wettability and therefore interfacial strength with systems that involve noble metals, and (b) control of the formation of the Ti-oxide layer which might be a weak point of the joint, in terms of its brittleness and the mismatch of the thermal expansion coefficient.

ACKNOWLEDGEMENTS

The first author acknowledges the support of the Foundation of Science and Technology of Portugal, (PRAXIS-grant XXI/BPD/1619/00) as well as the mentoring of Prof. P.Nikolopoulos, Dr. D.Sotiropoulou, Dr. S.Peteves and Dr. J.V.Emiliano for the acquired experience in zirconia/metal contacting systems in University of Patras in Greece and in the Joint Research Center (JRC/IAM, European Commission, Petten-site) in the Netherlands.

REFERENCES

[1] S.F. Hulbert, "The Use of Alumina and Zirconia in Surgical Implants"; pp.25-40 in *An Introduction to Bioceramics*. Edited by L.L. Hench and J. Wilson. World Scientific, Singapore, 1993.

[2] G.A. Gogotsi, E.E. Lamonova, Y.A. Furmanov and I.M. Savitskaya, "Zirconia Crystals Suitable for Medicine: 1. Implants," *Ceramics Int.*, **20** 343-8 (1994).

[3] C. Piconi and G. Maccauro, "Zirconia as a Ceramic Biomaterial," *Biomaterials*, **20** 1-25 (1999).

[4] A. Mortensen and I. Jin, "Solidification Processing of Metal Matrix Composites," *Inter.Mater.Rev.*, **37** [3] 101-28 (1992).

[5] M.G. Nicholas and S.D. Peteves, "Reactive Joining: Chemical Effects on the Formation and Properties of Brazed and Diffusion Bonded Interfaces," *Scripta Metallurgica et Materialia*, **31** [8] 1091-6 (1994).

[6] T. Young, "An Essay on the Cohesion of Fluids," *Phil.Trans.Royal Soc.London*, **95** 65-87 (1805).

[7] J.P. Garandet, B. Drevet and N. Eustathopoulos, "On the Validity of Young's Equation in the Presence of Gravitational and Other External Force Fields," *Scripta Materialia*, **38** [9] 1391-7 (1998).

[8] J.V. Naidich, "The Wettability of Solids by Liquid Metals," *Progress in Surface and Membrane Science*, **14** 353-484 (1981).

[9] P. Nikolopoulos and S. Agathopoulos, "Interfacial Phenomena in Al_2O_3-Liquid Metal and Al_2O_3-Liquid Alloy Systems," *J.Eur.Ceram.Soc.*, **10** 415-24 (1992).

[10] A.P. Tomsia, E. Saiz, B.J. Dalgleish and R.M. Cannon, "Wetting and Strength Issues in Ceramic/Metal Bonding"; pp.347-356 in *Challenging to Future Advanced Materials Aiming for Intelligence and Harmonization*, Proceedings of the 4th Japan International SAMPE Symposium, September 25-28, 1995.

[11] N. Eustathopoulos and B. Drevet, "Interfacial Bonding, Wettability and Reactivity in Metal/Oxide Systems," *J.Phys.III France*, **4** 1865-81 (1994).

[12] P. Nikolopoulos and D. Sotiropoulou, "Wettability between Zirconia Ceramics and the Liquid Metals Copper, Nickel and Cobalt," *J.Mater.Sci.Lett.*, **6** 1429-30 (1987).

[13] P. Nikolopoulos, G. Ondracek and D. Sotiropoulou, "Wettability and Interfacial Energies between Zirconia Ceramic and Liquid Metals," *Ceram.Int.*, **15** 201-6 (1989).

[14] S. Agathopoulos, "Characterization and Determination of Interfacial Properties of Bioceramic Oxides in Contact with Biological Liquids and Liquid Metallic Phases", Ph.D. Thesis (in Greek), University of Patras, Department of Chemical Enginneeing, Patras, Greece, 1994.

[15] P. Nikolopoulos, S.Agathopoulos and A. Tsoga, "A method for the Calculation of Interfacial Energies in Al_2O_3 and ZrO_2/Liquid-Metal and Liquid Alloy Systems," *J.Mater.Sci.*, **29** 4393-8 (1994).

[16] J.E. McDonald and J.G. Eberhart, "Adhesion in Aluminium Oxide-Metal Systems," *Trans.Metall.Soc. AIME*, **233** 512-7 (1965).

[17] D. Chatain, I. Rivollet and N. Eustathopoulos, "Adhesion Thermodynamique dans les Systems Non-Reactifs Metal Liquide-Alumine," *J.Chim.Phys.*, **83** 561-7 (1986).

[18] D. Sotiropoulou, and P. Nikolopoulos, "Work of Adhesion in ZrO_2-Liquid Metal Systems," *J.Mater.Sci.*, **28** 356-60 (1993).

[19]D. Sotiropoulou, S. Agathopoulos and P. Nikolopoulos, "Work of Adhesion in Ceramic Oxide/Liquid Metal Systems," *J.Adhesion Sci. Technol.*, **10** [10] 989-98 (1996).

[20]S. Agathopoulos, P. Moretto, S.D. Peteves, J.V. Emiliano and R.N. Correia, "Brazing of Zirconia to Ti an Ti6Al4V," *Ceramic Transactions*, **77** 75-82 (1997).

[21]R.N. Correia, J.V. Emiliano and P. Moretto, "Microstructure of Diffusional Zirconia-Titanium and Zirconia-(Ti-6wt%Al-4wt%V) Alloy Joints," *J.Mater.Sci.*, **33** 215-21 (1998).

[22]O. Kubaschewski and W.A. Dench, "The Dissociation Pressures in Zirconium-Oxygen System at 1000°C," *J.Inst.Metals*, **84** 440-4 (1955-56).

[23]E.G. Rauh and S.P. Garg, "The ZrO_{2-x}(cubic)-ZrO_{2-x}(cubic+tetragonal) Phase Boundary," *J.Am.Ceram.Soc.*, **63** [3-4] 239-40 (1980).

[24]J.L. Murray and H.A. Wriedt, "The O-Ti System," *Bulletin of Alloy Phase Diagrams*, **8** [2] 148-65 (1987).

[25]R.F. Dogamala, S.R. Lyon and R. Ruh, "The Pseudobinary Ti-ZrO_2," *J.Am.Ceram.Soc.*, **56** [11] 584-7 (1973).

[26]K.F. Lin and C.C. Lin, "Interfacial Reactions between Zirconia and Titanium," *Scripta Materialia*, **39** [10] 1333-8 (1998).

[27]K.F. Lin and C.C. Lin, "Transmission Electron Microscope Investigation of the Interface between Titanium and Zirconia," *J.Am.Ceram.Soc.*, **82** [11] 3179-85 (1999).

[28]J.V. Emiliano, R.N. Correia, P. Moretto and S.D. Peteves, "Zirconia-Titanium Joint Interfaces," *Mater.Sci.Forum*, **207-209** 145-8 (1996).

[29]A.J. Moorhead, H.M. Henson and T.J. Henson, "The Role of Interfacial Reactions on the Mechanical Properties of Ceramic Brazements"; pp.949-958 in *Ceramic Microstructures '86*. Edited by J.A. Pask and A.G. Evans. Plenum Press, New York, 1988.

[30]Y. Lee and J. Yu, "The Evolution of Interface Microstructures in a ZrO_2/Ag-Cu-Al-Ti System," *Scr.Metal.Mater.*, **29** 371-6 (1993).

[31]D. Imeson, J.N. Grant and M.C. Witt, "Interfacial Structure in a Zirconia to Steel Joint Formed by Active Metal Brazing"; pp.171-174 in *Inst.Phys.Conf.Ser. no 98*. IOP Publ.Ltd., 1990.

[32]G.P. Kelkar, K.E. Spear and A.H. Carim, "Thermodynamic Evaluation of Reaction Products and Layering in Brazed Alumina Joints," *J.Mater.Res.*, **9** [9] 2244-50 (1994).

[33]C. Peytour, P. Berthet, F. Barbier and A. Revcolevschi, "Interface Microstructure and Mechanical Behavior of Brazed TA6V/Zirconia Joints," *J.Mater.Sci.Lett.*, **9** 1129-31 (1990).

[34]C. Peytour, F. Barbier, P. Berthet, and A. Revcolevschi, "Characterization of Al_2O_3/TA6V and ZrO_2/TA6V Ceramic-Metal Interfaces," *Colloque de Physique 1*, **51**, C1-897 C1-902 (1990).

[35]M. Paulasto, F.J.J. van Loo and J.K. Kivilahti, "Thermodynamic and Experimental Study of Ti-Ag-Cu Alloys," *J.Alloys and Compounds*, **220** 136-41 (1995).

[36]J.L. Murray, "Pt-Ti"; p.2.348 in *Binary Alloy Phase Diagrams*, ASM Handbook, Vol.3, 1992.

[37]S. Agathopoulos, R.N. Correia, E. Joanni and J.R.A. Fernandes, "Interactions at Zirconia-Au-Ti Interfaces at High Temperatures," *Key Eng.Mater.*, **206-213** 487-90 (2002).

[38]M. Paulasto and J. Kivilahti, "Microstructural Study of Al_2O_3/Ti Joints Brazed with Different Ag-Cu Filler Metals," *Ceramic Transactions*, **35** 165-174 (1993).

[39]M. Paulasto, "Activation Mechanism and Interfacial Reactions in Brazing of Al_2O_3 and Si_3N_4 Ceramics with Ag-Cu-Ti Filler Alloys", Ph.D. Thesis, Helsinki University of Technology, Department of Materials Science and Engineering, Espoo, Finland, 1995.

JOINING ZIRCONIA AND ALUMINA BIOCERAMICS

H. W. Shin, E. D. Case, B.D. Brooks
Chemical Engineering and Materials Science Department

and

P. Kwon, C.K. Kok
Mechanical Engineering Department
Michigan State University
East Lansing, MI 48824

ABSTRACT
Bioceramics include both bioactive and bioinert ceramics. Zirconia and alumina are biocompatible but do not act to stimulate bond growth; thus zirconia and alumina are "bioinert" ceramics. This paper discusses joining of zirconia and alumina ceramics where the joined specimens have been fabricated both with and without surface or internal channels.

INTRODUCTION
A fundamental principle of design is that one seeks to optimize materials selection in terms of the service requirements of a given application. In order to most effectively utilize material properties it is often necessary to join materials. The ability to join alloys of differing physical properties has been exploited for a very long time for metallic materials. For ceramic materials, glass to metal seals were developed decades ago in response to the needs of the electronics industry in applications such as vacuum tubes and cathode ray tubes. However, it has only been recent that ceramic/ceramic joining has been performed for technical ceramic materials [1 - 9].

The materials included in this study, namely alumina, zirconia and hydroxyapatite (HAP), are each ceramic materials of current technological interest. Alumina is a widely used ceramic material with high hardness, high elastic modulus, and good resistance to acid and base attack. Uses of alumina include electronic packaging and insulation, cutting tools, and envelops for high intensity lamps [10]. In the fully stabilized form, zirconia has been used in solid oxide fuel cells (SOFC) and in the partially stabilized form it is a candidate for use as a structural material. In addition to the uses mentioned above, alumina and zirconia are of current interest as bioceramic materials. For example, alumina and zirconia have been used in hip replacements [11,12] and porous alumina is being studied as an implantable device for the slow release of medicine into the body [13]. Hydroxyapatite is a key bioceramic material. HAP is bioactive and biocompatible and is currently used as a coating on a variety of medical implants [14].

BACKGROUND: CHANNEL FABRICATION IN CERAMICS

The authors and co-workers have fabricated channels in ceramics using several different techniques. For example, exterior channels have been formed by both cutting the channels into the dense, sintered specimens using an ultrasonic vibratory mill [6,7] or a low speed diamond saw [8].

In addition, a fugitive phase burnout technique has been used, in which the fugitive phases employed include cotton thread [15], graphite pencil lead [16,17], monofilament polymeric fibers [15], or dense paper. In the fugitive technique, the fugitive phase material is first pressed into a powder compact (where the powder compact is formed in a uniaxial die). The specimens were then typically sintered to relative mass densities in the range of about 92 - 98 percent of theoretical density.

Interior channels in ceramics also have been fabricated by graphite pencil lead [17]. The "width" of both the internal and external channels fabricated by the authors and co-workers have been in the range of a few hundred microns to nearly a millimeter across. Channel lengths have been up to about 1.6 cm long, for disk-shaped specimens 1.8cm in diameter.

It should be noted that channels with depths of approximately 0.1 to 0.4 microns have been fabricated by Glaeser and co-workers [18 - 20]. However, the dimensions of the channels fabricated by Glaeser et al. [18 - 20] are quite different from the channels formed in this study, where in this study the channels have radii of roughly 300 to 500 microns and are thus about three orders or magnitude larger than the depth dimension of the channels fabricated by Glaeser et al. [18 - 20].

The dimensions of channels are significant, since they are very important in terms of the nature of the fluid flow that is feasible in the channel. When the channel dimensions drop below about 20 microns, it is impractical to pump a fluid through the channel. This fact is evident not only, for example, in the electronics cooling industry but in the human body. The smallest blood vessels, namely capillaries, distribute blood not as a function of the blood pressure exerted by the heart but (as their name implies) by capillary action. Channels that are from about 100 to several hundred microns across are of interest for both electronic cooling applications and biomedical applications [21]. Channels with sub-micron dimension fabricated by Glaeser et al. [18 - 20] have been used as model cracks in crack healing studies and as model systems to study diffusion-driven morphology changes in pores. In this study we successfully joined the two bioinert ceramics alumina and zirconia. In both the alumina and zirconia specimens, sub-micron internal and external channels were fabricated.

EXPERIMENTAL PROCEDURE

The powders were pressed and sintered from commercial zirconia, alumina and hydroxyapatite powders. The initial particle size, purity, and vendor of each of the powders are given in Table 1.

Each of the powders was pressed at roughly 35 MPa in a double-acting steel die, which produced disc-shaped specimens approximately 2.2 cm in diameter in the green state. The powder compacts of each material were then sintered in air in a conventional electric furnace, where the sintering temperature, sintering time and heating/cooling rate is given in Table 2. The mass of each alumina specimen was 2 grams while the mass of each zirconia specimen was 3 grams.

After the specimens were sintered, the specimens were polished using a series of diamond paste, as described elsewhere [7,8,16]. The mass density of the specimens was determined from the dimensions and mass of the sintered specimens.

Table 1. Characteristics of the starting powders used in this study

Material	Initial Particle Size (μm)	Chemical Purity	Vendor
Zirconia (TZ3YS)	0.59	99.9	Tosoh
Alumina	0.2	99.99	Tamii

Table 2. Sintering conditions for each of the materials used in this study

Material	Sintering Temperature (^{0}C)	Sintering Time (hours)	Heating and cooling rates
Zirconia	1475^{0}C	4 hrs	10^{0}C/min
Alumina	1475^{0}C	4 hrs	10^{0}C/min

After sintering and polishing, the specimens were spin-coated with a commercial organically-based pre-ceramic material, SilicaFilm™ (Emulistone Corp., Whippany, New Jersey). The SilicaFilm™ coated were then cured for 20 minutes in air at 200°C. When pyrolyzed in air, the SilicaFilm™ coating is converted into a high purity amorphous film [9,16].

Channels in the specimens were formed by pressing fugitive phase elements (graphite pencil leads) into the powder compacts [17]. The graphite pencil leads had nominal diameters of 0.5 mm to 0.9 mm. To form the surface channels, the powder was first added to the die cavity, the powder surface was leveled, then the fugitive phase elements were placed on top of the powder. The specimens were then pressed at 35 MPa. The fugitive phase elements were then burned out in air in an electric furnace by heating at 900^0C for 4 hours.

The specimens were joined by placing one specimen with a coated and polished surface in content with the polished surface of the other specimen to be joined. A dead weight of 20 to 50 grams was placed on top of the specimens. The specimens were heated in air in a conventional furnace for 4 hours at 1475^oC with a heating and cooling rate of 10^oC per minute.

In order to examine the microstructure of the joint region and to examine the exterior and/or internal channels in the specimens, the joined specimens were cut using a low speed diamond saw to reveal a cross section through the specimen. The specimens were then mounted in a polymeric mounting material and polished with diamond paste with grit sizes down to 1 micron. After polishing, the specimens were sputtered-coated with gold and examined using a scanning electron microscope.

RESULTS AND DISCUSSION

The microstructures of each material consisted of relatively equiaxed grains with average porosities of about 3 to 8 volume percent.

For all of the ceramic/ceramic joining performed in this study, the polished specimens were spin coated with SilicaFilm^{TM} ceramic precursor. The specimens were then fired in air in a conventional furnace.

The densified PSZ (3 mol% yttria partially stabilized zirconia) specimens that were joined with densified alumina specimens (Figures 1 and 2) show an interlocking microstructure at the interface between the PSZ and alumina. A similar microstructure was observed during microwave joining of PSZ/alumina specimens by Case and co-workers [22]. As was the case in the microwave joined specimens, the bond layer is not apparent in the region of the interlocking microstructure. For the microwave joined specimens, TEM examination of the PSZ/alumina did not reveal a bond layer [22].

Figure 3 is a low-magnification SEM micrograph of joined PSZ/alumina specimens that shows surface and internal channels formed by the burnout of the fugitive phase elements. The internal channels at the PSZ and alumina interface were formed by joining the PSZ specimen with external channels to the alumina specimen. As shown in Figure 3, the alumina specimen also contained external channels on the alumina specimen surface opposite the PSZ/alumina interface.

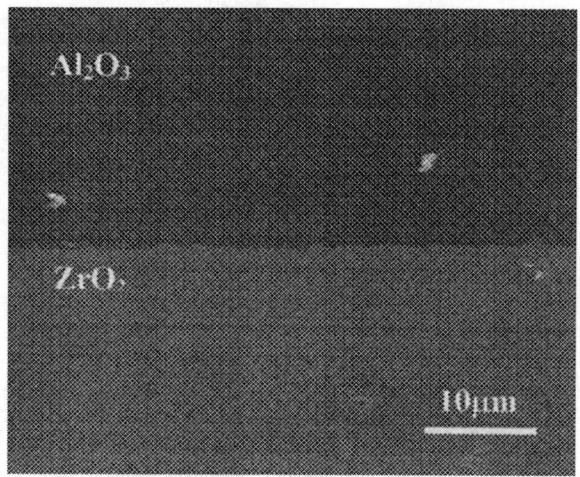

Figure 1. Partially stabilized zirconia (3 mol% yttria) conventionally joined at 1475°C for 4 hours using a 50 grams dead weight. Note interlocking microstructure at the PSZ-alumina interface.

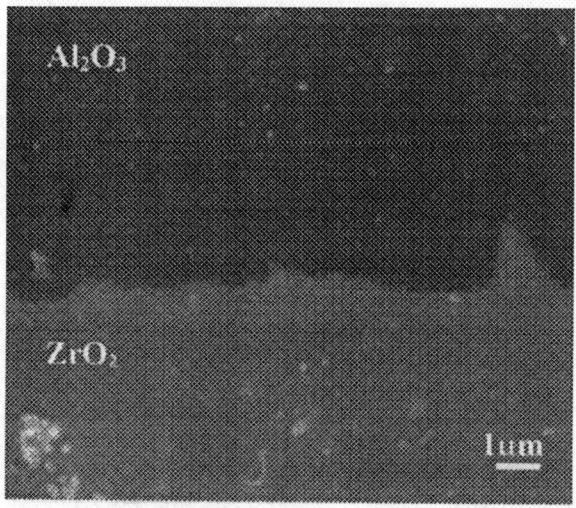

Figure 2. Higher magnification view of the same specimen as in Figure 1.

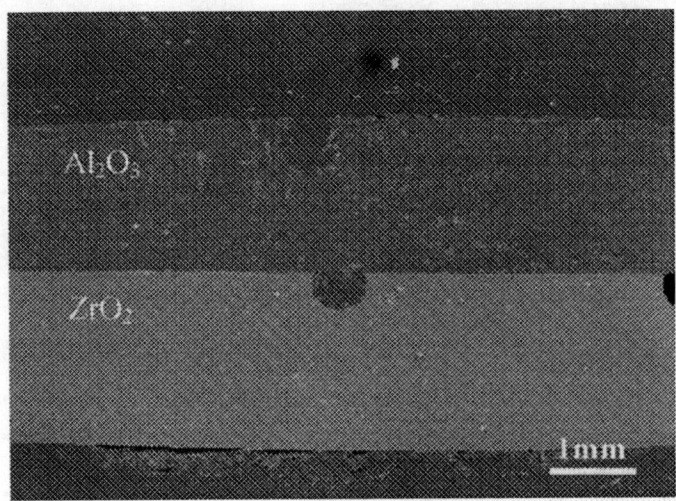

Figure 3. Cross-sectional view of PSZ joined with alumina. Note that in the alumina layer there is a surface channel fabricated from the burn out of a 0.5mm diameter fugitive phase element. Similar channels are located at the PSZ-alumina interface.

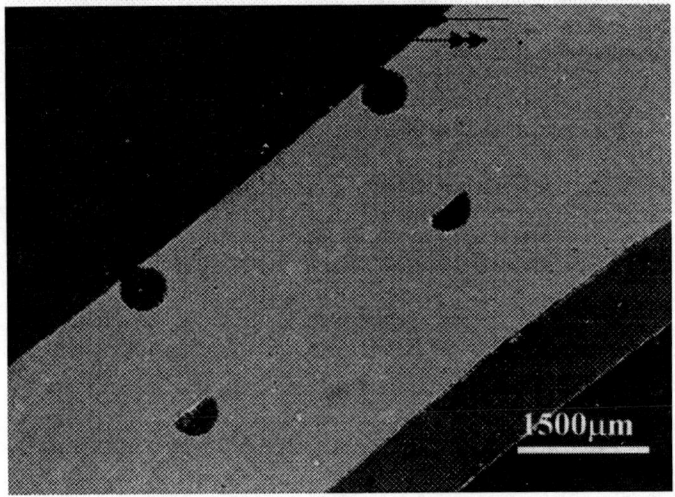

Figure 4. Partially stabilized zirconia (PSZ 3 mol % yttria) joined with PSZ, with external and internal channels. As in Figure 3, the internal channels were formed by joining.

External and internal channels were also fabricated in PSZ/PSZ joined specimens (Figure 4). As was the case for the PSZ/alumina specimens shown in Figure 3, the internal channels are formed by joining specimens with external channels with other PSZ specimens.

Figure 5 is a higher magnification SEM micrograph of the region near the bond layer in one the PSZ/PSZ specimens joined in this study. Two aspects of the micrograph shown in Figure 5 contrast with the PSZ/alumina micrographs shown in Figures 1 and 2. First, the bond layer in Figure 5 is roughly 2 microns thick, while the bond layer in the PSZ/alumina specimens was too small to be detected in the SEM. In addition, there are microcracks in the bond layer of the PSZ/PSZ specimens, while no microcracks are visible in the vicinity of the PSZ/alumina interface (Figures 1 and 2). In previous studies by the authors [6 - 9, 16, 22], that involved ceramic/ceramic joining by microwave heating, the bond layers were consistently thinner and were crack-free. The authors believe that likely the reason for the microcracking observe in this study is the thickness of the silica film. For example, in an earlier study by Mukherjee. [23] it was found that a silica coating on the polymer bismaleimide (BMI) cracked whenever the polymer coating was thicker than 0.3 microns.

Figure 6 shows an alumina/alumina specimen joined conventionally at 1475^0C for 4 hours. Joining a specimen with an external channel to another specimen again formed the internal channel in this specimen. In the micrograph, the polymer mounting solution in which the specimen was mounted has filled the channel. For the alumina/alumina specimen, the bond layer thickness was as thick as two microns in some locations along the interface.

Thus, for the alumina/PSZ joints, the conventional heating performed in this paper produced bonds that were crack free and very thin (Figures 1 and 2). However for the PSZ/PSZ joints, microcracks were visible in the bond layer.

SUMMARY AND CONCLUSIONS

Using conventional heating in air, the joints were fabricated between bioinert ceramics including alumina/alumina, alumina/zirconia and zirconia/zirconia materials. This effort compliments earlier work by the authors and co-workers involving both microwave and conventional joining of alumina, zirconia and hydroxyapatite (HAP) ceramics [7 - 9,16,17,22].

Under conventional heating, the best joints were of similar quality to those obtained under microwave heating, for example where an interlocking microstructure was observed at the alumina/PSZ interface. However, some of the joints fabricated by conventional heating were thicker than those obtained by microwave heating. In addition, numerous cracks were observed in PSZ/PSZ bond layers, where the bond layer was on the order of several microns thick. The

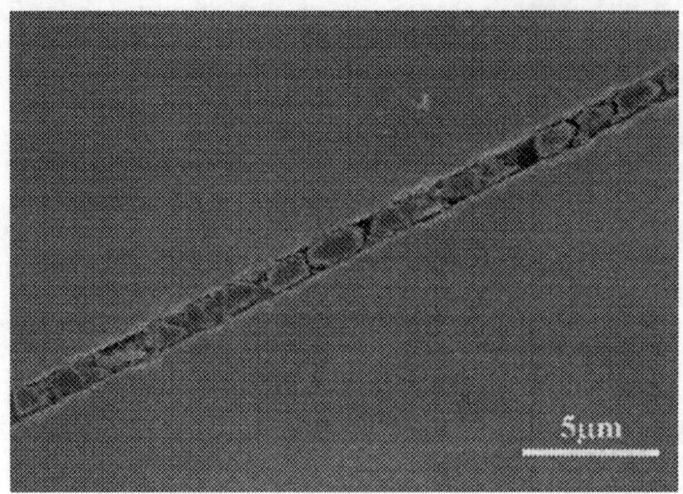

Figure 5. Interface between PSZ and PZS specimens joined at 1475°C for 4 hours

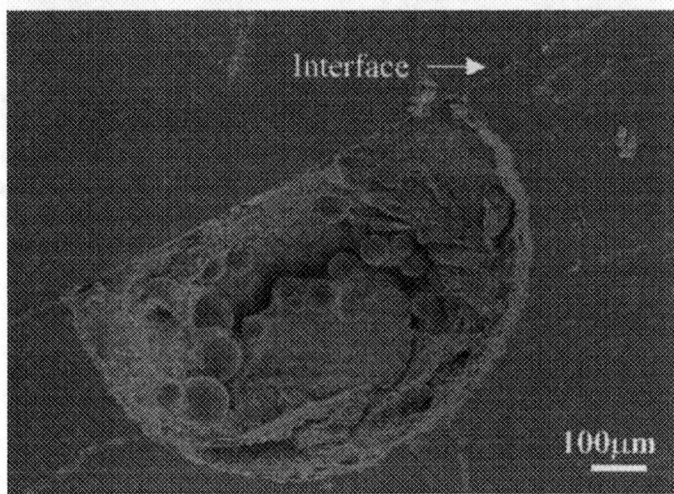

Figure 6. Alumina-alumina joined conventionally at 1475°C for 4 hours

difference in the final bond layer thickness could be due to either (i) differences in the as-cured thickness of the spin on the films or (ii) differences between the microwave and conventional heating techniques. At this time, it appears that microwave heating may result in ceramic/ceramic bonds that are more consistently crack-free and thin. However, the authors are continuing to investigate the differences between the bond layer microstructures for the conventionally joined ceramics versus the microwave joined ceramics.

REFERENCES

1. M. L. Mecartney, R Sinclair, and R. E. Loehman, "Silicon Nitride Joining," J. Amer. Ceram. Soc., 68:472-488, 1985.
2. H. Fukushima, T. Yamanaka, and M. Matsui, "Microwave Heating of Ceramics and Its Application to Joining," J. Mater. Res., 5 (2): 397-405, 84, 1990.
3. R. Silberglitt, D. Palaith, W. M. Black, H. S. Sa'adaldin, J. D. Katz and R. D. Blake, "Investigation of interlayer materials for microwave joining," Ceram. Trans., 21:487-495, 1991.
4. M. H. OBrien and D. N. Coon, Mechanistic analysis of time-dependent failure of oxynitride glass-joined silicon nitride below 1000^0C", J. Am. Ceram. Soc., 74[1]: 103 - 108, 1991.
5. P. A. Walls and M. Ueki, "Mechanical properties of beta-sialon ceramics joined using composite beta-sialon-glass adhesives", J. Am. Ceram. Soc., 78[4]: 999 - 1005, 1995.
6. K. N. Seiber, K. Y. Lee, and E. D. Case, "Microwave and Conventional Joining of Ceramics using Spin-on Materials," pp. 941-949 in Proceedings of the 12th Annual Advanced Composites Conference, Technomic Publishing Co., Lancaster, PA, 1997.
7. E. D. Case, K. Y. Lee, J. G. Lee, and T. Hoepfner, "Geometrical Stability of Holes and Channels During Joining of Ceramics and Ceramic Composites," pp. 27 - 34 in Joining of Advanced and Specialty Materials, M. Singh, J. E. Indacochea, and D. Hauser, eds., ASM International, Materials Park, OH, 1998.
8. J. G. Lee and E. D. Case, "Joining Ceramics to Produce Components with Precise Internal Channels", pp. 433 - 442 in Innovative Processing and Synthesis of Glass, Composite, and Ceramic Materials III, Volume 108, Ceramic Transactions, American Ceramic Society, 2000.
9. E. D. Case, K. Y. Lee, and J. G. Lee, "Joining of Polycrystalline Ceramics and Ceramic Composites Using Microwave Heating," pp. 17 - 20 in Proceedings of the 33rd International Microwave Power Symposium (IMPI), International Power Institute, Manassas, VA, 1998.
10. M. W. Barsoum, page 10 in Fundamentals of Ceramics, McGraw Hill, New York, 1997.

11. L. Sedel, "Evolution of alumina-on-alumina implants - A review", Clin. Orthop. Rel. Res., 379: 48 – 54, 2000.
12. R. B. Heimann and G. Willmann, "Irradiation induced colour changes in medical grade Y-TZP ceramics", Br. Ceram. Trans., 97[4]: 185 – 188, 1998.
13. A. Krajewski, A. Ravaglioli, A, E. Roncari, P. Pinasco and L. Montanari, "Porous ceramic bodies for drug delivery", J. Mater. Sci.-Mater. Med., 11[12]: 763 – 771, 2000.
14. J. R. Jones and L. L. Hench, "Materials perspective - Biomedical materials for new millenium: perspective on the future", Materials Science and Technology, 17[8]: 891 - 900, 2001.
15. J.G. Lee, Joining of Ceramic Materials Using Spin-On Interlayers, M. S. Thesis, Materials Science and Mechanics Department, Michigan State University, East Lansing, MI, 2000.
16. J. G. Lee, E. D. Case, H. Shin and P. Kwon, "Fabrication of Complex Channel Structures in Joined Ceramics", 21[4]: 103 - 110, Ceramic Engineering and Science Proceedings, American Ceramic Society, 2000.
17. H. W. Shin, E. D. Case, and P. Kwon, "Fabrication of internal channels in ceramics and ceramic composites", accepted for publication, Journal of Advanced Materials
18. A. M. Glaeser, "Model studies of Rayleigh instabilities via microdesigned interfaces", Interface Sci., 9[1 - 2]: 65 - 82, 2001.
19. T. Narushima and A. M. Glaeser, "High-temperature morphological evolution of lithographically introduced cavities in silicon carbide", J. Am. Ceram. Soc., 84[5]: 921 - 928, 2001.
20. M. Kitayama, T. Narushima and A. M. Glaeser, "The Wulff shape of alumina: II. Experimental measurements of pore shape evolution rates", J. Am. Ceram. Soc., 83[10]: 2572 - 2583, 2000.
21. T.M. G. Chu, J. W. Halloran, S. J. Hollister, S. E. Feinberg, Hydroxyapatite implants with designed internal architectures, J. Mater. Sci.-Mater. Med., 12 471 - 478, 2001.
22. E. D. Case, J. G. Lee, L. Zeng, and M. A. Crimp, "Joining of Dissimilar Ceramic Materials", pp 10 - 17 in Joining of Advanced and Specialty Materials II, ASM International, Materials Park, OH, 2000.
23. C.Mukherjee, pp.14-17 in "Silica Coatings on Bismaleimide Substrates", MS Thesis, Materials Science and Mechanics Department in Michigan State University, East Lansing Michigan 1999.

GRADED COATINGS FOR METALLIC IMPLANT ALLOYS

Eduardo Saiz and Antoni P. Tomsia
Lawrence Berkeley National Laboratory
Berkeley, CA 94720
USA

Shigeru Fujino
Kyushu University,
Kasuga-shi, Fukuoka 816-8580
Japan

Jose M. Gomez-Vega
Nagoya University
Furo-Cho, Chikkusa-ku, Nagoya 464-8603
Japan

ABSTRACT

Graded glass and glass-hydroxyapatite coatings on Ti-based and Co-Cr alloys have been prepared using a simple enameling technique. The composition of the glasses has been tailored to match the thermal expansion of the alloys. By controlling the firing time, and temperature, it has been possible to control the reactivity between the glass and the alloy and to fabricate coatings (25 to 150 µm thick) with excellent adhesion to the substrate, resistant to corrosion and able to precipitate hydroxyapatite during *in vitro* tests in simulated body fluid.

INTRODUCTION

Metals such as 316L stainless steel, Co-Cr or Ti alloys are widely used for skeletal repair.[1-3] However, one of the main drawbacks of using metallic implants is that they are bioinert and become encapsulated by dense fibrous tissue inside the body.[3] This impedes proper stress distribution at the implant-bone interface, which can result in an interfacial failure and loosening of the implant, with the possible consequence of fracture in the adjacent bone.[3,4] Therefore, a coating that enhances the adherence of the metal to the bone and protects the alloy from corrosion by the body fluids will accelerate the stabilization of the implant and extend its duration.

Coatings of hydroxyapatite (HA) fabricated by plasma spraying have been extensively investigated,[3,5-6] although there are several critical problems

---

To the extent authorized under the laws of the United States of America, all copyright interests in this publication are the property of The American Ceramic Society. Any duplication, reproduction, or republication of this publication or any part thereof, without the express written consent of The American Ceramic Society or fee paid to the Copyright Clearance Center, is prohibited.

associated with the degradation of HA due to the elevated temperature required in the process, and lack of strength at the metal/HA interface.[7-9] An alternative method is to coat the implant with a bioactive glass (able to form HA *in vivo*) that could provide the desired interfacial attachment to the bone. Several groups have attempted to coat metallic implants with bioactive glasses using enameling, rapid immersion in molten glass, or plasma-spraying techniques.[10-13] Although some coatings with excellent *in vitro* behavior have been obtained, most of the glass coatings are marred by cracking and poor reliability at the glass/metal interface.[10,12] In many cases glass/metal reactions lead to the formation of brittle interfacial layers and gas bubbles in the coating.[14,15]

It has been suggested that future progress in biomaterials must include the development of coatings with programmed dissolution of multilayer surfaces.[16] Such surfaces would provide new opportunities to optimize the biomaterial coating surface for different periods of the healing-in phase. This programmed dissolution can then be used to expose different micro-architectures, chemical patterns, and porosities at various times. Fabrication of coatings for medical applications involves a compromise between adhesion, mechanical stability, and bioactivity, but coatings that satisfy all these requirements are extremely difficult to develop. The aim of this work is to use a simple enameling technique to fabricate graded glass and glass-hydroxyapatite coatings on Co-Cr and Ti-based alloys that will combine good adhesion to the metal with rapid biofixation and long- term stability.

EXPERIMENTAL

Glasses in the system SiO_2-Na_2O-K_2O-CaO-MgO-P_2O_5 (Table I) were prepared by mixing SiO_2 (99.5%)[*], $CaCO_3$ (99.9%)[**], MgO (98.6%)[**], K_2CO_3 (99%)[#], $NaHCO_3$ (99.5%)[**] and $NaPO_3$ (99.7%)[#] using a high-speed stirrer. The mixture was dried at 80°C for 12 hours and then fired in air at 1400°C for 4 hours in a Pt crucible. The melt was cast into a graphite mold to obtain glass plates (~50×50×5 mm) that were subsequently annealed at 500°C for 6 hours to relieve stresses. The thermal expansion (α), softening (T_s) and transformation (T_g) temperatures were measured in a calibrated dilatometer with an alumina holder and push rod, using glass bars 25 mm long.

---

[*]Cerac, USA.
[**]JT Baker, USA.
[**]JT Baker, USA.
[#]Allied Chemical, USA
[**]JT Baker, USA.

To manufacture the coatings, the glass was milled in a planetary agate mill, and a suspension of the glass powder (particle size < 20 µm) in ethanol was deposited on the metallic substrates (Ti, Ti6Al4V or Vitallium® a Co-Cr alloy), which had been previously polished with diamond (1 µm particle size) and cleaned in acetone and ethanol. The resulting coatings were dried in air at 75°C for 12 hours and fired in air or N_2 at temperatures ranging between 650 to 850°C in order to make the glass flow and adhere to the metal. For the firings in air, the specimens were introduced in the furnace previously preheated to 600-650°C and heated at 40°C/min to the desired temperature. During heating, the furnace was evacuated to 0.1 atm. Once the maximum temperature was reached, air was let into the chamber. After the required time, they were quenched in air. Graded coatings have been manufactured by depositing two or three different glass or glass-HA layers on the metal substrates using the previously described method following by firing in air or N_2. The final coating thickness ranged between 25 to 150 µm.

Table I. Glass compositions

	SiO_2	Na_2O	K_2O	CaO	MgO	P_2O_5
Bioglass®	45.0	24.5		24.5		6.0
6P44-a	44.2	23.6	6.5	12.6	7.1	6.0
6P44-b	44.2	17.0	4.6	18.0	10.2	6.0
6P44-c	44.2	10.3	2.8	23.4	13.3	6.0
6P50	49.8	15.5	4.2	15.6	8.9	6.0
6P53-a	52.7	17.0	4.6	12.6	7.1	6.0
6P53-b	52.7	10.3	2.8	18.0	10.2	6.0
6P55	54.5	12.0	4.0	15.0	8.5	6.0
6P57	56.5	11.0	3.0	15.0	8.5	6.0
6P61	61.1	10.3	2.8	12.6	7.2	6.0
6P64	64.1	9.8	2.7	11.1	6.3	6.0
6P68	67.7	8.3	2.2	10.1	5.7	6.0

The crystallization of the coatings was evaluated by x-ray diffraction (XRD). The surfaces of the coatings, as well as polished cross sections, were examined by optical microscopy and scanning electron microscopy with associated energy dispersive spectroscopy analysis (SEM-EDS). The glass metal-interfaces were also analyzed using high resolution transmission electron microscopy (HRTEM).

In order to study the adherence of the coatings, the relative crack resistance was qualitatively evaluated by indentation. Vickers indentations on the coating surfaces were performed in air, with loads up to 6.2 Kg. Indentations on the coatings and glass/metal interfaces were also performed on polished cross sections, using loads ranging from 0.05 to 1.2 Kg.

Table II. Thermal properties of the metals and glasses (T_g and T_s are the transformation and softening points, respectively).

	α^* (10^{-6} °C^{-1})	T_g(°C)	T_s(°C)
Ti	~9.6		
Ti6Al4V	9.1-9.8		
Vitallium®	~14.0		
Bioglass®	15.1	511	557
6P44-a	15.6	449	503
6P44-b	13.0	516	560
6P44-c	11.3	527	599
6P50	12.2	522	560
6P53-a	12.9	530	565
6P53-b	11.5	531	608
6P55	11.0	548	602
6P57	10.8	557	609
6P61	10.2	564	624
6P64	9.1	565	622
6P68	8.8	565	644

*Measured between 200 and 400°C

The behavior of selected glass coatings in simulated body fluid (SBF) was studied by *in vitro* tests. The specimens (15×10×1 mm) were soaked in 20 ml of SBF at a constant temperature of 36.5°C for times up to 30 days. After soaking, the coatings were rinsed in distilled water, dried, and analyzed by XRD, SEM-EDS and Fourier Transform Infrared Spectromicroscopy (FTIRSM) in the Advanced Light Source (ALS) at Lawrence Berkeley National Laboratory.

RESULTS AND DISCUSSION

Table II shows the thermal properties of the fabricated glasses. As expected, an increase in SiO_2 and MgO contents reduces α and increases T_g and T_s. The softening temperature of all glasses is well below the $\alpha \rightarrow \beta$ transformation temperature of Ti (955-1010°C). XRD analysis of the synthesized glasses did not show any crystalline phase with the exception of 6P68, where sodium calcium phosphate ($2.4CaO \cdot 0.6Na_2O \cdot P_2O_5$) crystals were found.

Attempts to fabricate coatings with glasses 6P44-a 6P44-b, 6P53-a as well as the original Bioglass® composition developed by Hench always failed. Due to their hygroscopic nature caused by their high alkaline content (over 20 wt%) and the resultant presence of [OH⁻] ions on the surface of the glass powders, these glasses crystallize readily close to their flow temperature. Consequently these coatings crystallized almost completely even at the lowest firing temperatures (700°C), resulting in poor densification and lack of adhesion to the metal. The main crystalline phase present in the Bioglass® coatings was sodium calcium silicate ($Na_2Ca_2Si_3O_9$).

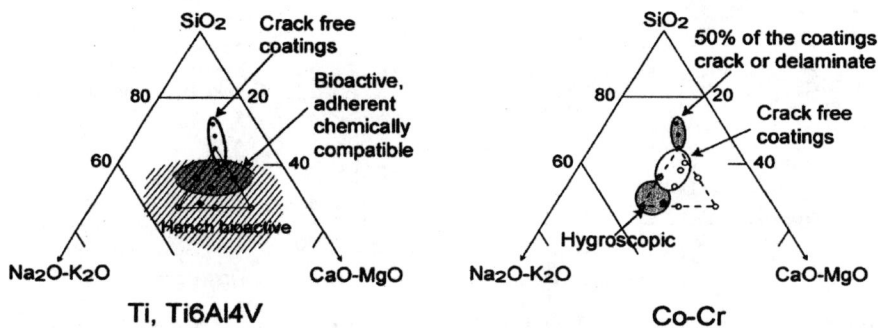

Figure 1. Behavior of single layer glass coatings on the different metallic alloys. All glass compositions have a constant 6 wt% P_2O_5 content.

Due to the difference in thermal expansion coefficient between the glass and the alloy, thermal stresses are generated in the coating during fabrication that can result in cracking and/or delamination. Figure 1 shows the range of glass compositions that can be used to prepare dense coatings that do not crack or delaminate on Ti and Ti6Al4V or Co-Cr alloys. Glasses with lower silica content have larger thermal expansion and can be used to coat Co-Cr, whereas SiO_2-rich glasses should be used to coat Ti-based alloys.

Similar results are obtained after firing in air or N_2, as an example, the effect of firing time and temperature on 6P57 coatings on Ti6Al4V and 6P50 on Co-Cr calcined in air is illustrated in Figure 2. Four regions can be distinguished. Below a critical time and temperature, the glass does not sinter. Then, at higher temperatures, the glass flows and forms a dense layer. Some of these coatings undergo delamination when a 6.2 Kg Vickers indentation is applied on the top surface. Nevertheless, a time and temperature region exists where the coatings are dense, exhibit good adhesion, and do not delaminate under indentation tests. In indentations performed at the glass/metal interface on polished cross sections of these coatings, cracks do not propagate along the interface, but rather tend to be driven into the glass (Figure 3). At longer times and temperatures, excessive reaction between the glass and the metal generates brittle reaction layers and/or gas bubbles at the interface, which result in porous coatings and poor adhesion to the substrate. Typically, slightly longer firings can be used in N_2 than in air to fabricate coatings with optimum adhesion.

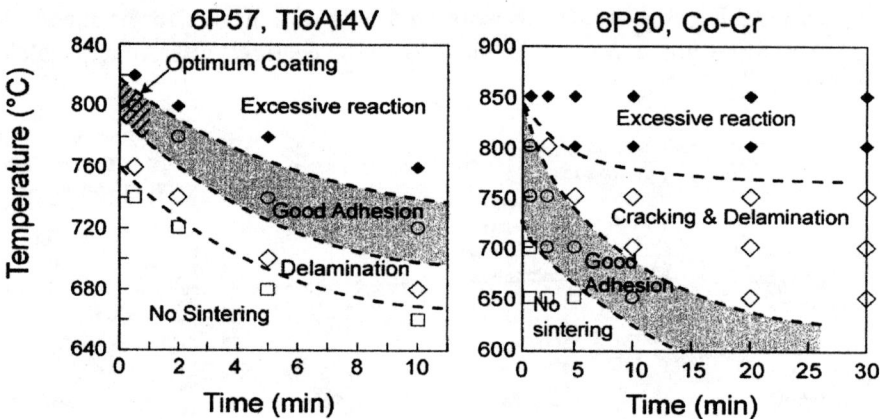

Figure 2. Influence of firing time and temperature on the adhesion of coatings manufactured with glass 6P57 on Ti6Al4V and glass 6P50 on Co-Cr (all the coatings were fired in air).

In the coatings with optimum adhesion on Ti or Co-Cr alloys, i.e., those that did not delaminate during indentation, it was not possible to detect any interfacial layer or change in the glass composition using SEM-EDS. However, a TEM image of the glass 6P57/Ti6Al4V interface annealed at 800°C for 30 seconds showed an interfacial Ti_5Si_3 layer ~150 nm thick (Figure 4). The layer was divided into two regions: a continuous nanocrystalline layer in contact with the alloy and, on top of it, a zone with isolated Ti_5Si_3 nanoparticles dispersed in the glass. The appearance of isolated particles on the TEM image can also result from the growth of elongated silicide grains, or dendrites, from the continuous layer into the glass. These dendrites may appear as isolated particles wherever they intersect the cross section. At the Ti_5Si_3/alloy interface the lattice fringes of Ti {100} and Ti_5Si_3 {121} were visible. A good lattice match exists between them, which can help in obtaining good adhesion. The SEM-EDS analysis of the cross section of a 6P50 coating on Co-Cr fired at 800 °C for 30min showed the presence of a thin CrO_x interfacial layer that promoted delamination of the coating.

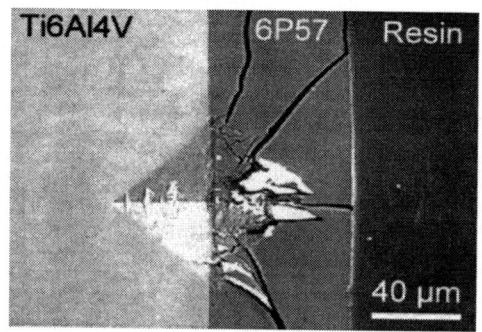

Figure 3. Vickers indentation at the glass 6P57/Ti6Al4V interface (fired at 800°C for 30 s) using 1.2 Kg load in ambient air. The cracks were driven towards the glass and the coating did not delaminate.

The following sequence of steps can be proposed for the coatings fired in air. During heating, gas flows easily through the porous deposited coating and forms an oxide layer on the alloy surface. When the glass softens and flows, it starts to dissolve the oxides and, once they have been completely dissolved, redox reactions can occur at the glass/metal interface. According to the interfacial analysis, the main reaction for the coatings on Ti-based alloys is the formation of Ti_5Si_3, whereas for coatings on Co-Cr alloys is the formation of chromium oxide, according to[14]:

$$8\ Ti + 3\ SiO_2\ \{glass\} \rightarrow Ti_5Si_3 + 3\ TiO_2\ \{glass\} \quad [1]$$

$$5\ Ti + 3\ SiO_2 \rightarrow Ti_5Si_3 + 3\ O_2 \uparrow \quad [2]$$

$$Cr + 3/2\ Na_2O \rightarrow 1/2\ Cr_2O_3 + 3Na(g) \uparrow \quad [3]$$

$$Cr + 1/2SiO_2 \rightarrow CrO + 1/2Si \quad [4]$$

If reactions [2] and [3] take place, the liberation of gas would form the bubbles observed in the overreacted samples. The bubbles and the brittle interfacial reaction layers result in weak coatings with poor adhesion to the metal.

The adequate fabrication temperature for each coating is related to the temperature at which the glass softens and flows. The higher the softening point, the higher the temperature needed for the glass to flow. Consequently, the temperature limits of the different regions described in Figure 2 (lack of sintering, delamination, good adhesion and excessive interfacial reactions) are proportional to the silica content of the glass. For example, 6P68 coatings on Ti6Al4V should be fired for 30 s at 840°C in order to achieve the optimum adhesion, whereas, for the same firing time, 6P57 should be fired at 800°C.

Figure 4. TEM image of the cross section of a 6P57 glass coating on Ti6Al4V annealed at 800°C for 30 min.

During *in vitro* testing in simulated body fluid, calcium phosphate crystals precipitated on the coatings with surface silica contents lower than 60 wt%. Fourier Transform Infrared Spectromicroscopy (FTIRSM) and x-ray analysis of the precipitates identify them as apatite (Figure 5). The apatite grows in the form of oriented nanocrystals, with the c-axis perpendicular to the substrate. The EDS analysis indicates that the apatite crystals incorporate 1 to 5 wt% MgO in their structure substituting for CaO. The mechanism of apatite formation is similar to the one described by Hench for glasses in the SiO_2-CaO-Na_2O-P_2O_5 system.[4] This involves the leaching of CaO, Na_2O, and P_2O_5 and the formation of an amorphous calcium phosphate layer on which the apatite crystallizes. Coatings with silica content higher than 60 wt % did not form apatite but were more resistant to corrosion in SBF, their composition did not change even after soaking in simulated body fluid for 4 months.

The experiments have shown that there is a narrow range of glass compositions that can be used to coat Ti or Ti6Al4V and that also form apatite (the mineral component of the bone) during *in vitro* tests in simulated body fluid.

Glasses with lower silica contents that readily form hydroxyapatite during *in vitro* testing in SBF can be prepared on Co-Cr. However, these coatings are not very resistant to corrosion and can crack during *in vitro* testing. Thus, one motivation for developing graded coatings is to reduce thermal stresses on the coatings on Ti and Ti6Al4V, so that a coating can be developed that has both a bioactive surface and an excellent adhesion to the metal. As an added advantage, the composition of the glass joining the metal can be such that its dissolution rate in body fluids is very limited (by using glasses with high SiO_2 content), thus enhancing the long-term coating stability.

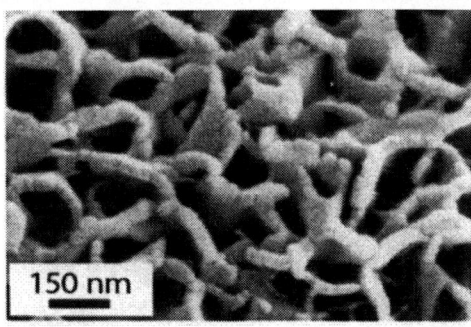
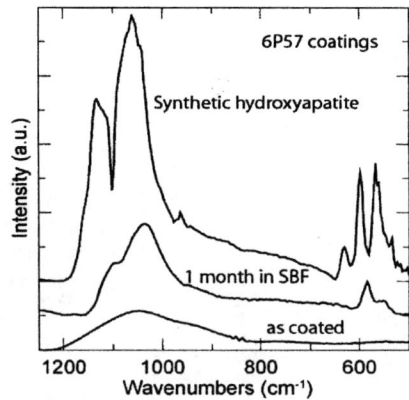

Figure 5. SEM micrographs and associated FTIRSM of the surface of a 6P57 coating on Ti6Al4V after 1 month in SBF showing the precipitation of hydroxyapatite crystals.

The basic enameling technique developed in this work was modified to prepare graded coatings. Layers of glasses with different compositions and mixtures of glass and HA were sequentially deposited on the metal and then fast-fired under the conditions that provide optimum adhesion for the glass in contact with the alloy. The elemental EDS analysis along the cross sections of multilayer coatings reveals a stepwise variation in the concentration of the glass components (with the exception of Na_2O) that corresponds to the composition of the different deposited glass layers (Figure 6). The concentration of Na_2O varied gradually across the coating.

The control of the gradient development during firing is critical in the fabrication of layered coatings. Two mechanisms control the development of the gradient during heat treatment: interdiffusion of the glass components and infiltration of one glass layer into another. Infiltration between adjacent glass layers can occur as a result of the different softening points (T_s) of the glasses.

Glasses with lower SiO_2 soften at lower temperature and, consequently, may infiltrate (during heating) a neighboring layer with higher silica content (which remains porous). The EDS analysis indicates that because of the short firing times, infiltration and interdiffusion (with the exception of sodium) are limited to a few micrometers (< 5 µm). The diffusion coefficient of Na^{+1} in soda-lima-silicate glasses ranges typically between 10^{-6}-10^{-7} cm²/s at temperatures between 800-900°C and is several orders of magnitude higher than for the other components.[17] During firing, sodium interdiffusion is fast enough to generate a smooth Na_2O profile even for the short firing times used in this work (Figure 6). The short firing times and low temperatures also allow the introduction of synthetic hydroxyapatite particles to improve bioactivity without any deleterious reaction.[18]

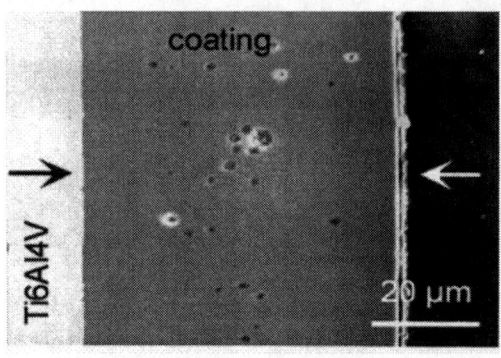
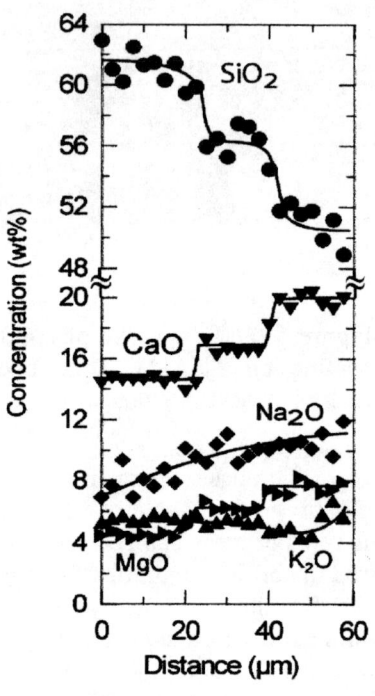

Figure 6. EDS elemental analysis along the cross section of a graded coating (6P61/6P55/6P53) on Ti6Al4V.

The low glass/metal thickness ratio of the coatings (<1:20) suggests that only a moderate relief of thermal stress on the external layer of multilayered coatings on Ti-based alloys should be expected using the graded approach. Nevertheless, for thin coatings, a gradient can markedly diminish the driving force for either cracking or delamination. In addition, stresses are singular where interfaces intersect the edges of samples, explaining why cracking originates at such places. These singularities are eliminated by continuous gradients; with multilayer coatings, the strength of these singularities is diminished inversely with the number of layers.[19] The mechanical benefits of the graded approach allowed the preparation of layers on Ti and Ti6Al4V with lower silica content (which consequently made the layers more bioactive) or with glass/HA composites, maintaining strong adhesion at the glass/metal interface. Layers with silica content as low as 53 wt% or containing as much as 50 wt% of synthetic hydroxyapatite were successfully prepared using the multilayer method. Because of the thermal expansion mismatch and the resulting high thermal stresses generated during processing, all those layers cracked or delaminated when applied directly to the alloy.

One advantage of the graded coatings containing hydroxyapatite is that the HA particles act as nucleation centers for the precipitation of new apatite and the time required for apatite precipitation *in vitro* is reduced on average by half with respect to the times observed in single-layer glass coatings.

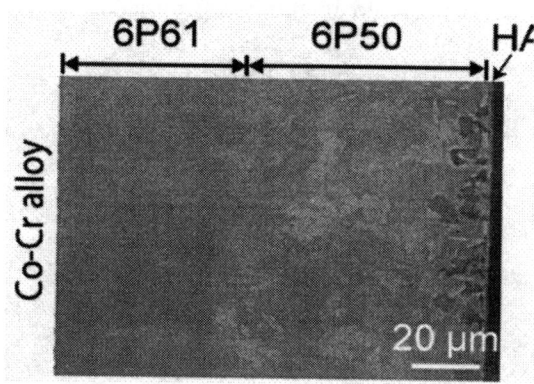

Figure 7. SEM micrograph of the cross section of a graded 6P61/6P50 coating on Co-Cr (fired at 800°C for 30s) after 30 days in SBF.

It is also possible to design gradients for which the residual stress distribution of the coating change from a surface under tension to a compressive stress for the glass in contact with the metal (using glasses in contact with the substrate with lower thermal expansion than the alloy). Recent theoretical and experimental studies have shown that such stress distributions are effective in arresting crack growth.[20-21] In this way, coatings are more resistant to fatigue and can be fabricated with more reliable mechanical properties.

Owing to their low silica content, single-layer bioactive coatings are prone to corrosion. In some cases during *in vitro* tests, cracks grow in the coating, reaching the metal and initiating delamination. The multilayer coatings with high silica glasses in contact with the metal present excellent long-term stability during *in vitro* tests in simulated body fluid. Figure 7 shows a 6P61/6P50 bilayer coating on Co-Cr after 30 days in SBF. A thin layer of HA has precipitated on the coating surface whereas the 6P61 layer in contact with the metal remains unaltered providing good adhesion and protection of the alloy from the body fluid.

CONCLUSIONS

A new family of silicate-based glasses with composition tailored to match the thermal expansion coefficient of Ti and Co-Cr based alloys has been developed to coat metallic implants, using a simple enameling technique. To better adjust the properties of the coating (in particular, to enhance bioactivity and increase chemical and mechanical stability) a multilayer approach has been used to fabricate graded glass coatings. Graded coatings with a corrosion-resistant glass composition protecting the metal and low surface silica contents were successfully fabricated. Also, layers containing as much as 50 wt% of synthetic hydroxyapatite were prepared with no appreciable degradation of the HA. The preliminary adhesion tests indicate a strong glass/metal bond, while at the same time the coatings form apatite on their surfaces when tested *in vitro*. The graded approach used in this work provides an exciting prospect for engineering new implant coatings.

ACKNOWLEDGEMENTS

This work was supported by the NIH/NIDCR grant 1R01DE11289. Jose M. Gomez-Vega wishes to thank the Spanish Ministry of Education (MEC) for financial support. S. Fujino wishes to thank the Japanese Ministry of Education, Culture and Sciences for a young researcher fellowship given to him in the National Program of Fellowships for young researchers in foreign countries, 2000. The Advanced Light Source is supported by the Director, Office of Science, Office of Basic Energy Sciences, Materials Sciences Division, of the U.S. Department of Energy under Contract No. DE-AC03-76SF00098 at Lawrence Berkeley National Laboratory.

REFERENCES

[1] M. Long and H.J. Rack, "Titanium Alloys in Total Joint Replacement–a Materials Science Perspective," *Biomaterials*, **19** 1621–1639 (1998).

[2] A. M. Weinstein and A. J. T. Clemov, "Cobalt-based Alloys for Biomedical Applications"; pp. 441-447 in *The Encyclopedia of Advanced Materials*, vol. 1, D. Edited by Bloor, R. J. Brook, M. C. Flemings, and S. Mahajan. Pergamon, New York, 1994

[3] Gerd Willmann, "Coating of Implants with Hydroxyapatite, Material Connections between Bone and Metal," *Advanced Engineering Materials*, 1[2], 95-105 (1999).

[4] L. L. Hench, "Bioceramics: From Concept to Clinic", *J. Am. Ceram. Soc.*, 74 [7] 1487-1510 (1991).

[5] C. L. Tisdel, V. M. Goldberg, J. A. Parr, J. S. Bensusan, L. S. Staikoff, and S. Stevenson, "The Iinfluence of a Hydroxyapatite and Tricalcium-Phosphate Coating on Bone Growth into Titanium Fiber-Metal Implants," *J. Bone Joint Surg. American Volume*, 76A[2], 159-171 (1994).

[6] J. C. Chae, J. P. Collier, M. B. Mayor, V. A. Surprenant, and L. A. Dauphinais, "Enhanced Ingrowth of Porous-Coated CoCr Implants Plasma-Sprayed with Tricalcium Phosphate," *Journal of Biomedical Materials Research*, 26[1] 93-102 (1992).

[7] S. R. Radin and P. Ducheyne, "Plasma Spraying Induced Changes of Calcium Phosphate Ceramic Characteristics and the Effect on *In Vitro* Stability," *Journal of Materials Science: Materials in Medicine*, 3[1] 33-42 **(1992)**.

[8] K. A. Gross, V. Gross, C. C. Berndt, "Thermal Analysis of Amorphous Phases in Hydroxyapatite Coatings," *Journal of the American Ceramic Society*, 81[1] 106-112 (1998).

[9] W. R. Lacefield, "Hydroxylapatite Coatings"; pp. 223-238 in *An Introduction to Bioceramics*. Edited by L. L. Hench and J.Wilson, World Scientific, Singapore 1993.

[10] L. Hench and Ö. Anderson, "Bioactive Glass Coatings"; pp. 239-260 in *An Introduction to Bioceramics*, Edited by L. L. Hench and J.Wilson, World Scientific, Singapore 1993.

[11] M. Lee, E. Chang, B. C. Wang and C. Y. Yang, "Characteristics of Plasma-sprayed bioactive glass coatings on Ti-6Al-4V alloy: An *in vitro* study," *Surface and Coatings Technology*, 79, 170-177 (1996).

[12] T. Kitsugi, T. Nakamura, M. Oka, Y. Senaha, T. Goto and T. Shibuya, "Bone-Bonding Behavior of Plasma-Sprayed Coatings of Bioglass®, AW-Glass Ceramic, and Tricalcium Phosphate on Titanium Alloy," *Journal of Biomedical Materials Research*, 30, 261-269 (1996).

[13] J. H. Chern Lin, K. S. Chen and C. P. Ju, "Corrosion Behavior of Hydroxyapatite/Bioactive Glass Plasma Sprayed on Ti6Al4V," *Materials Chemistry and Physics*, 41, 282-289 (1995).

[14] I. W. Donald, "Review: Preparation, Properties and Chemistry of Glass and Glass-Ceramic-to-Metal Seals and Coatings," *Journal of Materials Science*, **28**, 2841-2886 (1993).

[15] R. K. Brown and R. D. Watkins, "Reactions and bonding between glasses and titanium"; pp. 25-30 in *Technology of Glass, Ceramic or Glass-Ceramic to Metal Sealing*. Edited by W.E. Moddeman, C.W. Merten and D.P. Kramer, The American Society of Mechanical Engineers, New York, 1987.

[16] B. Kasemo and J. Gold, "Implant Surfaces and Interface Processes," *Advanced Dental Research*, 13 8-20 (1999).

[17] W. D. Kingery, H. K. Bowen and D. R. Uhlman, pp. 257-63 in *Introduction to Ceramics, 2nd Ed*, John Wiley & Sons, New York, 1976.

[18] A. Pazo, C. Santos, F. Guitian, A. P. Tomsia and J. S. Moya, "HA BioactiveGlass Composites - High Temperature Reactivity and *In Vitro* Behavior," *Scripta Materialia*, **34**[11] 1729-1733 (1996).

[19] F. Erdogan, "Fracture Mechanics of Functionally Graded Materials," *Composites Engineering*, **5**[7] 753-770 (1995).

[20] D.J. Green, R. Tandon and V. M. Sglavo, "Crack Arrest and Multiple Cracking in Glass Through the Use of Designed Residual Stress Profiles," *Science*, **283**[5406] 1295-1297 (1999).

[21] J. F. Bartolome, J. S. Moya, J. Requena, J. LLorca and M. Anglada, "Fatigue Crack Growth Behavior in Mullite/Alumina Functionally Graded Ceramics," *Journal of the American Ceramic Society*, **81**[6] 1502-1508 (1998).

High Temperature Applications

THERMAL CYCLING OF ADVANCED COMPRESSIVE SEALS FOR SOLID OXIDE FUEL CELLS

Yeong-shyung Chou, and Jeffry W. Stevenson

Pacific Northwest National Laboratories, Materials Resource Department, K2-44, P.O. Box 999, Richland, WA 99352

ABSTRACT

Thermal cycling was conducted on the compressive mica seals at 800°C in air. Thin (~0.1 mm) Muscovite mica was pressed between a metal tube and an alumina substrate and tested for leak rates at a stress of 100 psi in the advanced design and the plain design. The advanced design involves adding two glass interlayers and was found to greatly reduce the leak rates. Two metals (Inconel #600 and SS430) with high and low coefficients of thermal expansion (CTE) were used to evaluate the effect of CTE mismatch on thermal cycling. The results showed that the leak rates were lower for the advanced design than the plain micas. In addition, using the lower CTE (SS430) metal tube resulted in lower leak rates as compared to Inconel #600 metal (high CTE). In general, the leak rates abruptly increased during the first couple of cycles, and then tended to stabilize. Microstructure examination using scanning electron microscopy revealed damage to the mica after thermal cycling.

INTRODUCTION

Planar solid oxide fuel cells (SOFCs) appear to be the leading candidates for the next generation power sources due to their potential higher power density per unit volume compared to tubular designs [1-4]. However, many technical challenges must be overcome before planar SOFC technology can enter the marketplace; one of the most significant challenges is the need for satsifactory, cost-effective seals within the SOFC stack. The seals are required to prevent leakage of fuel gas from the stack, and to prevent mixing of fuel and oxidant gases within the stack. The seals must exhibit long-term stability in harsh environments (oxidizing, reducing, and humid) at elevated temperatures. In addition, the seals should not cause degradation (e.g., corrosion) of the materials with which they are in contact (e.g., stabilized zirconia, interconnect, and

---

To the extent authorized under the laws of the United States of America, all copyright interests in this publication are the property of The American Ceramic Society. Any duplication, reproduction, or republication of this publication or any part thereof, without the express written consent of The American Ceramic Society or fee paid to the Copyright Clearance Center, is prohibited.

electrodes). Finally, the seal has to survive many thermal cycles during routine operations.

Among the requirements for a successful seal listed above, thermal cycling may be the most critical one in the current seal development. To date, most of the seal development work has focused on the glass seals. Other approaches such as glass-ceramic seals, cement seals, mica glass-ceramics, brazes, and compressive seals have also been proposed [5-11]. None of these investigations addressed the issue of thermal cycling. SOFC stacks utilize components made from a variety of materials having different coefficients of thermal expansion (CTE). especially for SOFCs with metallic interconnects. The mismatch in CTE can result in undesirable residual stresses upon cooling if the stack components are rigidly bonded with each other (e.g., glass, glass-ceramics, cements, and brazes); the larger the CTE mismatch the larger the residual stresses. Such stresses can lead to structural failure. As a result, the candidates for metallic interconnects using glass seals are rather limited, as most high temperature alloys have relatively high CTE. The use of the compressive seals could potentially broaden the candidate list of alloys since the interconnect and the ceramic components would not be bonded with each other. Recently, Chou and Stevenson developed an advanced compressive mica seals and reported an ultra-low leak rates of $\sim 1.6 \times 10^{-4}$ sccm/cm at 800°C and a fairly low stress of 100 psi [10]. In this paper, we report results of a study investigating the effects of thermal cycling on the novel advanced compressive mica seal. Results of single layer mica seals with either glass or metallic interlayers are reported. The effect of mismatch in CTE is also addressed.

EXPERIMENTAL
Raw Materials
The mica investigated in this study is a natural cleaved single crystal Muscovite mica $(KAl_2(AlSi_3O_{10})(F,OH)_2)$ in the form of thin (~0.1 mm) sheet. The cleaved single crystal micas were found to have much lower leak rates as compared to other paper forms of mica and were therefore selected for this study [9,10]. For the advanced compressive seal tests, a borosilicate glass filter paper was used as the compliant interlayers.

Leak Test
Mica samples were cut into 1 1/2" squares with a ½" diameter central hole. The mica squares were then pressed between an Inconel #600 tube or a SS430 tube (outer diameter = 1.3" and inner diameter = 1.0") and a dense alumina substrate. For advanced compressive seals, an interlayer was placed between the Inconel tube/mica interface and the mica/alumina interface (Fig. 1). Samples

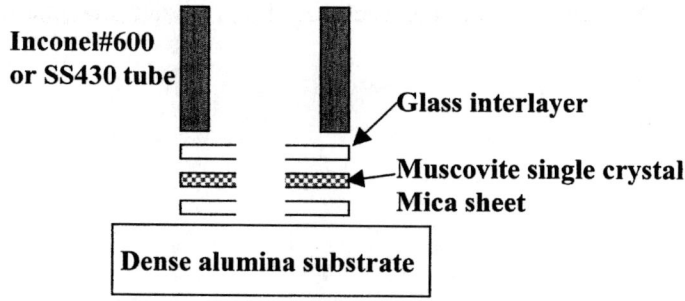

Fig.1. Schematic shows the assembly of advanced compressive design with two glass interlayers for thermal cycling.

were heated in a clamshell furnace at a heating rate of about ~3°C/min to 800°C in the first heating run. In the following thermal cycles, it was heated at a faster rate of 25°C/min to 800°C, then held at 800°C for one hour before cooling at 2.6°C/min to 100°C. The load was applied during the entire test using a universal mechanical tester with a constant load control (Model 5581, Instron, Canton, MA). The details of the experimental setup and the calculation of the normalized leak rates were given in an earlier paper [10].

RESULTS AND DISCUSSION
Thermal Cycling of Single Layer Muscovite Mica with Inconel#600 Tube

The 800°C leak rates for the Muscovite single crystal mica pressed between the Inconel #600 (high CTE=19 ppm/°C) and the alumina substrate are plotted in Fig. 2 as a function of the number of thermal cycles. Two runs were conducted for the advanced design and consistent results were obtained as shown in the figure. It is clear that the leak rates are lower for the advanced compressive seals than the conventional compressive seal (i.e., plain mica without the two glass interlayers placed at the interfaces of the metal/mica, and the mica/alumina substrate). However, the advanced design did exhibit major leaks during the first couples of cycles. For example, the leak rates were $1.6\sim3.0\times10^{-4}$ sccm/cm before cycling, and increased abruptly 19~36 times to 5.8×10^{-3} sccm/cm after 2 cycles. After that the behavior tended to stabilize. As for the plain mica, the leak rates appeared to increase with increasing thermal cycles. The average increase in leak rates per cycle (for the last 4 data points in Fig. 2) were 2.22×10^{-3} sccm/cm/cycle and 4.6×10^{-4} sccm/cm/cycle for the plain and the advanced design, respectively. It is evident the advanced mica design is superior to the plain mica. The initial abrupt increase in leak rates for the advanced mica design is likely due to the fracture of the mica sublayers adjacent to the interfaces, especially the

Inconel#600/mica interface since the mismatch in CTE is greater than that of the mica/alumina

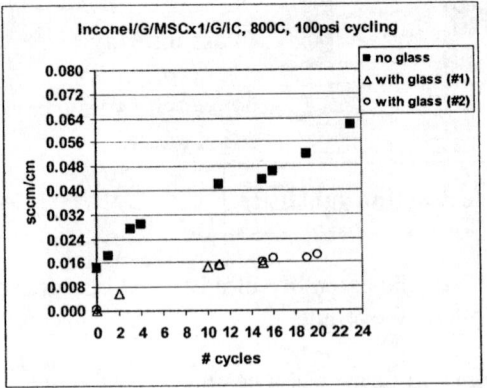

Fig. 2. Effect of thermal cycling on the normalized leak rates for a single layer Muscovite single crystal mica with and without the glass interlayers at 800°C and a compressive stress of 100 psi in air. The mica was pressed between an Inconel (CTE =19 ppm/°C) metal tube and an alumina substrate.

interface (CTE of the Muscovite mica was found to be ~6.9 ppm/°C, CTE of alumina is about 8~9 ppm/°C, and 19 ppm/°C for Inconel #600).

Thermal Cycling of Single Layer Muscovite Mica with SS430 Tube

Figure 3 shows the results of the effect of thermal cycling on the 800°C leak rates for single layer Muscovite mica pressed between a SS430 tube (CTE=12.5 ppm/°C) and an alumina substrate. For plain micas, the effect of surface finish was also tested on the SS430 metal tube. One run was with the as-machined (#32 ground finish) and flat surface. The other was with a smoother finish obtained using #800 grit paper. The advanced design mica showed lower leak rates than the plain micas, and the rougher surface finish yielded higher leak rates than the smoother surface for the plain micas. Both the advanced and the plain design micas showed the abrupt increase in leak rates during the initial couple of cycles, after which the leak rates tended to flatten out. Using the data points in the latter part of the curve (between cycle #18 to #30), the average increases in leak rate per cycle were found to be 1.9×10^{-4} sccm/cm/cycle, 4.3×10^{-4} sccm/cm/cycle, and 1.4×10^{-4} sccm/cm/cycle for the advanced design, plain design with #32 ground finish, and plain design with #800 grit finish on SS430 tube, respectively. The abrupt increase in leak rates during the initial couple of cycles is again likely due to the fragmentation of the mica sublayers adjacent to the SS430/mica interface, where the largest mismatch in CTE is present. Compared to the Inconel #600

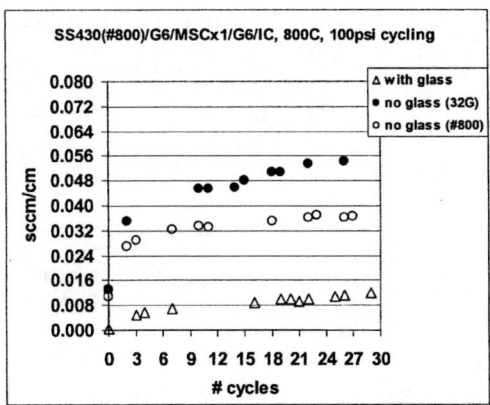

Fig. 3. Effect of thermal cycling on the normalized leak rates for a single layer Muscovite single crystal mica with and without the glass interlayers at 800°C and a compressive stress of 100 psi in air. The mica was pressed between a SS430 (CTE =12.5 ppm/°C) metal tube and an alumina substrate.

(higher CTE), SS430 (lower CTE) resulted in the lower leak rates and the smaller increase in leak rates per thermal cycle.

Materials Damage After Thermal Cycling

Degradation of the Muscovite mica after thermal cycling was examined using scanning electron microscopy. For the plain mica design (no glass interlayers), the mica surfaces in contact with the Inconel and the alumina substrate were both examined. Figure 4 shows the surface morphology of the mica in contact with the Inconel tube after 24 thermal cycles at 100 psi in air, and Figure 5 shows that in contact with the smoother alumina substrate. It is evident that the damage (fragmentation) was more severe on the Inconel side (Fig. 4B) as compared to the alumina side (Fig. 5B). This is not surprising since the alumina is much smoother (surface finish < 0.89 μm) as compared to the machined Inconel surface. The surface defects (machining grooves) on the Inconel after machining were found to be continuous and straight lines. The damages on the contact mica surfaces; however, were discrete. This may suggest that the compressive load was not evenly distributed on the mica surface at the microstructure level. The Muscovite thin mica appears to be flexible; however, it could not flow to accommodate the surface texture and evenly distribute the loads, and hence results in higher leak rates. For the advanced design, the damage appeared to be more uniform (Fig. 6) in that the mica fragmented into smaller particles (Fig. 6B). In addition, the mica tended to fracture through the thickness, and leaving "steps" on the fracture surfaces. Ideally, the Muscovite single crystal mica should cleave on the basal

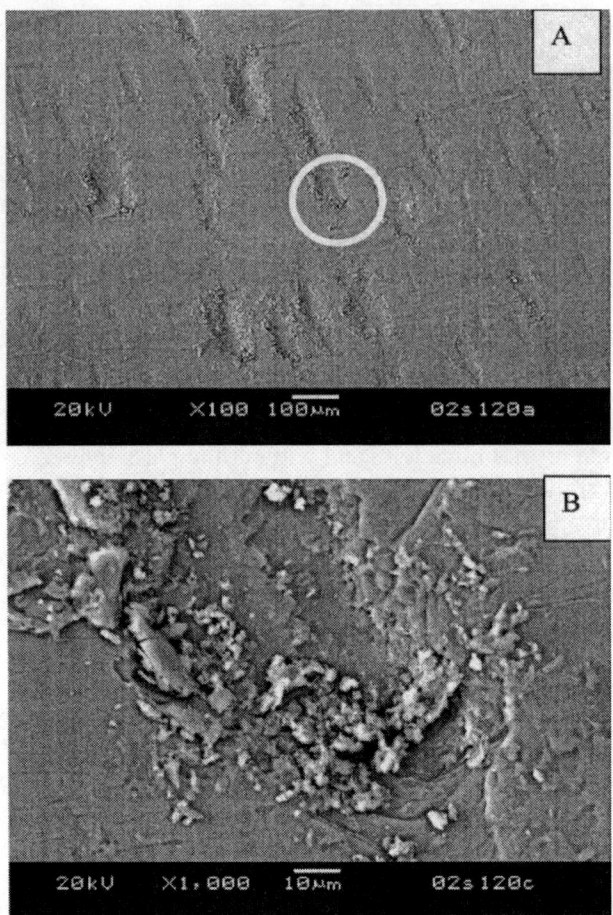

Fig. 4. Surface morphologies of the Muscovite single crystal mica in contact with the Inconel metal tube (without the glass interlayers) after 24 thermal cycles at 800°C and 100 psi in air: (A) a low magnification and (B) a high magnification of the circled area in (A). Picture clearly shows the degradation of mica at the circumference of the indentations.

planes and leaves parallel sublayers behind. In reality, local defects may affect the cleavage out of plane and leaves steps behind. The steps are believed to contribute to the abrupt increase in the leak rates for the first few cycles. The, as thermal cycling continues, the friction gradually wears the mica in sublayers into smaller particles.

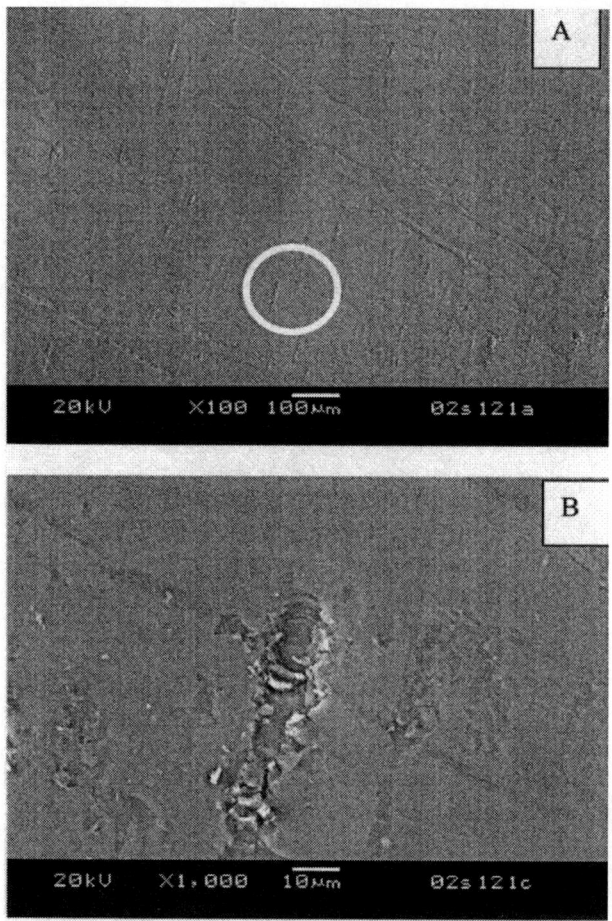

Fig. 5. Surface morphologies of the Muscovite single crystal mica in contact with the alumina substrate (without the glass interlayers) after 24 thermal cycles at 800°C and 100 psi in air: (A) a low magnification and (B) a high magnification of the circled area in (A). Picture clearly shows the degradation of mica at the circumference of the indentations.

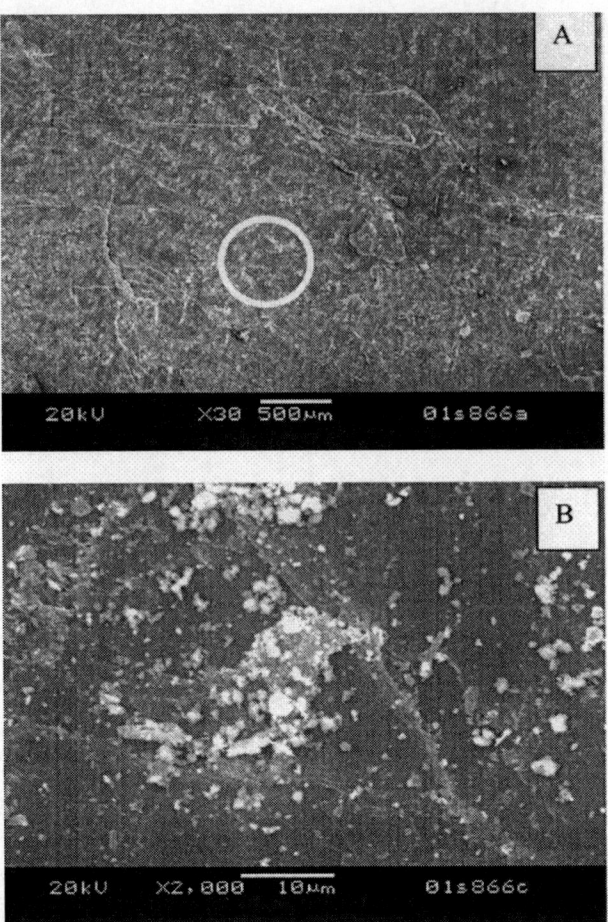

Fig. 6. Surface morphologies of the Muscovite single crystal mica after 21 thermal cycles at 800°C and 100 psi in air in the advanced seal design with the glass interlayers: (A) a low magnification and (B) a high magnification of the circled area in (A).

Application to SOFC Stacks

Low fuel leak rates are required if SOFC stacks are to operate safely and economically. Although the allowable leak rates remain to be experimentally determined and will be somewhat design-specific, common sense points to the use of sealing materials offering leak rates as low as possible at a compressive stress as low as possible. The advanced seal based on the Muscovite single crystal mica appears to be a viable candidate. For a 60-cell (6" x 6" per cell) stack of 4kW, 65% fuel utilization, 20% oxygen utilization, 0.5 W/cm^2, the total fuel flow rate is estimated to be ~1.36×10^5 sccm (STP) [11]. Assuming that the leak rate measured in this study (0.0119 sccm/cm after 29 thermal cycles, and increasing at 1.9×10^{-4} sccm/cm/cycle) applied to full size stacks, the total leak rate for a 60-cell stack at 800°C after 100 thermal cycles would be 48 sccm, only ~0.04% of the total fuel (majority of H_2 and CO) rate for the advanced Muscovite single crystal mica under a stress of 100 psi and a 2 psi pressure gradient (a leak length of 60 cm was assumed for each layer). It would increase to 707 sccm after 1000 thermal cycles, only 0.5% of the total fuel. According to open circuit voltage calculation, such a leak would be negligible. While this assumption is somewhat simplistic, the current results clearly demonstrate the potential applicability of the advanced-type compressive mica seals to SOFC applications. It must be emphasized, however, that other important aspects, such as thermal cycling and long-term stability in reducing and humid environments, must be evaluated. Results of studies examining these issues will be presented in the near future.

Conclusion

Thermal cycling of the compressive seals using Muscovite single crystal mica in both plain and advanced designs was studied. Results of 800°C leak rates showed the advanced design offered lower leak rates than the plain design. Tests on two metals (Inconel#600 and SS430) also demonstrated the effect of CTE mismatch on leak rates; the larger the mismatch, the higher the leak rates. Surface damage, and its contribution to the leak rates, was also investigated. The current leak rates from thermal cycling clearly suggest the advanced compressive seals are strong candidates for SOFC stacks.

Acknowledgement

The authors would like to thank N. Saenz and S. Carlson for SEM sample preparation, and J. Coleman for SEM analysis. Helpful discussions with L. Chick and S. Simner were also greatly appreciated. Funded as part of the Solid-State Energy Conversion Alliance (SECA) Core Technology Program by the US Department of Energy's National Energy Technology Laboratory (NETL). Pacific Northwest National Laboratory is operated by Battelle Memorial Institute for the US Department of Energy under Contract no. DE-AC06-76RLO 1830.

References

[1] N. Q. Minh, "Ceramic fuel cells," *J. Am. Ceram. Soc.*, **76** [3] 563-588 (1993).

[2] S. C. Singhal, "Progress in tubalar solid oxide fuel cell technology," in *Solid Oxide Fuel Cells* (SOFC VI) Proceedings of the Sixth International Symposium, edited by S. C. Singhal and M. Dokiya, The Electrochemical Society, Proceedings Volume **99-19**, 39-51 (1999).

[3] R. Bolden, K. Foger, and T. Pham, "Towards the development of a 25 kW planar SOFC system," in *Solid Oxide Fuel Cells* (SOFC VI) Proceedings of the Sixth International Symposium, edited by S. C. Singhal and M. Dokiya, The Electrochemical Society, Proceedings Volume **99-19**, 80-87 (1999).

[4] A. Khandkar, S. Elangovan, J. Hartvigsen, D. Rowley, R. Privette, and M. Tharp, "Status and progress in SOFCo's planar SOFC development," in *Solid Oxide Fuel Cells* (SOFC VI) Proceedings of the Sixth International Symposium, edited by S. C. Singhal and M. Dokiya, The Electrochemical Society, Proceedings Volume **99-19**, 88-94 (1999).

[5] N. Lahl, L. Singheiser, K. Hilpert, K. Singh, and D. Bahadur, "Aluminosilicate glass ceramics as sealant in SOFC stacks," in *Solid Oxide Fuel Cells* (SOFC VI) Proceedings of the Sixth International Symposium, edited by S. C. Singhal and M. Dokiya, The Electrochemical Society, Proceedings Volume **99-19**, 1057-1065 (1999).

[6] T. Yamamoto, H. Itoh, M. Mori, N. Mori, and T. Watanabe, "Compatibility of mica glass-ceramics as gas-sealing materials for SOFC," *Denki Kagaku* **64** [6] 575-581 (1996).

[7] K. Ley, M. Krumpelt, J. Meiser, I. Bloom, *J. Mater. Res.*, **11** 1489 (1996).

[8] P. Larsen, C. Bagger, M. Morgensen, J. Larsen, in M. Dokiya, O. Yamamoto, H. Tagawa, S. Singhal (Eds.), Solid Oxide Fuel Cells-IV, Vol. **69**, Electrochemical Society, Pennington, NJ, PV 95-1, 1995.

[9] S. P. Simner and J. W. Stevenson, " Compressive mica seals for SOFC applications," *J. Power Sources*, **102** [1-2] 310-316 (2001).

[10] Y-S Chou, J. W. Stevenson, and L. A. Chick, submitted to *J. Power Sources* 2002.

[11] L. A. Chick, unpublished work.

BRAZING A MIXED IONIC/ELECTRONIC CONDUCTOR TO AN OXIDATION RESISTANT METAL

K. Scott Weil and John S. Hardy
Pacific Northwest National Laboratory
P.O. Box 999
Richland, WA 99352

ABSTRACT

High temperature, solid-state electrochemical devices have received considerable attention in recent years because of their technological importance in a wide array of applications, including chemical sensors, solid oxide fuel cells, gas separation devices, and electrocatalyzers. While numerous advances have been made in the fabrication and performance of the ceramic materials that form the heart of the working device, less emphasis has been placed on the materials that will be used in the balance of the device; in particular, the seals that bond the functional ceramic to the metallic structural component. In an effort to begin addressing this issue, a new brazing concept referred to as reactive air brazing has been developed. This paper discusses the details of this joining technique and illustrates its use in bonding a potential oxygen separation material, $(La_{0.6}Sr_{0.4})(Co_{0.2}Fe_{0.8})O_3$, to an alumina scale-forming stainless steel alloy.

INTRODUCTION

Mixed ionic/electronic conducting (MIEC) oxides, such as $SrFeCo_{0.5}O_x$, $(La_{0.6}Sr_{0.4})(Co_{0.2}Fe_{0.8})O_3$, and $BaCeO_3$, are a class of ceramics that contain ionic and electronic carriers in high enough concentration that both forms of charge conduction are exhibited at high level, typically at temperatures in excess of 500°C. Because of their properties, the demand for MIEC oxide-based devices has grown considerably. The value of the present-day market is conservatively estimated to be $3 billion, with particularly high growth rates in automotive systems, environmental control, and energy generation technology where the devices are employed primarily as amperometric chemical sensors [1]. Solid oxide fuel cells (SOFCs) represent an even larger potential market than that established for chemical sensors. These electrochemical devices convert the chemical energy from fossil fuels into electricity in a highly efficient manner and

---

To the extent authorized under the laws of the United States of America, all copyright interests in this publication are the property of The American Ceramic Society. Any duplication, reproduction, or republication of this publication or any part thereof, without the express written consent of The American Ceramic Society or fee paid to the Copyright Clearance Center, is prohibited.

may find application in a number of energy generation applications, from auxillary power units in automobiles and trucks to megawatt generators helping to power the electrical grid. MIEC oxides are employed in SOFCs as electrodes, carrying out charge separation and charge transfer at the electrolyte/electrode interface, and as agents to increase the electrocatalytic activity of the electrodes with respect to fuel reformation [2]. If the ionic conductivity of a given MIEC oxide is high enough, it can be employed in electrically driven oxygen-ion transport membranes for oxygen gas separation, partial hydrocarbon oxidation, and waste reduction and recovery [3]. MIEC oxide-based membrane technology offers the potential to separate oxygen from air with far greater efficiency and at one-third lower cost than the cryogenic processing technology used today. And unlike cryo-separation, oxygen transport membranes operate at high temperature, making them ideally suited for direct integration with coal gasification plants [4].

Underlying the excitement over the potential of MIEC oxides is the engineering challenge of how to effectively incorporate these materials into practical devices. Opportunities to fully exploit the unique properties of these advanced ceramics depend in large part on our ability to develop reliable joining techniques. However, because MIEC-based device technology is essentially restricted to high temperature operation, only a limited number of joining technologies are applicable. In a review of ceramic-to-metal joining technology [5], Greenhut discusses a number of joining techniques, of which two, glass joining and active metal brazing, are most suitable for bonding a MIEC oxide to a metallic structural component. Figure 1 illustrates an example of this type of MIEC ceramic-to-metal bond in a portable oxygen generator being developed for medical application. The device operates nominally at 800°C and is likely to experience numerous thermal cycles over its lifetime, on the order of several thousand hours, during which it must remain hermetically sealed, structurally rugged, and chemically stable.

While glass bonding is potentially a viable joining solution, the maximum operating temperature to which a glass joint may be exposed is limited by the softening point of the glass. At present, high temperature glasses with appropriately matching coefficients of thermal expansion are limited to a narrow range of compositions within the borate-doped aluminosilicate family. These glasses typically display signs of devitrification within the first few hours of exposure at operating temperature [6]. As these glasses begin to crystallize, their carefully engineered thermal expansion properties change significantly, which ultimately limits the number of thermal cycles and the rate of cycling at which the joints are capable of surviving [7].

The second ceramic-to-metal joining technique, active metal brazing, utilizes a filler metal that when heated above its liquidus temperature, will flow and fill the gap between the two joining pieces by capillary action. Unlike metal-to-metal brazes, this particular family of braze alloys contains one or more reactive metals, often titanium, which will chemically reduce the ceramic at the interface with the braze, greatly improving wetting and adherence between the two materials [8,9].

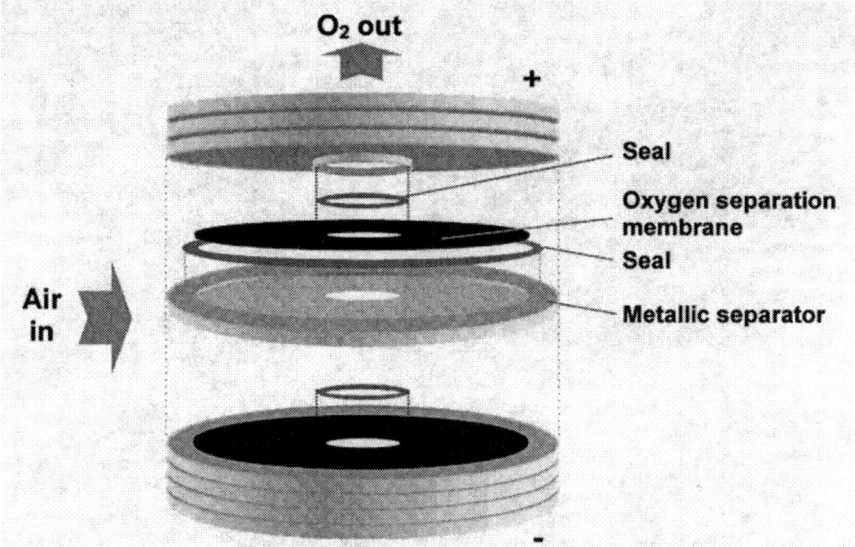

Figure 1   A schematic drawing of a MIEC oxide based oxygen generator (electrical interconnection not shown).

There are, however, at least two problems with using active metal brazing for the fabrication of solid-state electrochemical devices: 1) the complete oxidation of the active species in the braze during high temperature operation of the device will lead to rapid deterioration of the joint at the ceramic/braze metal interface [10,11] and an eventual loss in hermeticity and 2) exposure of the entire device to a reducing atmosphere at a temperature greater than ~800°C, typical processing conditions for active metal brazing, has been found to be too demanding for many of the oxide materials employed in these devices. MIEC oxides will tend to reduce during the joining operation, which can cause phase separation in the oxide. An example of this is shown in Figure 2, which displays a $(La_{0.6}Sr_{0.4})FeO_3$ specimen that after vacuum brazing with a commercial active metal gold braze, Nioro ABA, began to exhibit signs of surface spallation and eventually complete braze detachment after only a few hours exposure to ambient room temperature air. Moisture in the air caused the hydration of excess La_2O_3 in the sample, which had formed because of reduction and phase separation in the parent oxide during the brazing operation. Regardless of whether or not the braze remains intact, the oxide reduction phenomenon ultimately results in a severe loss in device performance due the irreversible deterioration of the functional ceramic [12]. To overcome these difficulties, an alternative reactive brazing approach was developed, referred to as reactive air brazing or RAB.

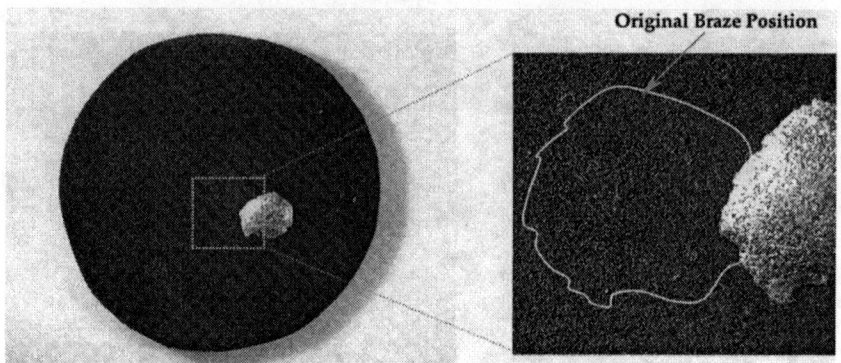

Figure 2   Spallation of a Nioro ABA braze drop from the surface of a $(La_{0.6}Sr_{0.4})FeO_3$ specimen. The oxide specimen has undergone reduction and phase separation. The resulting La_2O_3 at the substrate surface hydrates and swells in ambient air causing separation between the braze and the substrate. As seen at high magnification, the braze is fully detached from its original position on the substrate and is simply lying on the surface for comparison.

Since joining must be carried out in an oxidizing environment at a temperature greater than the device operating temperature, nominally 800°C, the bond that eventually forms will take place between the functional ceramic component and an oxide scale that grows on the structural metallic component under these conditions. The objective in RAB is to reactively modify one or both oxide faying surfaces with a compound that has been at least partially dissolved in a noble metal solvent, e.g. silver, gold, or platinum, such that the newly formed surface is readily wetted by the remaining molten filler material. In many respects, this concept is similar to active metal brazing, except that the joining operation can be conducted in air and the final joint should be resistant to oxidation at high temperature. Potentially, there are a number of metal oxide-noble metal systems that can be considered for RAB, including Ag-CuO, Ag-TeO$_3$, and Pt-Nb$_2$O$_5$ [13]. Schüler et al. [14] were the first to recognized that the Ag-CuO system could potentially be exploited to bond ceramic components in air, reporting the successful joining of alumina using a 99 mol%Ag-1 mol% CuO braze. Our interest is in investigating whether this system is suitable for air brazing functional ceramic-to-metal joints, such as those needed in practical electrochemical devices. In an effort to begin answering this question, a series of sessile drop measurements were performed to determine the wetting behavior of the different Ag-CuO-based braze compositions on a set of prototypical materials for a portable oxygen generating device. Microstructural and chemical analyses of the braze/substrate interfaces within the wetting specimens were also conducted to determine the nature of the wetting in these samples. The results from these studies and from initial RAB joining experiments are reported below.

EXPERIMENTAL
Copper Oxide-Silver Based Brazing

Past investigations of the Ag-CuO system [15] have determined that there two invariant points in the Ag-CuO phase diagram from which new braze compositions could be developed: a monotectic reaction at 964±3°C, where CuO and a liquid L_2 coexist with a second liquid phase L_1 at a composition of 30.65 mol.% Ag and 2) a eutectic reaction at 932±3°C, where Ag and CuO coexist with the liquid phase L_2 at a composition of 98.6 mol.% Ag. Extending between these three-phase reaction points is a two-phase liquid miscibility gap. Although Schüler et al. [14] did not conduct contact angle measurements in their experiments with the Ag-CuO braze, Meier et al. [16] demonstrated in a previous series of sessile drop experiments, conducted in inert atmosphere, that the contact angle between silver and alumina is greatly reduced by small additions of CuO. The improvement in wetting is apparently due to an increase in the oxygen activity of the melt and the formation of an interfacial compound, $CuAlO_2$ [17-19]. Furthermore, a recent phase study on the $CuO-TiO_2$ system demonstrates that this binary exhibits a eutectic reaction at 919°C with a wide compositional range centered on the eutectic composition of $X_{TiO_2} = 16.7 mol\%$ [20], suggesting to us that the addition of titania to a Ag-CuO braze may improve its wetting characteristics by modifying the CuO phase as the braze is heated to its molten state. Consequently, the use of TiO_2 as a wetting agent was also explored in this investigation.

Materials

$(La_{0.6}Sr_{0.4})(Co_{0.2}Fe_{0.8})O_3$ (LSCoF) and fecralloy were selected as the model joining system on which to carry out the initial RAB development effort. LSCoF was chosen because it is a well-known MIEC with excellent ionic and electronic transport propertes, making it a strong candidate for use in commercial oxygen generators [21]. In addition, it has been demonstrated that this oxide will undergo phase separation and cracking under typical active metal brazing conditions [22], making RAB essentially the only alternative to glass sealing. LSCoF pellets were fabricated by uniaxially compacting the oxide powder (99.9% purity; Praxair Specialty Ceramics, Inc.) in a carbon steel die under 7ksi of pressure. The cold pressed pellets were further densified by cold isostatic pressing at 20ksi, followed by sintering in air at 1250°C for two hours. The final pellets measured approximately 1" in diameter by ⅛" thick, with an average density of 96% of theoretical. The pellets were polished on one face to a 10μm finish using successively finer grit diamond paste, cleaned with acetone and rinsed with propanol, air dried, and finally heated in static air to 600°C for four hours to burn off any residual organic contamination.

Fecralloy (22% Cr, 4.8% Al, 0.3%Si, 0.3%Y, bal. Fe) was chosen as the metal component for joining because it is a low-cost, commercially available ferritic stainless steel of the type that is being strongly considered for use in SOFCs and other solid state electrochemical devices. Additionally, this alloy forms a protective aluminum oxide scale, which gives it excellent oxidation resistance properties at 800°C and which is also one of the reactants required for the RAB concept described above. As-received 20 mil thick fecralloy sheet was sheared into 1½" square coupons, which were polished on one side to a 10μm finish. The samples were flushed with de-ionized water to remove the polishing grit and ultrasonically cleaned in acetone for 10 minutes, then rinsed with propanol and dried in a stream of warm air. To form the reactive alumina layer, the samples were pre-oxidized at 1050°C for 2hrs in static air. The average thickness of the alumina scale formed on the fecralloy in this manner was ~0.6μm.

As listed in Table I, eight different braze compositions were formulated by dry mixing the appropriate amounts of silver (99.9%, 0.75μm average particle diameter; Alfa Aesar), copper (99%, 2.5μm average particle diameter; Alfa Aesar), and titanium hydride powders (-325 mesh, Alfa Aesar). The copper and TiH_2 oxidize in-situ as the braze is heated, respectively forming CuO and TiO_2. For the wetting studies, the mixtures were cold pressed into pellets measuring approximatley 7mm in diameter by 7mm thick. To prepare braze pastes for the joining experiments, a liquid binder (BX-18, Ferro Corp.) was added to the dry powder mixture in a 1:5 weight ratio and the resulting blend was thoroughly mixed on a three-roll mill. As formed, the paste was found to have acceptable thixotropic properties for the joining experiments.

Testing and Characterization

Wetting experiments were performed in a static air box furnace furnished with a large quartz window on the front door through which the heated specimen could be observed. A high speed video camera equipped with a zoom lens was used to record the wetting specimen during an entire heating cycle. Each braze pellet was placed on the polished side of the LSCoF pellet or pre-oxidized fecralloy substrates and heated at 30°C/min to 900°C, at which point the heating rate was reduced to 10°C/min. The furnace continued heating until it reached the first set point, 950°C, where the temperature remained for fifteen minutes, then resumed heating. In this way, the contact angle between the braze and substrate was allowed to stabilize for measurement at several different soak temperatures,

950°C, 1000°C, 1050°C, and 1100°C, during one heating cycle. Using Ulead™ software, select frames from the videotape were converted to computer images, from which the wetting angle between the braze and substrate could be measured and correlated with the temperature log for the heating run.

Table I. Target compositions of the brazes invetigated in this study

Braze I.D.	Ag Content (in mole%)	CuO Content (in mole%)	TiO_2 Content (in mole%)
Ag	100	0	0
Ag-½Ti	99.5	0	0.5
Ag-1Cu	99	1	0
Ag-1Cu-½Ti	98.5	1	0.5
Ag-2Cu	98	2	0
Ag-2Cu-½Ti	97.5	2	0.5
Ag-4Cu	96	4	0
Ag-4Cu-½Ti	95.5	4	0.5

Microstructural analysis of the wetting specimens was performed on polished cross-sectioned samples, by optical microscopy and by examination with a JEOL JSM-5900LV scanning electron microscope (SEM). The SEM is equipped with an Oxford energy dispersive X-ray analysis (EDX) system, which employs a windowless detector for quantitative detection of both light and heavy elements. To avoid electrical charging of the samples in the SEM, they were carbon coated and grounded. Elemental profiles were recorded across joint interfaces in the line-scan mode.

RESULTS AND DISCUSSION

Contact angle measurements of the molten Ag-CuO-TiO_2 brazes on polished LSCoF are shown as a function of temperature in Figure 3. Within a 10 - 20°C difference, melting of the binary silver-copper oxide braze compositions intitiated at the temperature predicted by the Ag-CuO phase diagram, indicating that the CuO and Ag are not impeded from reaching equilibrium by diffusion or solid state reaction kinetics. The fifteen minute hold time used in taking the sessile drop measurements appeared to be long enough for interfacial equilibrium to be established; in all cases the contact angle reached its stable value within five minutes. With the exception of the Ag-4 mol% CuO composition, the contact angles between the different brazes and the LSCoF surface are essentially invariant with respect to temperature over the 950 – 1100°C range. The wetting angle curves appear to fall into two distinct categories, those which exhibit little or no wetting and those which wet quite well, suggesting that a minimum concentration of CuO is required for wetting and that this minimum can be reduced by the introduction of TiO_2 to the braze. The two control compositions, Ag and Ag-0.5 mol% TiO_2, display no wetting with the ceramic. It is not until at least 4 mol% CuO is added to the binary Ag-CuO braze that sufficient wetting takes place, and this only occurs at 1100°C. However, when 0.5 mol% TiO_2 is added, the 2 mol% CuO braze wets the LSCoF at essentially the same contact angle as the best binary braze and does so at a temperature which is at least 150°C lower. No additional improvement in wetting occurs when the CuO content of this ternary braze is doubled.

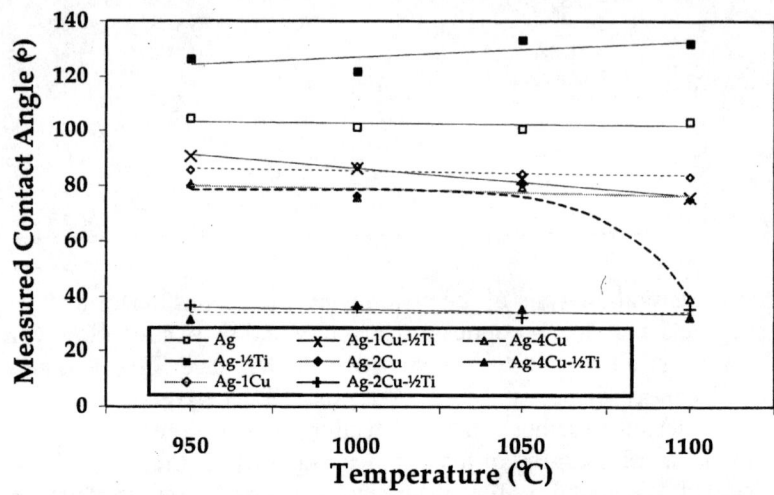

Figure 3 Contact angle of Ag-CuO-TiO_2 brazes on $(La_{0.6}Sr_{0.4})(Co_{0.2}Fe_{0.8})O_3$ in air as a function of temperature. The hold time at each soak temperature was fifteen minutes.

Shown in Figures 4(a) – (d) are back scattered electron images of the four braze compositions which exhibit the best wetting on the LSCoF substrate: Ag-2Cu, Ag-2Cu-½ Ti, Ag-4Cu, and Ag-4Cu-½ Ti. Each of these wetting specimens was heat treated under the conditions described for the in-situ wetting experiments, ultimately reaching a final soak temperature of 1100°C. It is apparent from all of the micrographs that the majority phase in the bulk of the braze is pure silver. Fine precipitates of CuO on the order of 1 – 5μm in size are typically found in the silver matrix away from the interface with the LSCoF. If the micrographs are paired, Figures 4(a) and (c) and Figures 4(b) and (d), the effect of the TiO_2 addition is readily seen. In the two cases where no titania was added, Ag-2Cu and Ag-4Cu, there is a thin interfacial zone where the CuO appears to preferentially wet the LSCoF. In Figure 4(a), which displays the Ag-2Cu braze, the CuO decorates the interface with the MIEC substrate, forming discrete, ~1μm half lens-shaped precipitates. An occasional silicate particle on this interface can also be found and is presumed to be an impurity introduced into the LSCoF powder during milling. The Ag-4Cu braze in Figure 4(c) exhibits a nearly continuous CuO phase along the braze/LSCoF interface which is occasionally disrupted by a short band of pure silver. Note in both figures signs of braze infiltration into the substrate, presumably via interconnected porosity, up to a depth of ~2μm.

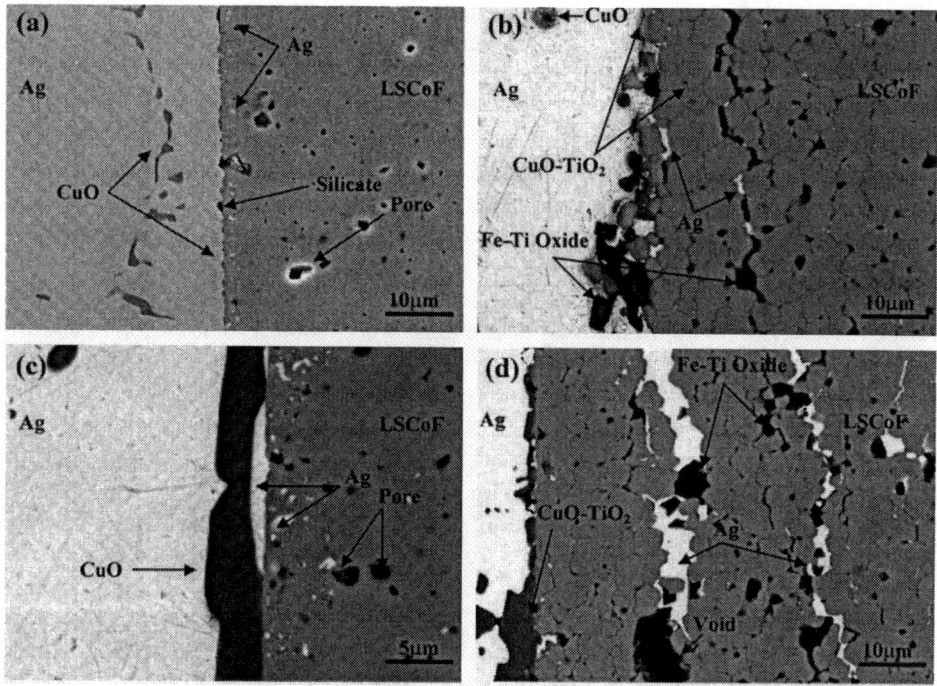

Figure 4 Cross-sectional SEM micrographs of braze/LSCoF interfaces: (a) Ag-2Cu, (b) Ag-Cu-½Ti, (c) Ag-4Cu, and (d) Ag-4Cu-½Ti. Each wetting specimen was heated in air at a final soak temperature of 1100°C.

Referring to Figure 3, our results suggest that the formation of a continuous layer of interfacial CuO improves the wetting of a Ag-CuO braze with LSCoF. It is possible that the two different CuO morphologies observed in Figure 4 are the direct result of the miscibility gap in the Ag-CuO phase diagram [15]. At 1100°C both brazes will form a single phase liquid. However, according to the Ag-CuO phase diagram, as the Ag-4Cu braze is cooled to ~1025°C, the system enters a miscibility gap. Below 1025°C, two liquids are formed, a minority phase which is rich in CuO and a majority phase which is CuO-poor. Because the phases are immiscible, it is expected they will segregate, with the CuO-rich liquid preferentially migrating to and wetting the LSCoF because of its higher oxide content and therefore lower expected interfacial energy with the MIEC oxide substrate. Upon further cooling to the monotectic temperature, 964°C, CuO will begin to precipitate from this liquid, nucleating at the interface with LSCoF. As it does so, the concentration of silver in the silver-rich liquid increases. At the eutectic temperature, solid CuO and Ag will simultaneously nucleate from the remaining liquid, presumably heterogeneously on the surface of the previously formed CuO layer which coats the boundary with LSCoF. The Ag-2Cu braze, on the other hand, does not enter a miscibility gap when cooled. Just below 964°C, a small amount of proeutectic CuO precipitates out of solution, nucleating heterogeneously at the interface with LSCoF. Upon cooling to the eutectic temperature, solid Ag and CuO form simultaneously from the eutectic liquid.

As is obvious from Figures 4(b) and (d), the addition of 0.5 mol% TiO_2 significantly changes the interfacial microstructure of the braze/LSCoF couple. In both cases, Ag-2Cu-½Ti and Ag-4Cu-½Ti, virtually no titanium was found in the bulk braze, even within the CuO precipitates. However, the samples exhibit a large affected zone, approximately 35μm and 50μm respectively, which contain a number of titanium-based reaction products. As expected, the CuO and TiO_2 form a low-melting eutectic (~919°C). This liquid segregates to the interface with the LSCoF, reacting with the substrate to form an iron-cobalt-titanium oxide phase and a copper oxide-rich phase that contains significant levels of lanthanum and strontium. Unexpectedly, however, the CuO-TiO_2 liquid attacks the LSCoF intergranularly, forming a low-melting complex oxide phase between grains, which displays high concentrations of copper, titanium, iron, and cobalt. Approximately 15μm into the oxide substrate of the Ag-2Cu-½Ti sample is a nearly continuous band of oxide running parallel to the braze/LSCoF interface. This oxide band contains Co, Fe, Cu, and Ti in roughly a 2:2:1:1 molar ratio. The EDS data suggests that the LSCoF grains adjacent to this band have become depleted of cobalt and iron, although the mechanism by which this occurs is not known, e.g. by dissolution or by micro-scale phase separation. The oxide band, which spans from one layer of LSCoF grains to the next, is occasionally disrupted by a short band of silver. The formation of reactions zones within the Ag-4Cu-½Ti sample is even more extreme. Two continuous bands form which are wider than the one observed in the lower CuO-content braze. In addition, a significant amount of silver has infiltrated these gaps that again appear to form via grain boundary melting and separation. Evidence of grain separation is apparent from the number of large voids that populate the two bands.

Figure 5 shows the effect of composition and temperature on the contact angle between the Ag-CuO-TiO_2 brazes and the alumina scale surface of pre-

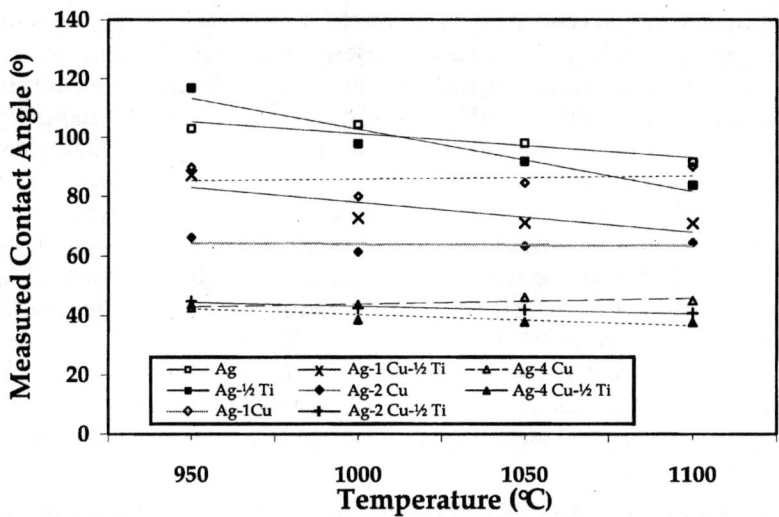

Figure 5 Contact angle of Ag-CuO-TiO$_2$ brazes on the alumina scale of pre-oxidized fecralloy in air as a function of temperature. The hold time at each soak temperature was fifteen minutes.

oxidized fecralloy. The brazes appeared to melt in the same manner observed in the LSCoF experiments and again reached interfacial equilibrium quickly, as a stable wetting angle was rapidly attained in each case. Again a number of the wetting angle curves are invariant with temperature. However, two braze compositions display a measurable dependence on temperature, both containing 0.5 mol% TiO$_2$ and less than 2 mol% CuO. If the braze has at least 2 mol% CuO, the temperature dependence due to TiO$_2$ is mitigated, indicating that the nature of wetting has changed for these braze compositions. With the pre-oxidized fecralloy surface, increasing the CuO content of the braze makes a continuous improvement in the wettability of the braze, although the effect is strongest for the binary Ag-CuO compositions. Only a small reduction in contact angle is observed for the ternary brazes beyond a CuO content of 1 mol%.

Back scattered electron images of the four braze compositions that display the best wetting behavior on the alumina scale surface of the pre-oxidized fecralloy are shown in Figures 6(a) – (d). By again pairing the micrographs for the brazes which contain no TiO$_2$ wetting aid, Ag-2Cu [Figure 6(a)] and Ag-4Cu [Figure 6(c)], and those which do, Ag-4Cu and Ag-4Cu-½ Ti shown in Figures 6(b) and 6(d) respectively, we observe microstructural similarities within each pair. The brazes containing no wetting aid display a continuous, ½ - 1µm thick alumina scale that contains a small amount of iron and chromium, ~5 mol% and 3 mol%

respectively. Both specimens also show the formation of a thin reaction zone which contains a mixture of discrete phases, including $CuAlO_2$, silver, and a mixed copper-aluminum oxide, assumed to be $CuO-Al_2O_3$ since CuO and Al_2O_3 exhibit complete solubility with each other [23]. EDX results indicate ~5 – 8 mol% each of iron and chromium is dissolved in this mixed oxide phase. Note that in the Ag-2Cu brazed sample the reaction zone is approximately 1μm thick, whereas in the Ag-4Cu sample the reaction zone is nearly seven times wider. However, the most significant difference is the thickness and continuity of the CuO phase adjacent to the reaction zone. In the case of the 2 mol% CuO braze, the copper oxide phase is about 2μm thick and has not yet become a continuous layer, having been penetrated at numerous points by one or more of the phases that populate the reaction zone. In the higher CuO-content braze however, the CuO layer is approximately 20 – 30μm thick and forms a continuous band that completely covers the reaction zone. The contact angle data for these brazes,

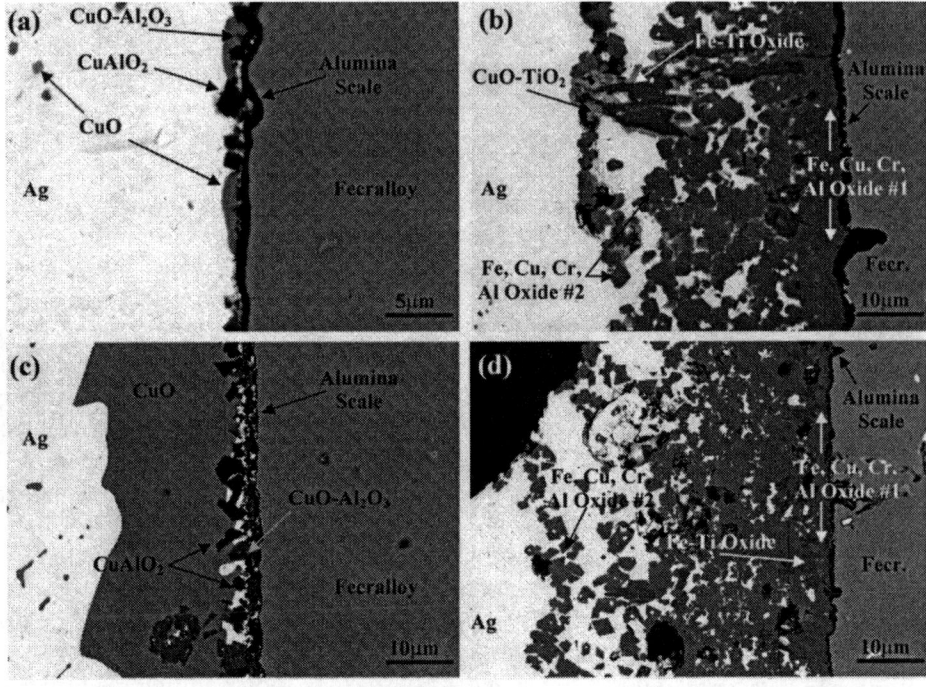

Figure 6 Cross-sectional SEM micrographs of braze/pre-oxidized fecralloy interfaces: (a) Ag-2Cu, (b) Ag-Cu-½Ti, (c) Ag-4Cu, and (d) Ag-4Cu-½Ti. Each wetting specimen was heated in air at a final soak temperature of 1100°C. Fe, Cu, Cr, Al oxides #1 and #2 are described in the text.

Figure 5, again bears out the wetting advantage that a continuous layer of CuO offers relative to the more discontinuous microstructure. As with the case of wetting on LSCoF, we assume that the difference in morphology between the two binary brazes results at least partially because of the miscibility gap in the Ag-CuO phase diagram.

As found with the LSCoF wetting specimens, TiO_2 has a significant effect on the composition and microstructure of the braze/pre-oxidized fecralloy interface. Both samples exhibit a wide affected zone, ~40μm in the case of the Ag-2Cu-½Ti sample and over 50μm for Ag-4Cu-½Ti. Near the interface with the 1μm alumina scale, a 10μm thick zone can be found in both specimens which consists primarily of two distinct but complex phases, one with a Fe, Cu, Cr, Al molar ratio of 1:1:1:1 and the second which appears to be primarily an iron-titanium oxide phase (possibly $FeTiO_3$) with a small fraction of Al and Cu. In general, this interfacial zone is relatively free of silver, although an occasionally precipitate can be found. Further into the bulk of the braze, roughly 15μm away from the alumina scale in the case of the Ag-2Cu-½Ti braze and 25μm for the higher CuO-content material, a second zone starts. Within this region, significantly more silver is found, forming a matrix that encapsulates two faceted oxide phases: (1) an iron-titanium oxide of the same Fe:Ti molar ratio and impurity composition as the interfacial product and (2) crystallites with an Fe, Cu, Cr, Al compositional ratio of 2:2:1:1. In addition, voids can be found in this zone, although the Ag-4Cu-½Ti specimen exhibits a far greater number than does Ag-2Cu-½Ti.

Based on the results of the wetting experiments and subsequent microstructural analyses, a joining study has been initiated using the Ag-2Cu and Ag-4Cu brazes. Joint samples have been prepared by placing a small, 6.5mm diameter x 1mm cold pressed braze pellet onto the pre-oxidized surface of the fecralloy. The LSCoF pellet was then placed polished side down on the braze pellet. In this way, the joint was kept under compression by the weight of the LSCoF. Thus far, joining has been conducted under the following heat treatment

Figure 7   Examples of a Ag-CuO braze LSCoF/Fecralloy joint (a) prior to and (b) after tensile testing. The specimen was prepared using the Ag-4Cu braze and was heated at 5°C/min to 1050°C, soaked at 1050°C for 1 hr, and cooled at 5°C/min to room temperature.

conditions: heat in static air at 5°C/min to 1050°C, hold at 1050°C for 1 hour, and cool to room temperature at 5°C/min. An example of a brazed joint prior to and after tensile testing is shown in Figures 7(a) and (b). The mechanical strength of the joints is currently under investigation and will be reported in the future.

CONCLUSIONS

Reaction air brazing using Ag-CuO and Ag-CuO-TiO_2 brazes was investigated as an alternative means of joining a mixed ionic/electronic conducting oxide, $(La_{0.6}Sr_{0.4})(Co_{0.2}Fe_{0.8})O_3$, to a structural alloy candidate, fecralloy, for an oxygen generator application. Wetting experiments demonstrated that copper oxide significantly improves the wetting behavior of silver on both the LSCoF and pre-oxidized fecralloy substrates, but that a minimum concentration is required. This minimum level of CuO can be reduced by adding a small amount of TiO_2 to the braze, but microstructural analysis indicates that a deleterious reaction zone may be formed at the substrate surface, particularly in the case of LSCoF, where evidence of grain boundary melting was observed. In general, it was found in the Ag-CuO brazes that the formation of a nearly continuous CuO layer along the interface with either substrate greatly improves the wetting characteristics of the braze. Based on the promising results obtained in the wetting experiments, a series of joining experiments have begun using the binary RAB brazes.

ACKNOWLEDGMENTS

The authors would like to thank Nat Saenz, Shelly Carlson, and Jim Coleman for their assistance in polishing the wetting samples and conducting the metallographic and SEM analysis work. This work was supported by the U. S. Department of Energy, Office of Fossil Energy, Advanced Research and Technology Development Program and by the U.S. Department of Energy's National Energy Technology Laboratory (NETL) under the Core Technology Program (CTP) of the Solid-State Energy Conversion Alliance (SECA). The Pacific Northwest National Laboratory is operated by Battelle Memorial Institute for the United States Department of Energy (U.S. DOE) under Contract DE-AC06-76RLO 1830.

REFERENCES

[1] G.R. Doughty and H. Hind, "The Applications of Ion-Conducting Ceramics," *Key Engineering Materials*, **122-124** [1] 145-62 (1996).

[2] N.Q. Minh, "Ceramic Fuel Cells," *Journal of the American Ceramic Society*, **76** [3] 563-88 (1993).

[3] A.V. Kovalesky, V.V. Kharton, V.N. Tikhonovich, E.N. Naumovich, A.A. Tonoyan, O.P. Reut, and L.S. Boginsky, "Oxygen Permeation Through

(Sr,Ln)CoO₃ (Ln=La, Nd, Sm, Gd) Ceramic Membranes," *Materials Science and Engineering B*, **52** [2-3] 105-16 (1998).

[4] A.K. Anand, C.S. Cook, J.C. Corman, and A.R. Smith, "New Technology Trends for Improved IGCC System Performance," *Transactions of the ASM. Journal of Engineering for Gas Turbines and Power*, **118** [4] 732-6 (1996).

[5] V.A. Greenhut, "Progress in Ceramic-Metal Joining and Metallization: An Overview of Techniques and Recent Advances"; pp. 130-17 in *Metal-Ceramic Joining*. Edited by P. Kumar and V.A. Greenhut. The Mineral, Metals, & Materials Society, 1991.

[6] N. Lahl, K. Singh, L. Singheiser, K. Hilpert, and D. Bahadur, "Crystallisation Kinetics in $AO-Al_2O_3-SiO_2-B_2O_3$ Glasses (A=Ba, Ca, Mg)," *Journal of Materials Science*, **35** [12] 3089-96 (2000).

[7] K. Eichler, G. Solow, P. Otschik, and W. Schaffrath, "Degradation Effects at Sealing Glasses for the SOFC"; pp. 899-906 in *Proceedings of the Fourth European Solid Oxide Fuel Cell Forum*. Edited by A.J. McEvoy. Oberrohrdorf, Switzerland (2000).

[8] C.W. Fox and G. M. Slaughter, "Brazing of Ceramics," *Welding Journal*, **43** [7] 591-7 (1964).

[9] O. M. Akselsen, "Advances in Brazing of Ceramics," *Journal of Materials Science*, **27** [9] 1989-2000 (1992).

[10] J-H Kim and Y-C Yoo, "Bonding of Alumina to Metals with Ag-Cu-Zr Brazing Alloy," *Journal of Materials Science Letters*, **16** [14] 1212-15 (1997).

[11] J.P. Rice, D.M. Paxton, and K.S. Weil, "Oxidation Behavior of a Commercial Gold-Based Braze Alloy for Ceramic-to-Metal Joining," Proceedings of the 26th Annual Conference on Composites, Advanced Ceramics, Materials, and Structures, in publication.

[12] K.D. Meinhardt, D.M. Paxton, and K.S. Weil, Unpublished Research on the Reduction of Mixed Ionic/Electronic Conducting Oxides, Pacific Northwest National Laboratory, P.O. Box 999, Richland, WA 99352.

[13] "Phase Diagrams for Ceramists, Volume VI," edited by R.S. Roth, J.R. Dennis, and H.F. McMurdie. The American Ceramic Society, Westerville, Ohio (1987).

[14] C.C. Shüler, A. Stuck, N. Beck, H. Keser, and U. Täck, "Direct Silver Bonding - An Alternative for Substrates in Power Semiconductor Packaging," *Journal of Materials Science: Materials in Electronics*, **11** [3] 389-96 (2000).

[15] Z.B. Shao, K.R. Liu, L.Q. Liu, H.K. Liu, S. Dou, "Equilibrium Phase Diagrams in the Systems PbO-Ag and CuO-Ag," *Journal of the American Ceramic Society*, **76** [10] 2663-4 (1993).

[16] A.M. Meier, P.R. Chidambaram, and G.R. Edwards, "A Comparison of the Wettability of Copper-Copper Oxide and Silver-Copper Oxide on Polycrystalline Alumina," *Journal of Materials Science*, **30** [19] 4781-6 (1995).

[17] Y. Yoshino, "Role of Oxygen in Bonding Copper to Alumina," *Journal of the American Ceramic Society*, **72** [8] 1322-7 (1989).

[18] C. Beraud, M. Courbiere, C. Esnouf, D. Juve, and D. Treheux, "Study of Copper-Alumina Bonding," *Journal of Materials Science*, **24** [12] 4545-54 (1989)

[19] Y. Yoshino and T. Shibata, "Structure and Bond Strength of a Copper-Alumina Interface," *Journal of the American Ceramic Society*, **75** [10] 2756-60 (1992).

[20] F-H. Lu, F-X. Fang, and Y-S. Chen, "Eutectic Reaction Between Copper Oxide and Titanium Dioxide," *Journal of the European Ceramic Society*, **21** [8] 1093-1099 (2001).

[21] A. Petric, P. Huang, and F. Tietz, "Evaluation of La-Sr-Co-Fe-O Perovskites for Solid Oxide Fuel Cells and Gas Separation Membranes, *Solid State Ionics*, **135** [1-4] 719-25 (2000).

[22] S.B. Adler, "Chemical Expansivity of Electrochemical Ceramics," *Journal of the American Ceramic Society*, **84** [9] 2117-19 (2001).

[23] S. K. Misra and A. C. D. Chaklader, *Journal of the American Ceramic Society*, **46** [10] 609- (1963).

BRAZELESS APPROACHES TO JOINING OF SILICON CARBIDE-BASED CERAMICS FOR HIGH TEMPERATURE APPLICATIONS

C.A. Lewinsohn
Ceramatec, Inc.
2425 South 900 West
Salt Lake City, UT 84119, USA

C.H. Henager, Jr.
Pacific Northwest National Laboratory
PO Box 999
Richland, WA 99352, USA

M. Singh
QSS Group, Inc.
NASA Glenn Research Center
Cleveland, OH 44135, USA

ABSTRACT

Silicon carbide has attractive thermal and mechanical properties for use in a number of high temperature applications such as gas-to-liquid fuel processing, glass and aluminum melting, gas turbine hot-section components, and fusion energy systems. Robust and reliable methods for joining of silicon carbide components are required in order to fabricate large components from smaller ones, or to assemble systems comprised of different materials. Conventional approaches to joining ceramics rely on reactive metal brazes that have limited durability at elevated temperatures (>1000°C). In this paper, advantages and disadvantages of three methods for joining of silicon carbide ceramics without the use of brazes will be discussed.

INTRODUCTION

Although ceramic materials, especially non-oxide compositions, possess properties that make them suitable for applications at temperatures above 1000°C, satisfactory joining methods, required for assembling large components from similar materials or for attaching parts of dissimilar materials, are not available or have significant limitations [1]. In some cases, this barrier precludes the selection of ceramic materials, such as silicon carbide, in applications where their use would result in significant energy savings or environmental benefits. For example, diffusion bonding requires the use of high temperatures and pressures and the shape of components that can be joined is limited. Brazing must be performed

---

To the extent authorized under the laws of the United States of America, all copyright interests in this publication are the property of The American Ceramic Society. Any duplication, reproduction, or republication of this publication or any part thereof, without the express written consent of The American Ceramic Society or fee paid to the Copyright Clearance Center, is prohibited.

under vacuum. Thermal expansion mismatch at the joints and the formation of brittle reactants, particularly when silicides and carbide phases can form, can limit durability. Therefore, there is a need for methods of joining ceramics that are appropriate for applications involving exposure to elevated temperatures. This paper will focus on three recently developed methods for joining of silicon carbide ceramics that are designed for use at elevated temperatures: reaction-forming, in-situ displacement reaction-bonding, and preceramic precursor pyrolysis. Various aspects of each of these methods are compared in Table I.

Table I. Comparison of Brazeless Methods for Joining Silicon Carbide Ceramics

Joining Technology	Reaction-Forming	In-situ Displacement Reactions	Precursor Pyrolysis
Joint composition	SiC + ≈5% Si	$TiSi_2$, SiC, and Ti_3SiC_2	mixed amorphous/nano-crystalline Si-O-B-C-N
Strength	good	good	reasonable
Processing temperature	> 1425 °C (*)	≈1300°C	> 850°C
Applied pressure	not required	required	improves strength
Compatibility	Si-based ceramics	Si-based ceramics, possibly metals	oxide and non-oxide ceramics, metals

* The joining temperature could be lowered using silicon-refractory metal alloys.

The reaction-forming method studied in this work can provide joints with tailored microstructures [2-4]. The process consists of joining parts together with a carbonaceous preform followed by impregnation by molten silicon or silicon-refractory metal alloys. No external pressure is applied during the joining process. The formation of joints by this approach is attractive since the thermomechanical properties of the joint interlayer can be tailored to be very close to those of silicon carbide-based materials.

Consideration of phase equilibria at high temperature suggests that compounds that would react with silicon carbide (SiC) naturally occur in the Ti-Si-C system and may be suitable joining compounds for silicon carbide-based materials. Materials synthesized via in-situ displacement reactions, based on the reactions between silicon (Si) and titanium carbide (TiC), have attractive high temperature mechanical properties [5]. In this study, a process where joints were fabricated by hot pressing TiC and Si powders between plates of silicon carbide was investigated. According to the Ti-Si-C phase diagram a complete reaction would lead to the formation of a mixture of $TiSi_2$, SiC, and Ti_3SiC_2.

The use of organic, preceramic precursors for joining ceramics also offers the potential to form robust, high temperature joints at relatively low temperatures [6-10]. Preceramic precursors are available as solids or liquids that can be applied to surfaces easily and then pyrolyzed to form joints. Typically, careful processing and the addition of fillers are required to obtain robust joints with good mechanical properties.

EXPERIMENTAL METHODS

A detailed description of the reaction-forming joining process (ARCJoinT) has been presented elsewhere [3, 11]. To study joining by reaction forming, large plates of sintered silicon carbide[1] were cut into small (65 mm long by 25 mm wide by 4 mm-thick) pieces. A carbonaceous mixture was applied to the surfaces to be joined and cured at 110-120°C for 10 to 20 minutes. Subsequently, silicon powder paste was applied to the surface of the joint region and heated to 1425°C for 5-10 minutes. Capillary forces drew the molten silicon into the joint where it reacted with the carbon to form silicon carbide[2].

Silicon carbide specimens were joined using in-situ displacement reaction compounds with a one to one mole ratio of TiC to Si in the starting materials. Plates of sintered, alpha silicon carbide[1] were joined[3] using various amounts of applied pressure ranging from 0-30 MPa at 1300°C, in argon, for 1 h in a graphite element hot press.

To study joining by preceramic precursors, plates of monolithic, chemically vapor deposited (CVD) SiC[4] were joined[5] using allyl-hydridopolycarbosilane (aHPCS)[6] containing 42 wt% SiC powders[7]. Two plates of CVD SiC, approximately 4 mm thick, were cut into 25 mm long by 30 mm-wide pieces. The 30 x 4 mm faces were cleaned using hexane. Polymer paste was applied by hand, and then the pieces were fastened together in a special fixture. The material was cured and pyrolysed at 850°C for 1 h in inert gas, using a heating and cooling rate of 1°C/min. After pyrolysis the joint was re-impregnated with polymer and pyrolyzed again. The resulting joints were 20-32.5 μm thick.

After joining the joined plates were cut into mechanical test specimens that were approximately 50 x 4 x 3 mm in size. The specimens were fabricated

---

[1] Hexoloy-SA, Carborundum Co., Niagara, NY.
[2] Joints fabricated at NASA Glenn Research Center, Cleveland, OH.
[3] Joints fabricated by Sienna Technologies, Woodinville, WA.
[4] Morton Advanced Materials, Woburn, MA
[5] Joints fabricated by Starfire Systems, Inc., Watervliet, NY.
[6] Starfire Systems, Inc., Watervliet, NY.
[7] F800 powder from UK Abrasives - Lot No: SZ0802A7

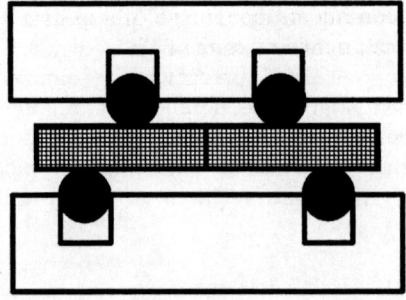

Figure 1. Schematic drawing illustrating the orientation of the joint relative to the load applied by the four point bend fixture. Dark vertical line, at the specimen midpoint, indicates the joint.

such that the joint was at the midpoint of the largest dimension of the specimen (Fig. 1). The specimens were loaded in four-point bending, using a fully articulated silicon carbide fixture, in ambient air at room temperature or 1000°C. The maximum load was used to calculate the stress on the tensile side of the joint at failure. Although this is not a true measure of the strength of the joints, all of the joints failed cohesively (in the joint material near the interface between the joint and the substrate) and therefore the results can be used to qualitatively compare treatments.

RESULTS

An optical micrograph of a reaction formed joint in sintered silicon ceramics (Hexoloy-SA) is shown in Fig. 2. The white and grey areas are Si and SiC, respectively. The silicon is finely distributed in regions of approximately the same size as the SiC areas. The joint thickness' were about 50-55 $\pm$ 0.6 μm. The volume fraction of silicon in the joint was 7.3 $\pm$ 2.2 %.

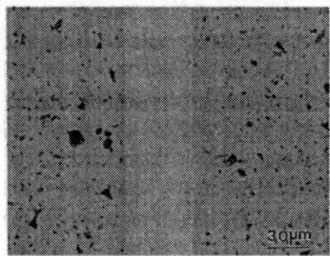

Figure 2. Typical optical micrograph of reaction formed joints in Hexoloy-SA.

A scanning electron microscope image of a typical joint fabricated by the in-situ displacement reaction method is shown in Figure 3.

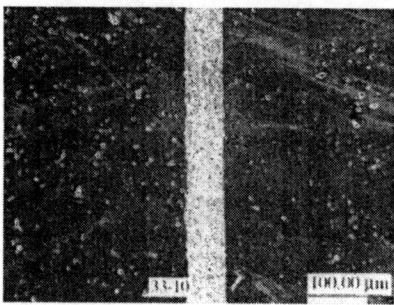

Figure 3: Scanning electron microscope image of a joint formed by the in-situ displacement reaction method..

The experimental results are summarized in Table II. The average strength of the joints fabricated by the reaction forming method was the highest. Earlier studies have also found the strength of joints fabricated using this method to be 255 MPa [11]. Detailed characterization of joint and interface microstructure by transmission electron microscopy and the joint strengths for reaction formed joints has been completed and will be reported elsewhere [12]. The strength of the joints formed by the displacement reaction method varied with the amount of applied pressure used during joining and with the test temperature (Fig. 4). Only two specimens were tested for each condition at room temperature.

Table II. Room Temperature Strength of Joints

Joint Material	Substrate	Max. Process Temp. (°C)	Joint Thickness (μm)	Average Strength (MPa)	Std. Deviation (MPa)
Reaction-formed SiC	Sintered SiC	1425	50	275	12.9
In-situ displacement reaction, $Ti_xSi_yC_z$	Sintered SiC	1300	94	187	-
aHPCS	CVD SiC	850	20-32.5	85.0	11.0

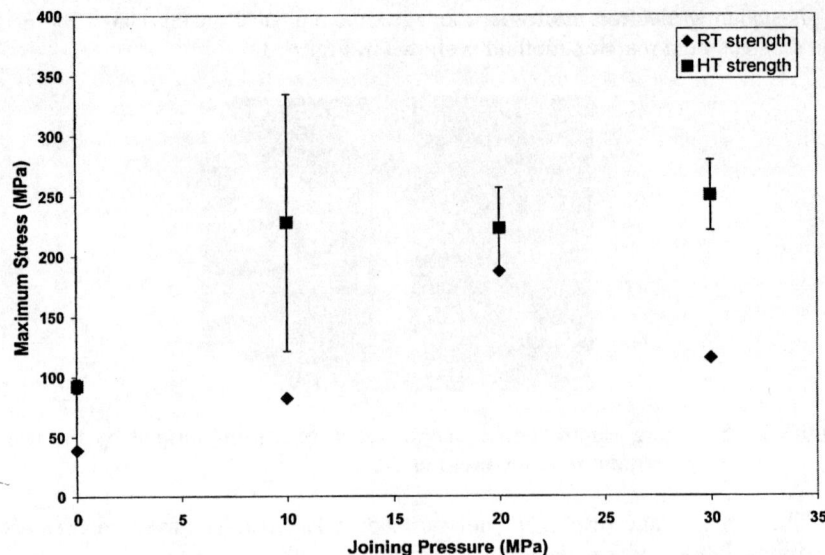

Figure 4. The average maximum tensile stress, on the outer surface of specimens, joined using the in-situ displacement reaction method, as a function of the test temperature and applied pressure used during joining.

and, hence, confidence intervals were not calculated. Ninety-five percent confidence intervals are plotted for the results measured at 1000°C. Since the difference between the maximum tensile stress measured on specimens that were fabricated without pressure was at least 100 MPa lower than that for specimens fabricated with pressure, it can be safely stated that the use of pressure increases the strength of the joints subject to flexural loading.

The strength of the samples joined using the displacement reaction method was higher when measured at 1000°C than at room temperature (Fig. 4). Although this might indicate the presence of residual stress in the samples a comparison of the difference between the values of strength measured at room temperature and at high-temperature does not reveal a consistent amount of residual stress. Alternatively, since these titanium-silico-carbide based composites exhibit a ductile-brittle transition at about 900°C, the joints may become less flaw sensitive at higher temperatures and exhibit higher fracture strengths.

The value of the maximum tensile stress at failure of the joints formed by pyrolysis of a preceramic precursor were the lowest of all those measured, due to the presence of shrinkage cracks in the joining material [13]. Therefore, it is likely that the strength of the joints can be enhanced by improved processing schedules. Since the joints were processed at the lowest temperature, however, the use of preceramic polymers as joining compounds is attractive, despite the lowest values of strength measured in this study.

SUMMARY

Three methods of fabricating joints between silicon carbide, without using brazes, were investigated. Reaction-forming methods were sensitive to process control, but were capable of providing joints with high strength. The in-situ displacement reaction method was also capable of producing joints with high strength. The application of pressure during fabrication of joints using the in-situ displacement reaction process improved their strength. Joints could also be fabricated by pyrolysis of preceramic polymers, however the strength was somewhat lower than that measured for the other two methods. Nevertheless, due to the relatively low processing temperature, and the possibility for process optimization, this method appears promising.

ACKNOWLEDGEMENTS

This work was supported by the National Aeronautics and Space Administration (NASA), The National Institute for Fusion Science under the Japan-USA Program of Irradiation Test for Fusion Research (JUPITER), Kyoto University, Core Research for Evolutional Science and Technology (CREST) Japan Science and Technology Corporation, and the Office of Fusion Energy Science under U.S. Department of Energy (DOE) contract DE-AC06-76RLO 1830 with Pacific Northwest National Laboratory, which is operated for DOE by Battelle.

REFERENCES

1. J.M. Fragomeni and S.K. El-Rahaiby, Review of Ceramic Joining Technology, Rept. No. 9, Ceramic Information Analysis Center, Purdue University, Indiana (1995).
2. M. Singh, S.C. Farmer, and J.D. Kiser, "Joining of Silicon Carbide-based Ceramics by Reaction Forming Approach," Ceramic Eng, Sci. Proc., 18 [3], 161-166 (1997).
3. M. Singh, "A Recation Forming Method for Joining of Silicon Carbide-based Ceramics," Scripta Mater., 37 [8], 1151-1154 (1997).

4. J. Martinez-Fernandez, F.M. Varela-Feria, M. Singh, "Characetrization of Microstructure and Mechanical Properties of Joints in Silicon Carbide-based Ceramics," pp. 35-43 in Proc. of Materials Solutions '98 International Conference on Joining of Advanced and Specialty Materials, Rosemont, Ill., October 12-15, ASM International (1998).
5. Chuck, in-situ disp rcn matl.s
6. L.M. Ewart, "A study of process variables and bond strength in the use of polycarbosilane to join SiC," pp. 125-132 in *Proc. 19th Army Science Conference*, Orlando FL, June 20-23, 1994, Department of the Army, Washington DC (1994).
7. A. Donato, P. Colombo and M.O. Abdirashid, "Joining of SiC to SiC using a preceramic polymer," pp. 471-476 in *High-Temperature Ceramic-Matrix Composites I: Design, durability and performance, Ceramic Transactions* Vol. 57. Edited by A.G. Evans and R. Naslain. The American Ceramic Society, Westerville OH, 1995.
8. I. Ahmad, R. Silberglitt, Y.L. Tian and J.D. Katz, "Microwave joining of SiC ceramics and composites," pp. 455-463 in *Microwaves: Theory and Application in Materials Processing IV*, Ceramic Transactions 80. Edited by D.E. Clark, W.H. Sutton and D.A. Lewis, The American Ceramic Society, Westerville, OH, 1997.
9. W.J. Sherwood, C.K. Whitmarsh, J.M. Jacobs and L.V. Interrante, "Joining ceramic composites using active metal/HPCS preceramic polymer slurries," *Cer.Eng.Sci.Proc.*, **18**, 177-184 (1997).
10. I.E. Anderson, S. Ijadi-Maghsoodi, Ö. Ünal, M. Nostrati and W.E. Bustamante, "Development of a compound for low temperature joining of SiC ceramics and CFCC composites," pp. 25-40 in *Ceramic Joining*, Ceramic Transactions **77**. Edited by I.E. Reimanis, C.H. Henager and A.P. Tomsia. The American Ceramic Society, Westerville OH, 1997.
11. M. Singh, "Joining of Sintered Silicon Carbide Ceramics for High Temperature Applications" Journal of Materials Science Letters, **17** [6] 459-461 (1998).
12. M. Singh and J. Martinez-Fernandez, "Characterization of Microstructure and Mechanical Properties of Reaction Formed Joints in Sintered Silicon Carbide Ceramics", unpublished work (2002).
13. C.A. Lewinsohn, P. Colombo, I. Reimanis, and O. Unal "Joining Ceramics For Use at High Temperatures with Inorganic Polymer, Preceramic Precursors" J. Am. Ceram. Soc., **84** [10], 2240-2244 (2001).

PROCESSING ISSUES IN FABRICATING CERAMIC MICRO-HEAT EXCHANGERS BY JOINING COMPONENTS

P. Kwon, C. K. Kok, D. Fickes and C. W. Somerton,
Department of Mechanical Engineering

H. W. Shin and E. D. Case,
Department of Chemical Engineering and Materials Science
Michigan State University
East Lansing, MI 48824

ABSTRACT

With the miniaturization of electronic circuitry, a very important technological challenge is the development and fabrication of an efficient cooling of electrical circuit elements. The authors have been developing the fabrication technology for prototypical meso-heat exchangers with channels using alumina and other ceramics. One route to produce such-heat exchangers is ceramic/ceramic joining subcomponents having either surface or bulk channels. The joining and testing of subcomponents for multi-pass cooling channels will be discussed.

INTRODUCTION

The ever-increasing demand for powerful chips has been limited by the development and fabrication of an efficient cooling system. A conventional method for such cooling system is to dissipate and spread the heat rapidly by employing highly conductive and high heat capacity materials and forcing air through pin arrays or fins or by cooling naturally [1,2,3]. A more efficient way to dissipate the heat is to circulate the coolants through networked channels and manifolds in a closed system.

Tuckerman and Pease [4] made a unidirectional micro-channeled heat sink by etching onto a silicon wafer the channels, which were anodically bonded by a Pyrex plate over the wafer. Instead of the channels, pins are fabricated to enhance the heat transfer into the coolants [5]. Harpole and Eninger [6] and Copeland et al. [7] added simple manifold by covering the middle section of the channel, where one side of the uncovered section is used as inlet and the other side as outlet. Another processing technique used by Zhong et al., [8] is to laminate the ceramic tapes (ceramic powders and organic binders) where each tape has been cut out to form the channels. Each tape is layer on top of another in a predetermine sequence to make the medium with channels and manifold. The laminates are then sintered for a substantial amount of time to burn out the binder phase and eventually to form a homogeneous body with channels. Paul et al. [9] and Alman et al. [10] use a technique where Ni and Al foils with the cuts for channels are laminated. During heating, the Ni and Al foils transform the intermetallic phases such as NiAl or Ni_3Al.

This paper explores the processing technology to fabricate an advanced meso-scale heat exchanger characterized by two unique features, micro-configuration and micro-texturing. The schematic of the meso-scale heat exchanger is shown in Figure 1 with the channels and manifolds. Micro-configuration means to introduce micro-geometric features such as channels and manifolds that are necessary to circulate a cooling fluid. Micro-texturing means to segregate at least two distinct powders spatially that results in inhomogeneous properties. By controlling the resulting inhomogeniety in the materials, the temperature gradiency that will inherently exist in a heat exchanger can be compensated. These two features require exploring new methods to fabricate such medium for the meso-scale heat-exchanger. Individual components can then be joined to fabricate more complex structures.

This paper presents the successful processing routes that enable us to produce the gradient materials and to introduce the channels and manifolds in the bulk of the gradient medium. In addition this paper reports on the testing set-up being developed, which will enable us to test for an optimal gradiency in a medium as well as for an optimal layout of channels and manifolds.

MATERIALS USED

We have used several different types of powders and dense billets of machinable ceramic called MaCor™ manufactured by Corning. TMDAR is alumina powder manufactured by Taimai Co., Japan, whose average size is about 0.2 micron, TZ-3YS is the partially stabilized zirconia (PSZ) powders manufactured by Tosoh, whose average size was about 0.6 microns. Two fully stabilized zirconia (FSZ) powders were designated TZ-8YS manufactured by Tosoh Corp., Japan and 5.2 weight percentage (w/o) Y_2O_3 zirconia manufactured by CERAC, respectively. The average size of the TZ-8YS (Tosoh) powder was about 0.54 microns. The average size of the CERAC powder was about 1.23 microns. We have also used hydroxyapatite (HAP). The average size of the HAP powder was about 2~3 microns. The various powders are used to achieve the micro-texturing and micro-configuring of the medium that will be used to form the heat exchanger.

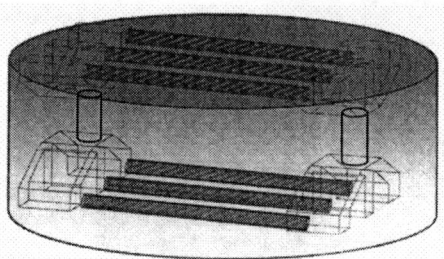

Figure 1: The Micro-textured and Micro-configured Medium for Meso-Scale Heat Exchanger

MICRO-TEXTURING VIA DIE DESIGN

Segregating the powders to form a desirable gradiency can be achieved in various ways. One way explored in this study is to achieve the gradiency by layering the powder mixtures. Ideally starting from 100% of powder A, we can gradually increase the concentration of powder B as each layer is added to the layers already deposited into the die. To repeat this process successfully, we have design the special die where the layers of a certain mixture can be deposited into the cavity from the top. As each layer with a different mixture deposited into the cavity, the thickness of each layer can be controlled by taking out the spacer with a right thickness. Figure 1 shows the picture of the die with only one spacer. However, the spacers are made with four different size (thickness) spacers to control the thickness of the layer. When one of the spacers is taken out, the die lowers for the thickness of the spacer and the layer with a designed mixture can be deposited. In addition, a simple uniaxial steel die, which consists of top and bottom plungers and die, was also used to press some of the specimens in this study. In both cases, a pressure of approximately 35 MPa was used to press the powders deposited into the die.

The normal thickness of powder compacts ranges from 2 to 3 mm, which can be controlled by the mass of the powder depositing into the die. To prepare various 'composite' powder mixtures of TM-DAR and PSZ in separate containers, a layer of one mixture, another layer of another mixture and so on were deposited to form a micro-textured medium for the heat exchanger.

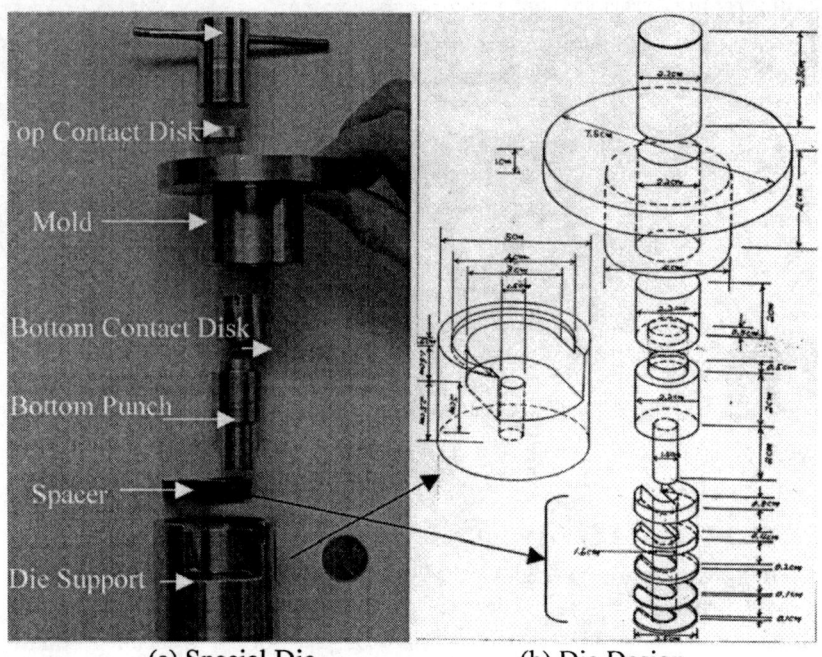

(a) Special Die (b) Die Design
Figure 2: The Die Used for Micro-Texturing

RESIDUAL STRESS CONTROL

The layers of powders deposited into the die are compacted using the press and fired in a conventional or microwave sintering unit. When the compact is fired, the inhomogeneous properties such as coefficient of thermal expansion (CTE) create severe residual stress to damage the sintered sample. However, the CTE difference can be compensated with the differences in densification. One way to control the densification is by manipulating the initial packing of a powder [11,12,13]. For example, if one powder has a higher CTE than the other powder, the shrinkage differences between two solid phases resulting from sintering causes the residual stress after sintering. The powder with a higher CTE must be obtained by mixing two different batches with distinct powder size. McGeary [14] has shown that the ratio between two 'monosize' powders is 2.4 or 6.5:1 depending on how the powders are arranged. The powders used in this study are not definitely mono-sized. For a first approximation, the same ratio of average powder sizes was used.

The packing of two powder mixtures can be achieved at a higher packing ratio than a typical value of 50%. Thus, the final shrinkage of this powder is minimized. Using this logic, we have prepared the sample with two layers (alumina and zirconia layers) where the zirconia layer is prepared by mixing two batches (CERAC and Tosoh). The ratio of the average powder size between CERAC and Tosoh PSZ powders is 2.12. To determine the optimum weight ratio between the two powder, various mixtures were prepared. The double layer samples with one layer being the TMDAR alumina powder and the other layer being one of the mixtures of CERAC and Tosoh PSZ powders were compacted and sintered. Due to process-induced residual stress, the samples were usually warped. The samples were measured using the dial gauge at the locations shown in Figure 3. Figure 4 has been generated to show the optimum mixture (weight ratio) between two zirconia powders.

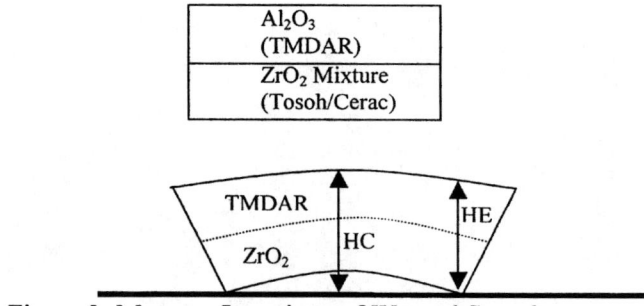

Figure 3: Measure Locations of Warped Sample

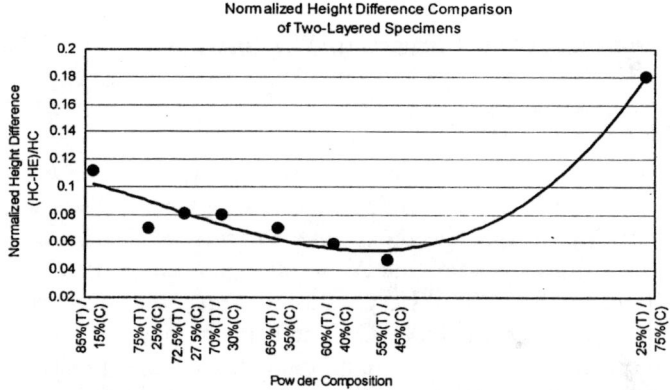

Figure 4. Comparison of the out-of-plane height at the center of zirconia/alumina specimens, based on a variation of particle-size mixture in the zirconia component.

MICRO-CONFIGURATION

The micro-scale geometric features such as micro-channels and manifolds are introduced into the gradient medium by imbedding the fugitive phase in the desired shape of channels or manifold. Among the various fugitive phases used, the graphite phase was most successful in making internal channels and manifolds. To make internal channels, we deposited a portion of the powder, the fugitive phase and the rest of the powder into the die. To make external channels, the powder is deposited and then the fugitive phase is placed on the powder. The powder is then compacted using the press and sintered at 1475°C. During pre-sintering at 900°C for 4 hours, the fugitive phase decomposes leaving channels and manifolds. Both internal and external channels were shown on Figure 5.

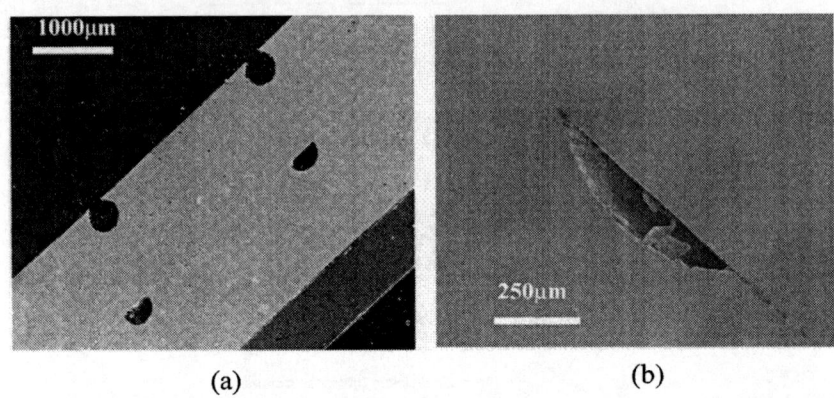

(a)   (b)

Figure 5: Joined Samples with Channels (a) PSZ joined with PSZ (b) PSZ joined with FSZ

CERAMIC/CERAMIC JOINING

The powders chosen for processing are alumina and zirconia, whose coefficient of thermal expansion (CTE) are not so different. Large CTE difference can lead to warping or cracking if the specimens are formed in the green state since differences in the initial particle packing may not be sufficient to offset a substantial difference in CTE. However, problems with fabricating internal channels using ceramics with large CTE mismatch may be resolved by first densifying the specimens and then joining the densified specimens [15]. If the densified specimens have external surface channels that have been formed, for example, by the burnout of fugitive phase elements [16], then joining can convert the external surface channels into internal channels. In addition, even when internal channels are fabricated in a given specimen [17], joining two or more "subcomponents" can be used to fabricate a more complex component.

Using the technique discussed below, in previous studies we have joined: (i) hydroxyapatite (HAP) with MaCor™ and (ii) FSZ, alumina with alumina, and (iii) an alumina-PSZ particulate composite (25 volume % alumina, 75 volume % PSZ) [16, 17]. For HAP and MaCor™, the CTE differences are substantial. Despite the large CTE differences, residual stresses do not damage the HAP-MaCor™ specimens (no warping or cracking is observed).

In this study, we have joined the following ceramic specimens that included surface channels: (i) alumina with alumina, (ii) alumina with PSZ, (iii) PSZ with PSZ and (iv) FSZ with PSZ. As noted for the previous studies [16,17], no significant cracking or warping was observed for the specimens in this study that were densified prior to joining. Figures 5a and 5b show, respectively, ceramic/ceramic bonds between the joined specimens of PSZ/PSZ and FSZ/PSZ. After joining the specimens were cut using a low speed diamond saw in order to obtain a cross-sectional view of the channels. In Figure 5a and 5b, densified specimens having open, external surface channels have been joined to fabricate a joined specimen that has both internal and external channels. In Figure 5b, the debris inside the channel result from the polymeric mounting compound in which the specimen was mounted after cutting, the debris were not present prior to mounting the specimen.

Among the joined specimens, the interface between the alumina and zirconia (PSZ) is especially interesting (Figure 6). The interlocking microstructure that is observed in this study at the alumina/zirconia interface (Figure 6) is similar to the interlocking microstructure that is seen in microwave-joined alumina/zirconia systems [15].

In this study, for all of the specimens that were densified prior to joining, the specimen surfaces were polished using diamond paste. The diamond paste grit sizes were changed gradually ranging from 25 microns to 1 micron. After each polishing step, the specimens were cleaned using an ultrasonic bath and de-ionized water. At least one side of the specimens were spin-coated with a pre-ceramic solution called Silcafilm™ (manufactured by Emulsitone Company, Whippany, New Jersey). The coating was applied in the liquid state using a commercial substrate spinner operating at 3000 rpm for 20 seconds. The spin-coated samples were cured in air at 200°C for 20 min. at the heating/cooling rate of 3°C/ min. The joining process takes place via diffusion bonding at 1475°C in a conventional sintering unit for 4 hours with the heating/cooling rate of 10°C per min. Before the heating began, a 50-grams dead weight was place on the samples to provide additional pressure.

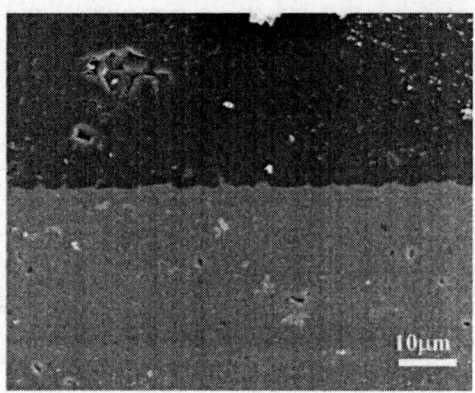

Figure 6: Joined interface of PSZ/ alumina

THERMAL TESTING

An apparatus has been designed and is being fabricated that will test the thermal performance of the microscale heat exchanger. This apparatus is shown in Figure 8. A small disk shaped electric heater is used to simulate the energy dissipation of the computer chip. In order to position the heat exchanger in the flow system a small cylindrical copper billet is mounted on the heater, with the heat exchanger mounted on the billet. The high thermal conductivity of the billet insures that nearly all of the energy provided by the heater will be supplied to the heat exchanger. As is seen in the drawing, insulation is packed around the heater and billet to guarantee little or no heat loss to the surroundings. In this way, the heat delivered to the heat exchanger is determined by measuring the electric current and voltage drop through the heater. The heat exchanger is situated in a Plexiglas channel through which water flows. Three temperature measurements are made with thermocouples: water inlet (T_1), water outlet (T_2), and heat exchanger lower surface (T_3).

The performance of the heat exchanger will be characterized by the overall heat transfer coefficient of the heat exchanger, U. In this specific instance, the overall heat transfer coefficient will be calculated from the heater voltage measurement (V), the heater current measurement (I), and the temperature measurements with the equation

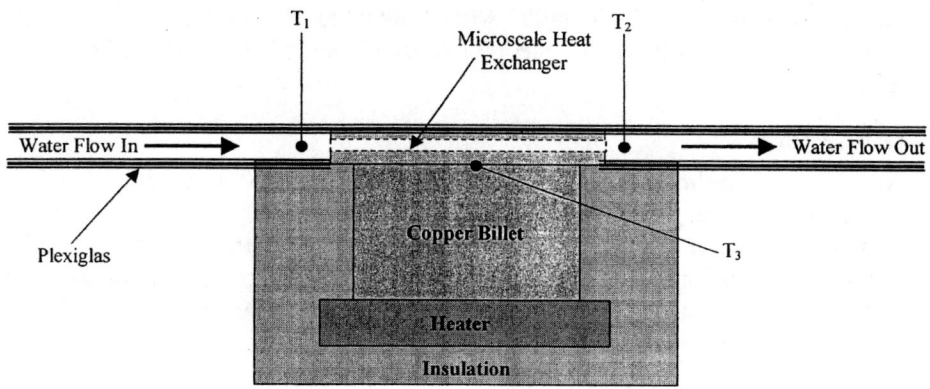

Figure 8: Thermal Testing Apparatus

$$U = \frac{V \cdot I}{T_3 - T_{water}}$$

where T_{water} will be the average water temperature as it flows through the heat exchanger and will be approximated as the linear average of the inlet and outlet water temperatures. The traditional parameter in characterizing heat exchanger performance is the number of transfer units, NTU, which may be thought of as the ratio of the heat exchanger's ability to transfer heat to its ability to carry energy away. With the overall heat transfer coefficient known, the number of transfer unit for the microscale heat exchanger may be determined from

$$NTU = \frac{U}{(\dot{m} c_P)_{water}}$$

where $\dot{m}$ is the mass flow rate of water through the heat exchanger and c_P is the specific heat of water. Current plans calls for the testing of heat exchangers with several different geometries, number and position of the flow passages. The NTU's for these heat exchangers will serve as a measure of their performance, and will allow prediction of performance in the actual application. This testing will also allow for the exploration of the effect of channel roughness on heat exchanger performance.

Running parallel to the development of the thermal testing is the development of a finite element model for the heat exchanger. A finite element model is being developed for the solid. This model will allow us to predict the behavior of the heat exchanger, and will yield a theoretical calculation of the overall heat transfer coefficient.

CONCLUSIONS

The processing techniques presented in this paper have been developed, which will be used to fabricate the micro-heat exchanger. The set-up to test the effectiveness of the heat exchanger is being built. Ceramic/ceramic joining facilitates the fabrication of ceramic micro-heat exchangers in two ways. First, the intricate channels needed for a successful micro-heat exchanger (Figure 1) are difficult to form as internal channels or manifolds. Thus, ceramic/ceramic joining allows one to form complicated channels on the surface of the specimen and convert the surface channels into internal channels via joining. The second way in which ceramic/ceramic joining can enable the fabrication of micro-heat exchangers is that joining ceramics with large CTE differences can be difficult if the ceramics are formed from powders and then sintered to fabricate the ceramic/ceramic join. In contrast, the process by which specimens are first densified and then joined can avoid the warping and cracking that can accompany densification of powders having large CTE differences. Thus, ceramic/ceramic joining is a key technology in the fabrication of ceramic micro-heat exchangers.

ACKNOWLEDGEMENT

This work has been supported with the funding from Air Force Office of Scientific Research (AFOSR).

REFERENCES

1. Gray, K. J., 2000, "Effective Thermal Conductivity of a Diamond Coated Heat Spreader," Diamond and Related Materials, 9: (2), pp. 201-204.
2. Jagannadham, K., 1999, "Model of interfacial thermal resistance of diamond composites," J. Vac. Sci. Technol., A17: (2), pp. 373-379.
3. Hui, P., Tan, H. S. and Lye, Y. S., 1997, "Design of circular Heat Spreaders on Semi-Infinite Heat Sinks in Microelectronics Device Applications," IEEE Tran. Comp. Pack. & Manuf. Tech. Part A, 20: (4); pp. 452-457.
4. Tuckerman, D. B. and Pease, R. F. W., 1981 "High Performance Heat Sink for VLSI," *IEEE Electron. Devices Lett.*, vol. EDL-2, pp. 126-129.
5. Yin, X. and Bau, H. H., 1997, "Micro Heat Exchangers Consisting of Pin Arrays," Journal of Electronic Packaging, 119, pp. 51-57.

6. Harpole, G. M. and Eniger, J. E., 1991, "Microchannel Heat Exchanger Optimization," Proc. 7th IEEE Semi-Therm. Symp., pp. 59-63.

7. Copeland, D., Behnia, M. and Nakayama, W., 1997, "Manifold Microchannel Heat Sinks: Isothermal Analysis," IEEE Trans Comp. Packaging. Manuf. Tech., A, 20: (2) PP.96-102

8. Zhong, J., Yi, M. and Bau, H. H., 1999, "A Thermal Cycler Fabricated with Low Temperature, Co-fired Ceramic Tape," MEMS-Vol 1, Micro Electromechanical Syatems (MEMS), ASME, pp. 123-128.

9. Paul, B. K., Wilson, R. D. and Alman, D., 2001, "Limits on Aspect Ratio in Two-Fluid Micro-scale Heat Exchangers," Transactions of NAMRI/SME, V. XXXIX, pp. 461-468.

10. Alman, D. E., Wilson, R. D. and Paul, B. K., 2001, "Fabrication of NiAl Intermetallic Reactors for Microtechnology-based Energy Chemical Systems (MECS)," Transactions of NAMRI/SME, V. XXXIX, pp. 453-459.

11. Ting, T. -M. and Lin, R. Y., 1994, "Effect of Particle-size Distribution on Sintering: Part I Modelling," *J. Mat. Sci.*, pp. 1867-1872.

12. Ting, T. -M., and Lin, R. Y., 1995, "Effect of Particle-size Distribution on Sintering: Part II Sintering Alumina," *J. Mat. Sci.*, pp. 2382-2389.

13. Yeh, T. and Sacks, M. D., 1988,"Effect of Particle Size Distribution on Sintering of Alumina," *J. Am. Ceram. Soc.*, **71**, 12, pp. C484-V487.

14. McGeary, R. K., 1961, "Mechanical Packing of Spherical Particles," *J. Am. Ceram. Soc.*, **44**, 10, pp. 613-522.

15. Case, E. D., Lee, J. G. Zeng L. and Crimp, M. A. 2000, "Joining of Dissimilar Ceramic Materials", in Joining of Advanced and Specialty Materials II, ASM International, Materials Park, OH, pp 10 - 17.

16. Shin, H. W., Kwon, P. and Case, E. D., "Fabrication of internal channels without machining in joined alumina and zirconia ceramics", ASM Fall 2000 Proceedings, pp. 23-30.

17. Shin, H. W., Case, E. D. and Kwon, P. "Joining of Bioactive and Bioactive Ceramics", ASM Fall 2000 Proceedings, pp. 15-22.

KEYWORD AND AUTHOR INDEX

Agathopoulos, S., 135
Alumina, 103, 149, 209

Bioactive, 159
Biomaterials, 135, 149
Bond strength, 61
Brazeless joining, 201
Brazing, 103, 119
Brooks, B.D., 149

Case, E.D., 3, 149, 209
Ceramic–metal bonding, 29, 61, 135, 185
Chapa-Cabrera, J., 49
Chapman, T.R., 61
Chou, Y.-S., 175
Cobalt–Chromium, 159
Conquest, D.B., 103
Copper oxide–silver, 119
Copper–silica, 29
Correia, R.N., 135

Dissimilar materials, 29

Ecclestone, L.J., 103
Electrochemical devices, 185
Enamel, 159
Evaluation, 61

Fernie, J.A., 103
Fickes, D., 209
Finite element modeling, 49
Fuel cell, 175, 185
Fujino, S., 159

Glass, 159
Gomez-Vega, J.M., 159

Graded layers, 49
Greenhut, V.A., 61

Hardy, J.S., 185
Heat exchanger, 209
Henager Jr., C.H., 201
Hydroxyapatite, 149, 159

Implants, 159
Interlayer fabrication, 3

Kim, J.Y., 119
Knowles, K.M., 103
Kok, C.K., 149, 209
Kwon, P., 149, 209

Lewinsohn, C.A., 201
Liquid phase joining, 61

Mica, 175
Micro-channeled heat sink, 209
Microwave, 149
Numerical modeling, 29

Ormston, D.R., 103

Particulate loading, 103
Pina, S., 135

Reactive air brazing, 119
Reimanis, I.E., 49

Saiz, E., 159
Seal, 175
Selection, 3
Sensors, 185
Shin, H.W., 149, 209
Silicon carbide, 103, 201

Singh, M., 201
Solid state bonding, 29
Solide oxide fuel cell, 175
Somerton, C.W., 209
Stamile, J., 49
Stevenson, J.W., 175

Takahashi, Y., 29
Thermal cycling, 175
Titanium, 103, 135, 159
Titanium–alumina, 29
Tomsia, A.P., 159

Weil, K.S., 119, 185
Wettability, 119

Zirconia, 135, 149